Z-80 Microcomputer Design Projects

by

William Barden, Jr.

Howard W. Sams & Co., Inc.
4300 WEST 62ND ST. INDIANAPOLIS, INDIANA 46268 USA

FIRST EDITION
FIRST PRINTING—1980

International Standard Book Number: 0-672-21682-5
Library of Congress Catalog Card Number: 80-50046

Printed in the United States of America.

Preface

This book is dedicated to one proposition—that it is relatively easy to use today's *microprocessors,* "computers on a chip," to perform a variety of sophisticated tasks. The digital computer has made the transition from paraphernalia that required government funding to build and use, to a circuit component that is used in hundreds of applications. Microprocessor chips are "designed into" mixers, radio tuners, microwave ovens, and many other devices.

The microprocessor has become a standard engineering building block, just as vacuum tubes and flip-flops were standard components several years ago. The appeal of a microprocessor over *discrete logic* is that a microprocessor does not have to be dedicated to performing a single defined task. Because a microprocessor is a computer, by its very nature it is a general-purpose device. The same circuitry may be *programmed* to perform any number of functions. Rather than designing a dozen separate circuits to perform a dozen separate functions, the computer program may simply be changed to perform each function.

This book, *Z-80 Microcomputer Design Projects,* may be used by the electronics enthusiast who has a background in electronics other than microprocessors as a training course in microprocessor fundamentals. It may be used by the interested nontechnician to let him or her see how easy it really is to construct a complete microcomputer. It may be used by the hobbyist who wants to use a microcomputer primarily for the *application* or end result.

This book provides a step-by-step guide in building a complete microcomputer, the EZ-80, and for implementing a number of different applications. Although some kit-building experience may be of help, every attempt has been made to provide a trouble-free guide to construction even for the neophyte. The applications range from a music synthesizer that will play one-voice musical scores with special effects, to a Morse code generator that generates code for practice or transmission, to a telephone dialer, to a timer that times external events over 100 days. Each application is fully documented in detail. For those readers who are interested in implementing their own unique applications, this book provides the ground work in programming methods so that they may create their own programmed "applications packages" using the *input* and *output* lines of the microcomputer to talk to the external world.

The EZ-80 Microcomputer is built around the popular Z-80 microprocessor chip. The Z-80 microprocessor is a complete computer on a chip. It has a repertoire of hundreds of instructions and operates at speeds of up to hundreds of thousands of operations per second.

In addition to the Z-80, about 12 other semiconductor devices are used. Some of these are memory, others enable the Z-80 to *interface* to the outside world, and others perform clocking and control functions. The complete set of parts to build the EZ-80 may be purchased for about $50—inexpensive indeed for the processing power that is available. Two methods of construction are possible.

The microcomputer may be *wire-wrapped* using simple techniques and tools. Alternatively, plans are provided for a *printed-circuit board* construction for those readers who have the wherewithal to produce printed circuits. Total construction time using wire-wrapping is approximately 2 hours.

The book is divided into three sections. Section 1 covers the hardware and software basics of the Z-80 microprocessor. Since the microcomputer is built around the Z-80, discussion of the hardware signals and operation of the microprocessor are essential to a complete understanding of the *microcomputer*. Similarly, the programs presented in the book all use the built-in instruction set of the Z-80, and a discussion of basic Z-80 instructions is helpful in understanding operation of the microcomputer programs for the application.

Section 2 describes the EZ-80 microcomputer built from the Z-80. The relationship of the Z-80 to other system components, such as memory, peripheral interface, and clock, is explored. Complete construction details on the EZ-80 are presented in this section. If you choose to program or "burn in" an applications program in the EPROM (*E*rasable *P*rogrammable *R*ead-*O*nly *M*emory) chip, you may do so by constructing the simple auxiliary EPROM programmer described in this section (or you may choose one of several other alternatives). A *diagnostic program* and step-by-step troubleshooting procedures are also provided in this section. These help in checkout of the EZ-80 after construction has been completed, and verify that the EZ-80 is working properly.

Section 3 describes the applications that may be implemented with the EZ-80. A *Morse Code Generator* is described that will generate random code characters for code practice, and a *Morse Code Sender* that will send predefined messages is also discussed. Speed may be varied as desired. A *Music Synthesizer* is defined that will play prerecorded or user-defined scores. The *envelope* of the notes may be shaped to create special effects. A *Timer with presets* is described that enables six outputs with programmable times from seconds to days. Two security applications, a *Burglar Alarm* and *Combination Lock,* are described. The *Burglar Alarm* monitors five inputs for switch closures and provides an audio alarm and visual report. The *Combination Lock* provides a virtually unbreakable combination that may be used to open doors or for control functions. A *Frequency Counter/Tachometer* application describes a general counter that counts at rates of less than one event per second to tens of thousands of events per second. A *Telephone Dialer* application provides automatic dialing of a number of commonly used telephone numbers. A *Microcomputer Educator* program permits the user to construct his or her own assembly-language program to learn the basics of this type of programming.

All of the applications presented in Section 3 are described in detail with complete applications programs that are ready to be used. Section 3 also describes how the user may implement other EZ-80 control projects, perform *distributed processing* and implement *intelligent controllers* using the EZ-80. A complete set of appendices provides information on binary and hexadecimal number systems and the Z-80 instruction set.

The projects in this book are really a starting point in two senses. Firstly, they will convince the reader that it *is* possible to use a microprocessor in place of a great deal of other electronic circuitry and to have as a result a much more adaptable piece of equipment. Secondly, they may give the reader the initiative to implement his or her own projects, using the EZ-80 as a high-speed computer communicating with the external world.

Special thanks are due John Albu for his pc board artwork.

WILLIAM BARDEN, JR.

To Barb, John, Jon, and Danny

Contents

Section 1

EZ-80 Theory

CHAPTER 1

CHAPTER 2

CHAPTER 3

CHAPTER 4

CHAPTER 5

CHAPTER 6

Section 2

EZ-80 Construction

CHAPTER 7

CHAPTER 8

CHAPTER 9

Section 3

EZ-80 Projects

CHAPTER 10

CHAPTER 11

CHAPTER 12

CHAPTER 13

CHAPTER 14

CHAPTER 15

CHAPTER 16

CHAPTER 17

CHAPTER 18

CHAPTER 19

CHAPTER 20

Appendices

APPENDIX A

APPENDIX B

APPENDIX C

APPENDIX D

APPENDIX E

APPENDIX F

SECTION 1

EZ-80 Theory

CHAPTER 1

EZ-80 Component Parts

This chapter discusses the general theory behind the EZ-80. Rather than discussing abstract computer design theory, we are going to rush into the general approach used on the EZ-80. The EZ-80 design is very similar in concept to most other *microcomputers* and *minicomputers* (and even much larger computers) and we will not lose any background in computer theory by this approach. As a mater of fact, since this is a concrete example of a working computer, the reader will have a sound basis in computer fundamentals if he or she studies the EZ-80 theory in the following chapters.

Suppose that you don't want to get into the nuts and bolts of computer theory as used for the EZ-80. That's fine. You may bypass these chapters and go directly into the construction of the EZ-80 and the specific projects in which you are interested. You may wish to come back to the theory *after* you have a working microcomputer. If your interests are in programming, another possible approach is to scan the theory chapter, construct the EZ-80, and then use the applications programs presented here or design your own.

Still another alternative is possible. Suppose you do not even want to build the EZ-80. The author's feelings will not be hurt if you wish to use the book as a reference text on simple microcomputers. The techniques presented here are adaptable to any microcomputer, and you may wish to design your own with some reference to this book.

This section, EZ-80 Theory, describes the general theory of the EZ-80. An overall picture is first presented, and the EZ-80 is broken down into component parts of central processing unit (cpu), memory, input/output (i/o), and software. Each of these components is then studied in some detail, as it relates to the EZ-80. Finally, in the last chapter of this section, the component parts are studied together as a package—the EZ-80.

EZ-80 CPU

The EZ-80 system in block diagram form is shown in Fig. 1-1. The *cpu,* or *c*entral *p*rocessing *u*nit, is the main controlling component of the system. Its functions are:

- To *fetch* and *execute* instructions from memory
- To store and retrieve *data* from memory
- To store and retrieve *data* from the input/output section
- To oversee all system functions

The cpu used in the EZ-80 is a microprocessor called the Z-80. The Z stands for Zilog, the original manufacturer of the Z-80 (several companies now manufacture it). The 80 has no particular significance, except that the microprocessor is an 8-bit microprocessor and supersedes another microprocessor, the Intel 8080.

The physical appearance of the Z-80 in the EZ-80 is shown in Fig. 1-2. As you can see, it is basically a 40-pin (40 legs, 20 per side) semiconductor integrated circuit. It is about 2 inches long by ½ inch wide.

Packed within that 1 square inch are tens of thousands of transistors that connect to implement a fully functional digital computer roughly comparable to the cpu of a small IBM computer of several years ago! The Z-80 can add hundreds of thousands of numbers per second and, by executing a variety of different types of instructions, can perform virtually any data processing task.

The *instruction set* of the cpu consists of about 200 different instruction *types.* Typical instructions are instructions to add two numbers, to subtract two numbers, to store a number in memory, or to retrieve a number from the outside world via input/output. The instructions are generic in nature so that many

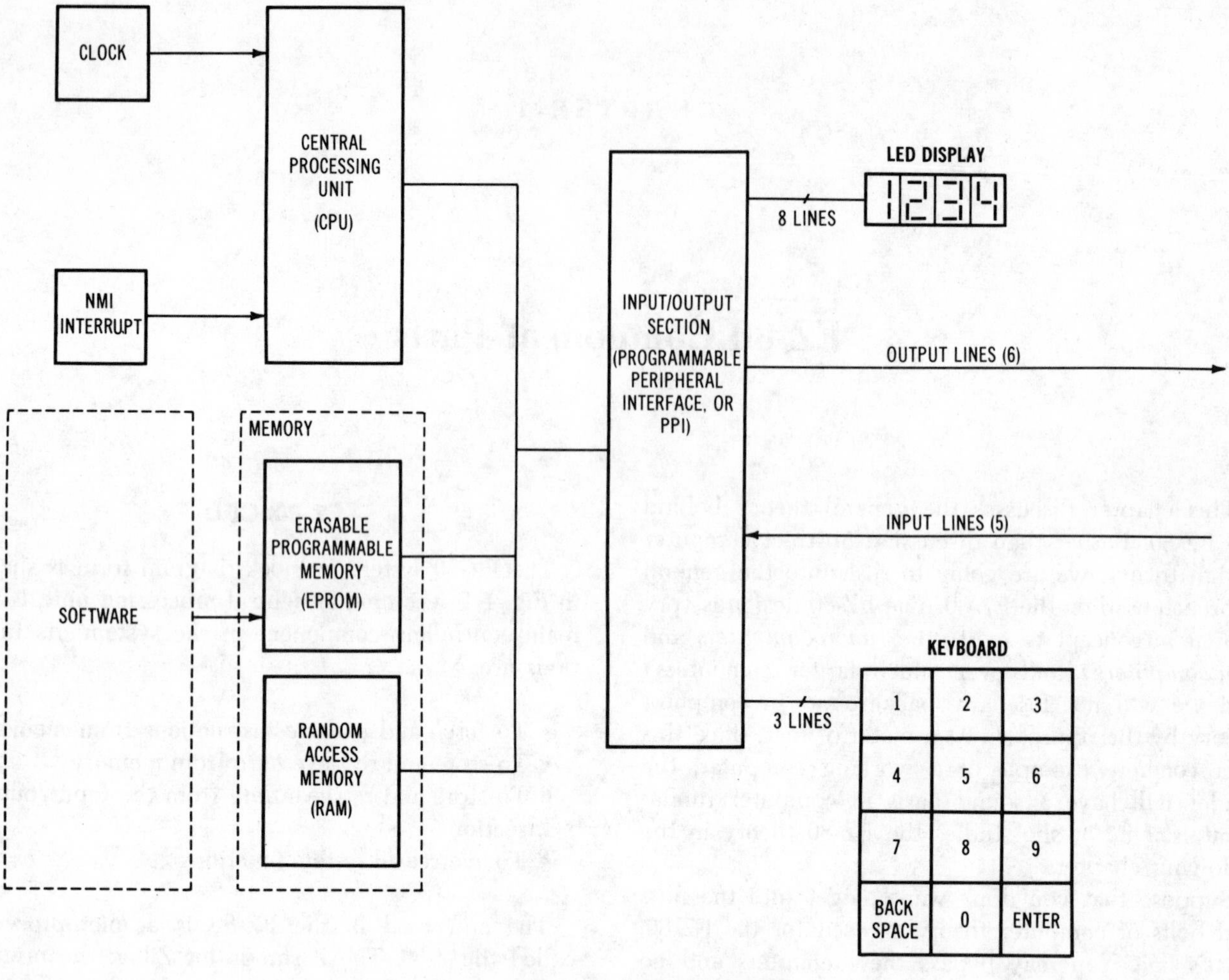

Fig. 1-1. EZ-80 system block diagram.

different applications may be built up from a sequence of hundreds of instructions called *programs*.

The cpu operates at a constant rate called the *clock frequency*. Every action within the cpu is broken down into increments of this clock frequency. The Z-80 microprocessor is capable of operating at clock frequencies of up to 4 million cycles per second. The clock frequency chosen for the EZ-80 is 1 million cycles per second to utilize a less expensive version of the Z-80 and to provide a good design safety margin. The block called "clock" (Fig. 1-1) is the circuitry that generates the 1 million cycles per second, or 1 megahertz (abbreviated 1 MHz), clock frequency. One megahertz simply means one million (mega) cycles per second (hertz).

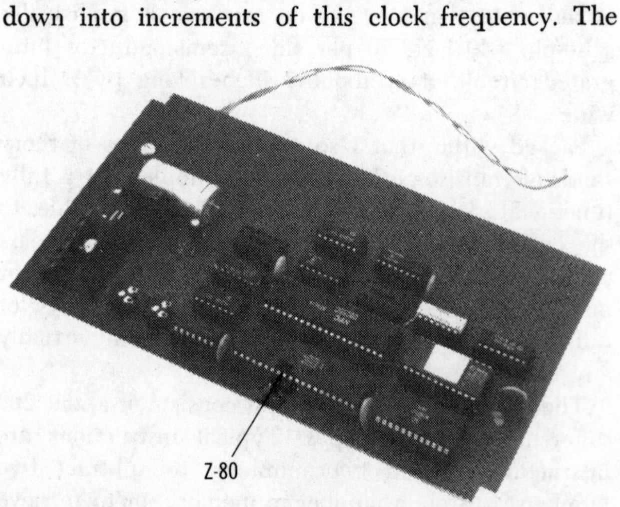

Fig. 1-2. Board with Z-80 microprocessor chip.

The *period* of the clock frequency is 1 microsecond (1 μs), or 1 millionth of a second (micro = millionth). Every action taken in the cpu occurs in increments of half the period. Each instruction that the cpu *executes* varies from 4 clock periods to over 20 clock periods, so the reader can see that instructions may be anywhere from 4 microseconds to over 20 microseconds long.

The NMI *interrupt* block is used to signal the cpu that another 1/100 of a second in the real world has passed. The clock (1 megahertz) and interrupt are separate functions. This 1/100 second, or *10/1000* second, or *10-millisecond* (10-ms) interrupt (milli = 1/1000) is used by the EZ-80 to keep track of time, as many program functions, such as using the EZ-80 as a timer, must have some provision for handling *real-time*. The 1-megahertz cpu clock cannot be used for this function because the cpu cannot reasonably keep track of how many clock cycles have elapsed.

EZ-80 MEMORY

The *memory* block of Fig. 1-1 is another major system component. Every computer has a memory to store programs and data. Programs are a sequence of instructions to be performed. Each instruction is *coded* as a unique numeric value. For example, an instruction that adds two numbers in the cpu is a 128, while an instruction that tests whether one number is larger than another is 184. Instructions are built up with a number of these numeric values ranging from one value (such as the 184) to four values, such as 221, 54, 0, 23, which transfers a value of 23 to a memory *location*. Every value in an instruction is some number from 0 to 255. We will see why this is true shortly.

Data is also stored in memory and, on a transient basis, in the cpu. "Data" is a generic term that describes a variety of information types. If the data is a telephone number such as 555-7004, for example, the data may be broken up into seven pieces and stored in seven *locations* in memory, each representing one digit (the dash is not stored in this example, but it could have been). If the data is an employee number of an Al-Joe-Eddie's Pizzeria employee, a small operation, the data might consist of one location in memory, as the employee number will never exceed 255. Data, in short, can be anything that can be broken down into digital form, and just about everything can.

Why is the range of numbers from 0 to 255 important? All instructions and data are stored in segments called *bytes*. A byte is a collection of eight *bits*. *Bit* is a contraction of the term *binary* digit. The EZ-80 is a *digital* computer. All data and instructions are in binary digital form in the EZ-80, as they are in all digital computers.

BINARY NOTATION

Binary numbers are made up of combinations of two digits: 0 and 1. One (1) represents an on condition, while zero (0) represents an off condition. Think of a room light switch as a binary device as it turns the light on (1) or off (0).

In our decimal notation system, a number represents powers of 10 as in the example in Fig. 1-3. Note

$$4 \times 10^0 = 4$$
$$3 \times 10^1 = 30$$
$$2 \times 10^2 = 200$$
$$1 \times 10^3 = \underline{1000}$$
$$1234$$

Fig. 1-3. Decimal number notation of 1234.

$$1 \times 2^0 = 1$$
$$0 \times 2^1 = 0$$
$$1 \times 2^2 = 4$$
$$1 \times 2^3 = 8$$
$$1 \times 2^4 = 16$$
$$0 \times 2^5 = 0$$
$$1 \times 2^6 = 64$$
$$1 \times 2^7 = \underline{128}$$
$$221$$

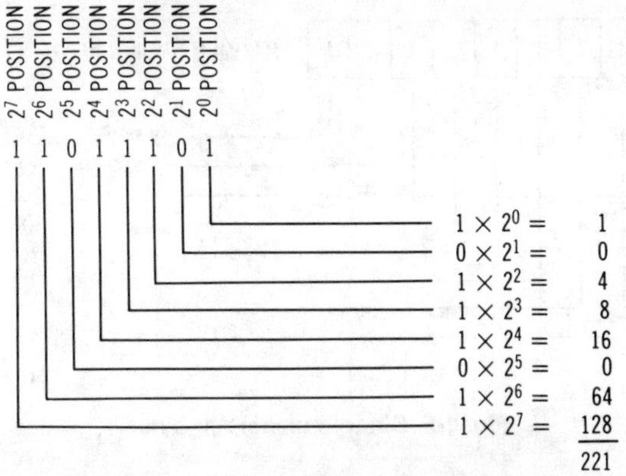

Fig. 1-4. Binary number notation for decimal 221.

that any number to the zero power is always 1. Just as our decimal system uses *positional notation* to represent powers of 10, the binary system uses positional notation to represent powers of 2. The binary number 11011101, for example, translates to the decimal number 221 as shown in Fig. 1-4.

The binary number above is made up of eight bits (binary digits) and represents the decimal equivalent, 221. In the EZ-80 and in many digital computers, each memory *location* holds one 8-bit number, or one byte. Each bit of the byte is held as an electrical condition of on or off, similar to the on/off condition of a switch. What is the maximum number that can be held in one byte? That number is the binary value 11111111, which represents the value shown in Fig. 1-5. Hence, there is the limitation on the values that we spoke of earlier. The range of values that can be held in 8 bits, or one byte, is 0 through 255 (00000000 to 11111111). Note that this does not mean that we cannot work with values larger than 255. It simply means that all data and instructions are broken up into 8-bit chunks.

To get back to the memory of the EZ-80, the EZ-80 memory is made up of two chips, each slightly smaller than the Z-80 microprocessor. The memory chips are much less complicated than the Z-80 in that they have only two functions: storage and retrieval of data. One of the chips is a 2758 EPROM (*Erasable Programmable Read-Only Memory*) while the other is 6810 RAM (*Random Access Memory*). The number assignments are not significant, but reflect the manufacturer's designation.

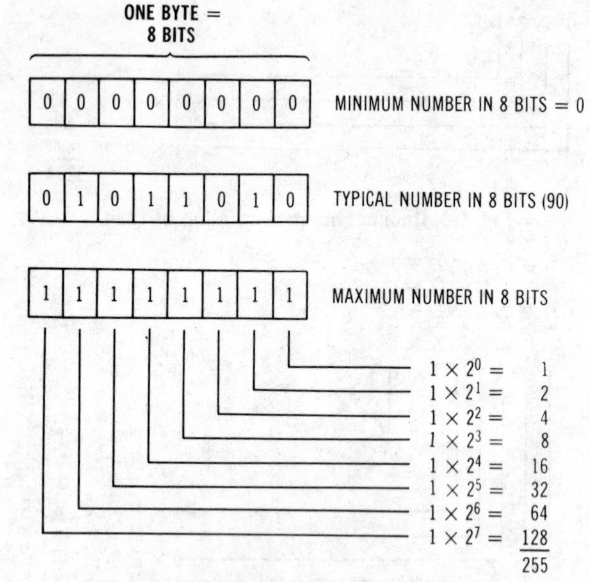

Fig. 1-5. Binary numbers in bytes.

EPROM MEMORY

The 2758 EPROM *architecture* is shown in Fig. 1-6. It is made up of 1024 memory locations, each 8 bits or one byte wide. The 2758 is sometimes designated a 1K×8 memory chip, where K stands for 1024 and 8 stands for 8 bits per location. Within the 1024 (2^{10}) locations, instructions or data for the cpu may be stored.

In the EZ-80 the EPROM locations are numbered 0 through 1023, for a total of 1024, counting 0. The cpu retrieves data a byte at a time from the EPROM by sending out an address over 16 address lines. The address is a collection of 16 bits, one for each address line. To retrieve the data stored in EPROM location 100, for example, the cpu puts the value of 100 on the 16 address lines, as shown in Fig. 1-7. As the maximum location in the EPROM is location 1023, the cpu will never *address* the EPROM with a binary value greater than 0000 0011 1111 1111.

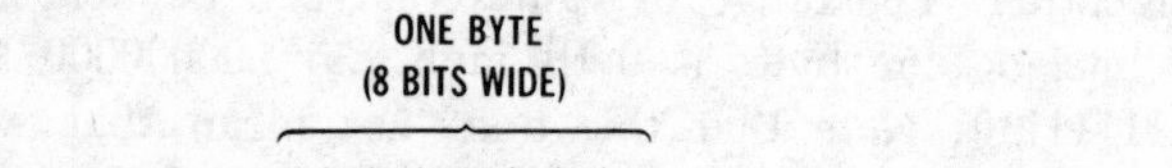

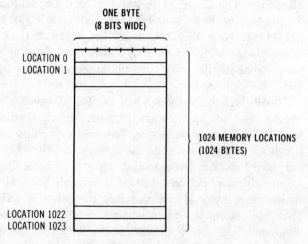

Fig. 1-6. EPROM architecture.

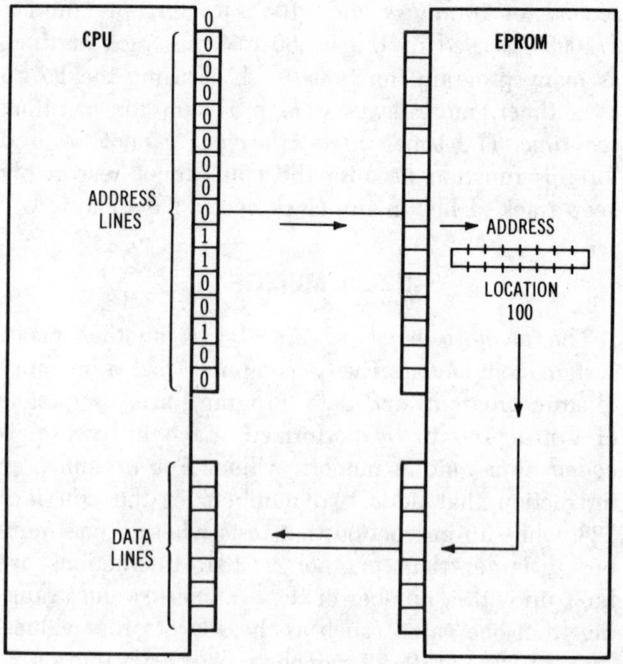

Fig. 1-7. EPROM operation.

At about the same instant that the cpu puts the EPROM address on the 16 address lines, it *reads in* the data from 8 data lines that connect to the memory. The data lines hold the 8 bits of data from the EPROM memory location that was addressed. In the course of executing a program the EPROM is addressed for new data and instructions hundreds of thousands of times per second. In the EZ-80 system the EPROM memory holds both the computer *program* broken up into 8-bit bytes and also some constant *data.* An example of the latter would be a constant value of 116, recorded in EPROM as a binary value of 0111 0100. In future references to data, we may mean *either* instructions or *data,* as they amount to the same thing. We will differentiate between instructions and data only when we mean one or the other.

The EPROM is a *read-only* memory. That means that data can be read out from the memory, but that nothing can be *written* to the memory. Since the EPROM is used in the EZ-80 to store programs and constant data (that never change), it is not necessary to write data into the EPROM. The term "EPROM," however, is a misnomer. The EPROM *must* have been loaded with the program and constant data at some point. That's obvious. The EPROM should really be called a *mostly* read and *seldom* write memory. To write data into the EPROM it is necessary to remove the EPROM from the system, *erase* old data by exposure to ultraviolet light, electrically *program* the EPROM a location at a time, and then put the EPROM back in the system with the new program and data. As the procedure does not lend itself to writing data tens of thousands of times per second, the EPROM was developed specifically for storing seldom-changing programs and constant data.

RAM MEMORY

The RAM memory used in the EZ-80, however, *is* a *read/write* memory. Data can be both written into the RAM and read from the RAM. The number of bytes that the RAM can hold is one-eighth the number of the EPROM, or 128 bytes. This is just an arbitrary size for the RAM which has been dictated by two factors: cost and storage requirements for the EZ-80. The size of RAM might have been much greater. Many microcomputers use up to 65,536 bytes of RAM rather than 128, but 128 bytes of RAM allow a great deal of storage for many applications. The principles of memory/cpu communication also apply to 128 bytes of RAM just as they do in larger configurations.

The 6810 RAM architecture used in the EZ-80 is shown in Fig. 1-8. The addresses of the 128 RAM locations are 2048 through 2175 (binary 0000 1000 0000 0000 through 0000 1000 0111 1111). The cpu addresses RAM by putting a 16-bit address in this range on the address lines and then *reading* 8 bits of data from the RAM or *writing* 8 bits of data to the RAM. The read or write function is sent to the RAM via the control lines.

Data is continually being transferred between the cpu and RAM memory. RAM is used to hold temporary results and data that will be used in the applications program. Note that EPROM data is permanent (or at least lasts 30 years or so); RAM data is destroyed once the power to the system is turned off. A term used for this type of storage is *volatile* memory—it remains only as long as power to the system is on.

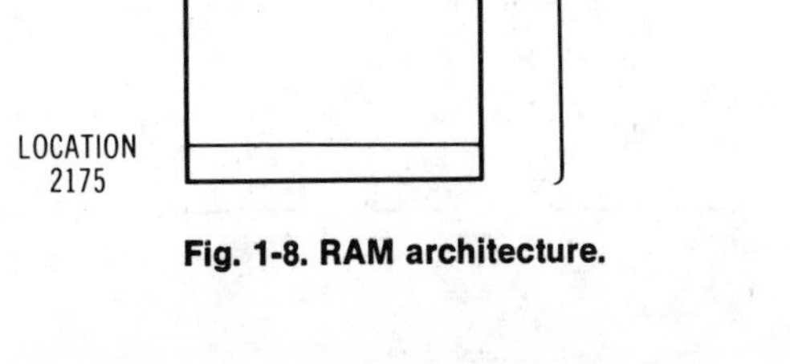

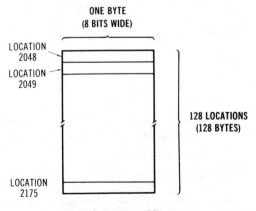

Fig. 1-8. RAM architecture.

EZ-80 INPUT/OUTPUT

Referring back to Fig. 1-1, let's look at another element of a typical microcomputer system. The *input/output* section, or *i/o*, is the system component that allows communication with the outside world. In the EZ-80 the outside world is connected by 24 lines from an 8255 PPI, or *p*rogrammable *p*eripheral *i*nterface chip. The 8255 is the same size as the Z-80 microprocessor chip and between the microprocessor and memory in complexity.

The 24 lines of the PPI represent 24 bits of binary data. There are four groups of the 24 lines in the EZ-80. Eight of the lines go to the LED display. The LED (*l*ight *e*mitting *d*iode) display is a common calculator-type display that allows four decimal digits to be displayed. Another 3 lines are *input* lines that come from the keyboard. The keyboard is similar to a telephone-style push-button keypad. The digits 0 through 9 and two other buttons may be input to the Z-80 via the PPI. Another 5 lines are input lines from the outside world. These may connect to burglar alarm switches, to fire sensors, or to other on/off devices. The remaining 6 lines are output lines that are used to send data from the EZ-80 to the outside world to open doors, send audio signals to a speaker, and so forth.

The PPI is an i/o *interface* that is *addressed* similarly to a memory location. The cpu can send one byte of data to the PPI and the PPI will then route it to the appropriate set of lines to display LED data or to signal the outside world. The cpu may also read one byte of data representing the state (0 or 1) of the five input lines or a digit from the keyboard.

EZ-80 SOFTWARE

Another element shown in Fig. 1-1 is the EZ-80 *software*. The system software depends upon the application. For the applications of this book, from 600 to 1200 bytes of software may be required, representing a complete program. Since the average instruction is about 2 bytes long, the programs in this book consist of about 300 to 600 instructions, all stored in the EPROM. The chief advantage of the EZ-80 over a comparable "hard-wired" piece of equipment is that the latter cannot be changed except by rewiring whereas the EZ-80 may be much more easily changed by rewriting the program. As a consequence the EZ-80 is much more flexible and can be put to a variety of uses. We'll be talking a great deal more about software and programming in later chapters.

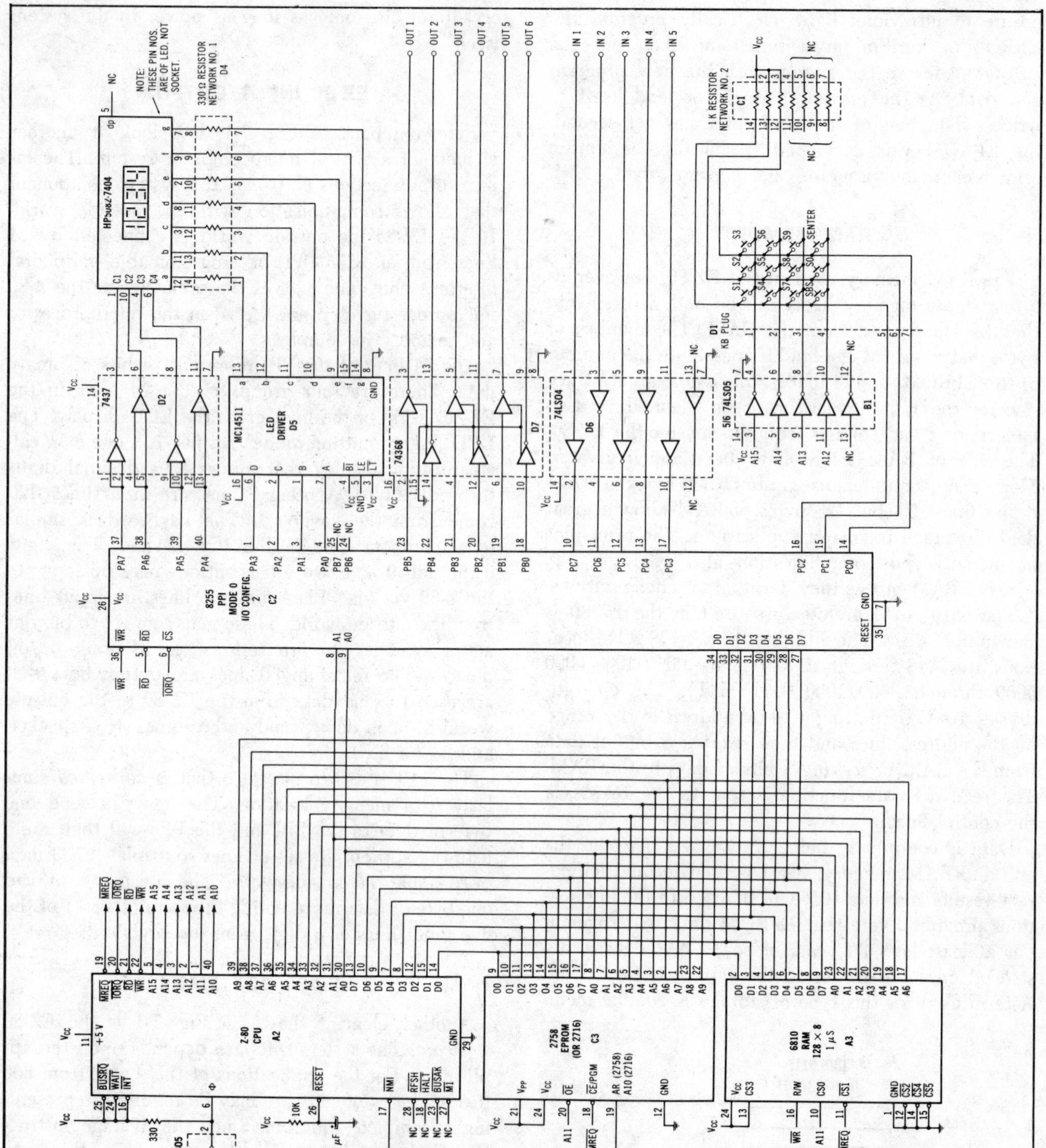

Fig. 1-9. EZ-80 logic diagram.

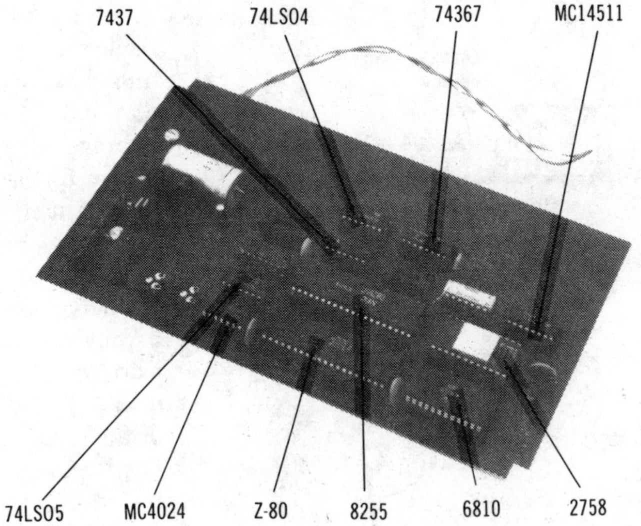

Fig. 1-10. EZ-80 microcomputer board.

EZ-80 LOGIC DIAGRAM

Fig. 1-9 is the *logic diagram* of the complete EZ-80. Each rectangle (sold-line or broken line) represents a semiconductor integrated circuit. The layout of Fig. 1-9 roughly corresponds to the layout in Fig. 1-1. The physical counterpart to Fig. 1-9 is shown in Fig. 1-10, which shows the parts mounted on a board and identifies each semiconductor. The construction of the EZ-80 involves connecting the lines shown in Fig. 1-9. Each line represents a *signal* from a semiconductor pin. The A9 (Address Line 9) pin of the Z-80, for example, connects from pin 39 of the Z-80 to pin 22 (A9) of the 2758 EPROM. We'll be discussing each of the component parts of the EZ-80 in detail in the chapters of this section.

Let's discuss some of the symbology used in Fig. 1-9. Different symbols shown in Fig. 1-9 represent semiconductors, resistors, capacitors, switches, and, within the semiconductor rectangles, inverters.

As Figs. 1-9 and 1-10 show, there are four sizes of semiconductors in the EZ-80. The Z-80 and PPI are 40-pin devices with 20 pins on each side. The 2758 EPROM and 6810 RAM are 24-pin devices with 12 pins per side. The remaining devices are either 14-pin devices (7 per side) or 16-pin devices (8 per side). Fig. 1-9 shows all pins on the devices, their signal names (within the rectangle), the pin number (outside of the rectangle), and the connections to other components or devices within the system.

The capacitors are *discrete* components (not semiconductors). The capacitor is a device for storing energy and is used in the clock and interrupt circuits. The symbols for the capacitors are shown in Fig. 1-11A. Physically, they appear as disks or small tubular components as shown in Fig. 1-11B.

Resistors come in two types. A device that holds seven resistors is used to simplify wiring. The appearance of such a resistor pack is similar to a semiconductor chip. Another type is a discrete resistor, which is shown in Fig. 1-12A along with the symbol for the resistor. A resistor is used to limit current. In the EZ-80 it is used primarily as a "pull-up," that is, a connection to a positive voltage. Fig. 1-12B shows a potentiometer, or a variable-resistance resistor.

There is only one set of switches used in the EZ-80 proper (there is a power supply switch)—the switches on the keyboard. The symbol for the switch is shown in Fig. 1-9.

The inverters within some of the broken lines are represented by a triangle with a circle at the apex.

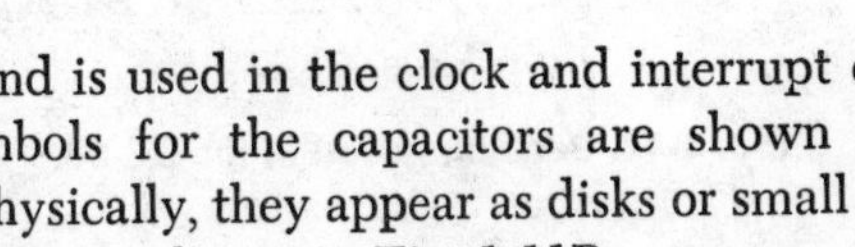

(A) Symbols.

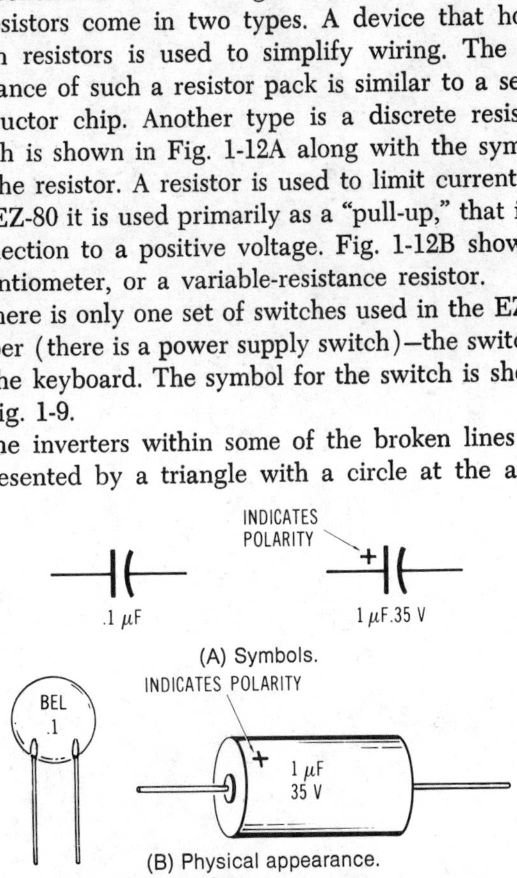

(B) Physical appearance.

Fig. 1-11. Capacitors used in the EZ-80.

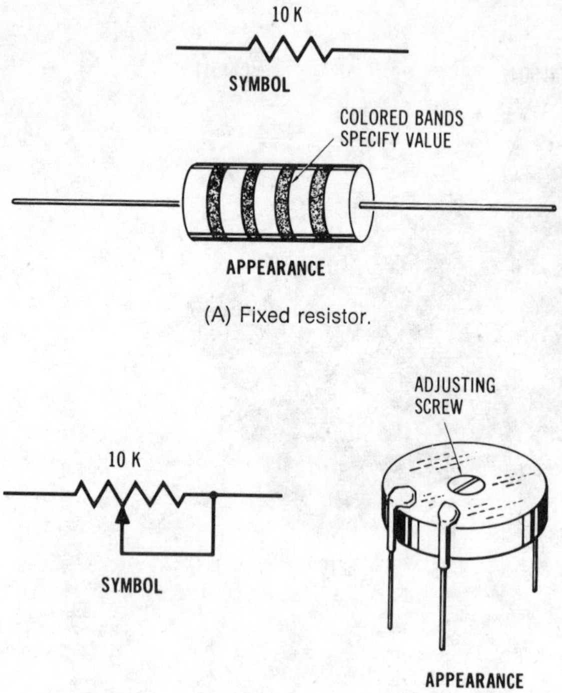

(B) Potentiometer.

Fig. 1-12. Resistors used in the EZ-80.

The only function of an inverter is to invert a binary value from a 1 to a 0 or from a 0 to a 1. This is usually necessary to match the logical requirements of one device to another. For example, the LED display must have a logical 0 on pin 1 for the leftmost digit on the display to light. The inverters within the 7437 package invert the binary 1 which appears on the output of the PPI to a binary 0 to enable the display of a digit in the leftmost position. (Another function of the inverter in this case is to provide higher current than is normally available from the PPI chip.)

The voltage used for the EZ-80 is +5 volts dc. The 5 volts is a common voltage used with MOS (metal-oxide semiconductors—the Z-80 and larger semiconductors) and TTL (transistor-transistor logic—most of the remaining parts). When binary levels are translated into physical voltages, a binary 1 is expressed by +3.0 to +5 volts, while a binary 0 is expressed by about 0 volts. The V_{CC} represents the +5 volts and the GND or ⏚ symbol represents the ground line of the +5-volt power supply.

In the following chapters of this section we'll be looking in detail at the cpu, memory and i/o sections of the EZ-80, using this introductory chapter as a basis.

CHAPTER 2

The CPU Section

The cpu section of the EZ-80 is discussed in detail in this chapter. The basis of the cpu is the Zilog Z-80 microprocessor, an 8-bit microprocessor that has become extremely popular for all types of designs incorporating a general-purpose microprocessor. The Z-80 requires a minimum of *support circuitry,* that is, a working microcomputer can be implemented using just a few additional components with the Z-80. In this chapter we'll discuss the internal structure of the Z-80, the *pinouts* or signals going into or originating from the Z-80, and the processing *cycles* of the Z-80. In other chapters in this section we'll see how memory, i/o, and software relate to the Z-80.

GENERAL CHARACTERISTICS OF THE Z-80

The Z-80 is a "third-generation" microprocessor. Its grandfather was the Intel 8008 and its father was the Intel 8080. The built-in instruction set of the Z-80 contains instructions that were used in the 8008 and 8080, and the internal layout, or architecture, of the Z-80 is built along the same lines as the 8008 and 8080.

The instruction set of the 8008 is 58 instructions and the instruction set of the 8080 is 78 instructions. The Z-80 includes all of the 78 instructions of the 8080 and adds quite a few more to provide about 158 total instruction types. In addition, the speed at which instructions can be *executed* is about twice as fast on the Z-80 than in the 8080, and an order of magnitude faster than the 8008. In addition, the Z-80 requires far fewer *support* chips than either the 8080 or 8008. Both the 8008 and 8080 required quite a few chips (8–12) just to generate a clock signal, to decode the signals originating from the microprocessor, and to drive other parts of the system.

ARCHITECTURE OF THE Z-80

Let's take a look at the internal architecture of the Z-80 in light of its predecessors. The most elemental part of the Z-80 and any other microprocessor as far as data handling is concerned is a *register.* In this case the register is termed *cpu register* since it is in the microprocessor. A register is simply a storage cell or memory location in the cpu. Like other memory locations in many microcomputer systems, it is 8 bits wide, that is, it can hold 8 bits of data as shown in Fig. 2-1.

The main register for data handling in the Z-80 is the *A register.* The A register's name is derived from the term accumulator register. It is the register in many systems that accumulates the results of adds, subtracts, and other operations. If two *operands* are added in the Z-80, for example, one of the operands is held in the A register, the operands are added, and *result* of the add is put back in the A register. As the A register is 8 bits wide, the operands must be decimal 0 to 255 and the result must be 0 to 255. Adds of larger numbers are performed by other methods which we'll discuss later. Almost *all* arithmetic operations are performed by use of the A register, however. The A register is shown in Fig. 2-2.

One of the chief functions of the Z-80 cpu and of any microprocessor is to perform *arithmetic* operations, that is, adds or subtracts. The portion of the Z-80 that implements this is called the *arithmetic and logic unit,* or *alu.* One of the inputs to the alu is the A register, as shown in Fig. 2-3. The second input to the alu is an 8-bit operand from a *memory location* or from *another cpu general-purpose register.* The output of the alu generally goes to the A register, destroying the previous contents of the A register. Suppose that the A register contained decimal 53 and that a memory location used as the second operand contained decimal 27. An ADD instruction that added the contents of the A register and the memory location would add 53 (A register) and 27 (the location in external memory), and the result of 80 would be put back into the A register, replacing the 53. The alu can perform adds, subtracts, logical operations such

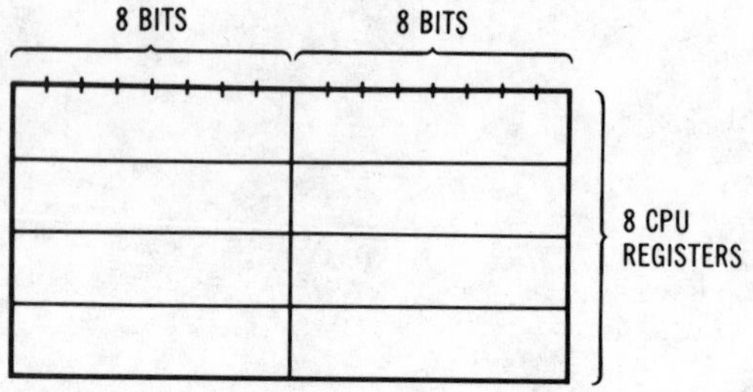

Fig. 2-1. Registers of the cpu.

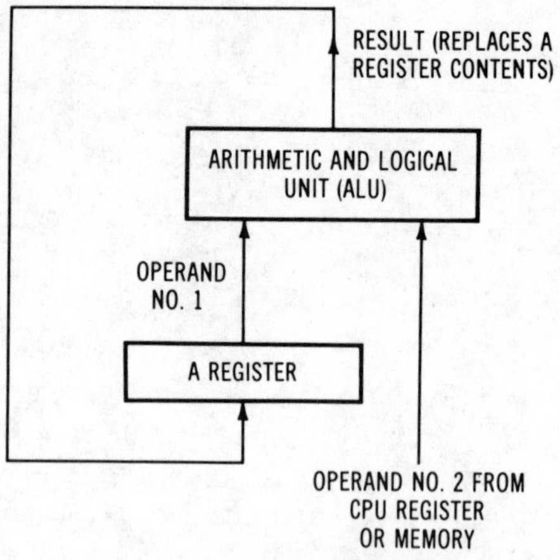

Fig. 2-3. Arithmetic and logical operations.

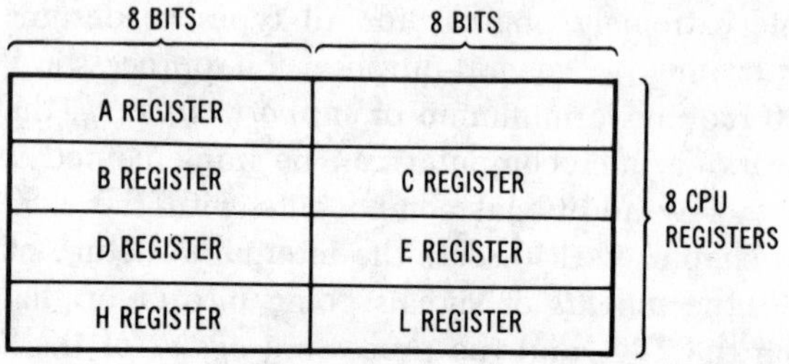

Fig. 2-4. General-purpose registers.

as ANDS and ORS, shifts—such as moving the contents of a register one bit to the right—and other operations. We'll discuss these in later chapters.

While the Z-80 A register is generally dedicated to being used for arithmetic operations and other functions, the Z-80 contains other general-purpose registers. For reasons which may become obvious, six of these are designated B, C, D, E, H, and L. They are shown in Fig. 2-4. Each of them is 8 bits wide, as is the A register, so they can hold binary values of 0000 0000 (0) to 1111 1111 (255). These general-purpose registers are used to hold intermediate results or for temporary storage. For example, the result of an ADD could be moved from the A register to the D register by the Z-80 instruction LD D,A, *Load D with A.* In general, these registers are continually being used in programs to hold intermediate results. Why not use external memory for this purpose? The cpu registers can be accessed much more rapidly and simply than an external memory location. (It takes over three times as long to store the A register into a given external memory location than into the B register—for example, 13 microseconds versus 4 microseconds in the EZ-80.)

As the reader can see from Fig. 2-4, we have grouped the seven registers in the Z-80 in sets of two. Register B is associated with C, D with E, and H with L. The registers taken two at a time constitute *register pairs* of BC, DE, and HL. Certain instructions in the Z-80 allow the registers to be treated this way. When register pairs are used in this fashion, they are really a single *16-bit* register rather than two separate 8-bit registers. The HL register pair, for example, now looks like the register shown in Fig. 2-5, a 16-bit register with bit positions numbered from 15 to 0, left to right. When registers are used in this manner, they can hold 16 bits of information, allowing arithmetic operations of 16 bits at a time. An operand in the BC register pair can be added to an operand in the HL register pair through the alu, for example. The result is put into the HL register pair. Sixteen-bit adds and subtracts use the HL register pair in a manner analogous to the A register. It is the "16-bit accumulator" that holds one of the operands before the add or subtract and the result after the operation. Fig. 2-5 shows the 8- and 16-bit arrangement of the general-purpose registers in the Z-80.

There is an eighth register in the cpu that fills the vacant space for the register associated with the A

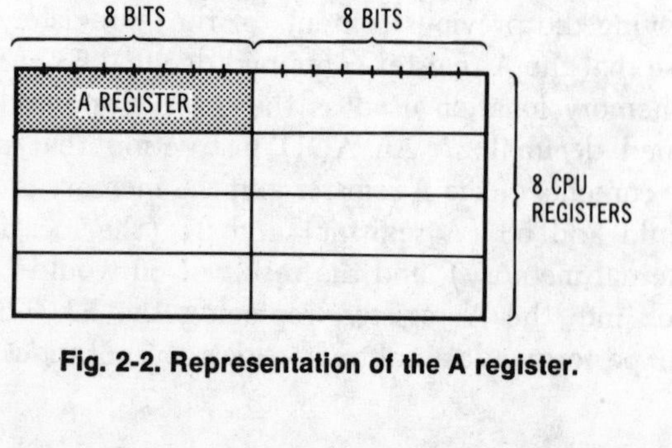

Fig. 2-2. Representation of the A register.

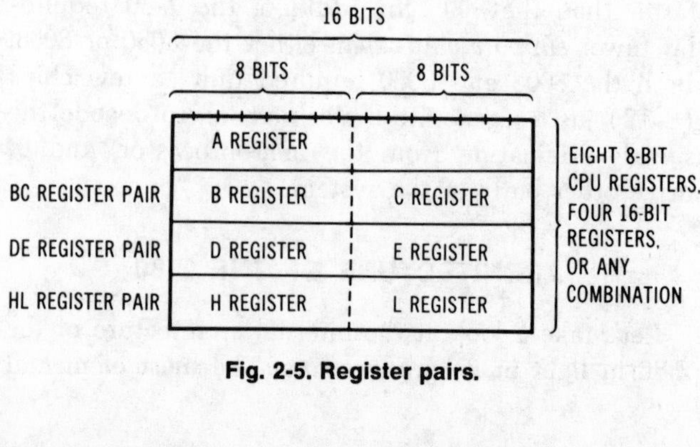

Fig. 2-5. Register pairs.

register. This is the *flags register*, or F. The flags are 1-bit cells within the Z-80 cpu that contain information about the results of operations. Adding two operands, for example, sets the Z(ero) flag if the result of the add is zero, and sets the S(ign) flag if the result is a negative number. The flags are grouped as the F register and make up the second register of the AF register pair, as shown in Fig. 2-6. The flags can be tested by certain instructions within the program such as JP M,1234, which causes a jump to location 1234 if the result is minus, or negative. In general, the flags are set by the alu and are shown as being associated with it.

The register pairs BC, DE, and HL are not only used to hold 16-bit data for arithmetic operations. The original use of the HL register pair in the 8008 was to act as a *pointer* to an external memory location. The H(igh) register contained the 8 high-order bits of the memory address, while the L(ow) register contained the 8 low-order bits of the memory address. This use is carried over into the Z-80. In the EZ-80, for example, the HL register pair can be loaded with the value of decimal 1023 (0000 0011 1111 1111) and an instruction such as LD A,(HL) executed. In this example the A register would be loaded with the 8-bit value from memory location 1023. The HL register pair would have been used as a pointer to the memory location for the load operation. Although HL was the original register pair used for this type of addressing, instructions to use BC and DE were added in the 8080 and Z-80. Use of register pairs in

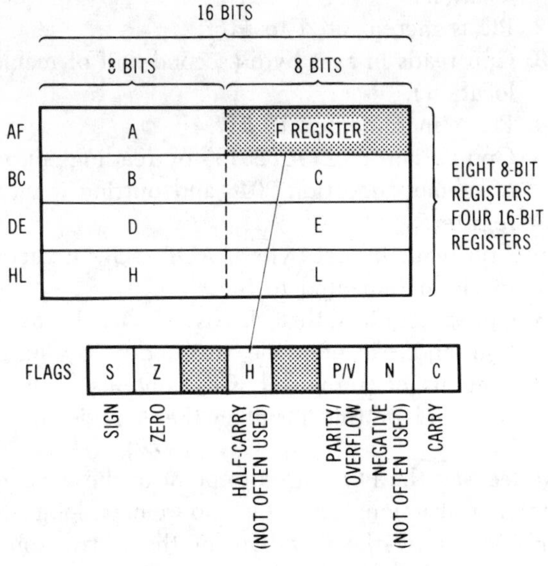

Fig. 2-6. Flag register and general-purpose registers.

addressing will be covered in the software chapter of this section.

Actually, we haven't been quite complete in discussing the general registers in the cpu. The registers we've been discussing consist of eight general-purpose registers including the flags, as shown in Fig. 2-6. There is really a *duplicate* set of these registers, designated the primed (′) set, as shown in Fig. 2-7. However, only eight of the sixteen can be used at any given time. The choice between one or the other is made by two Z-80 instructions that select either AF or AF′, and B through L or B′ through L′. At any given time, then, the program has only eight of the sixteen available although the other set can be selected in a few millionths of a second. Why have two sets? For one thing, extra storage capability in the cpu is sometimes required. Since the second set can be switched to rapidly, a second reason is that two sets make *interrupt handling* more efficient. We'll cover the second reason later in this book.

In addition to the sixteen general-purpose registers, the Z-80 cpu has six other registers that are available to the EZ-80 user through programming (see Fig. 2-8). Two of these are 16-bit index registers designated IX and IY. The index registers were not in the 8080 and have been added in the Z-80 to enable a type of addressing capability called *indexing*. Indexing allows the IX or IY register to be used as a type of indirect pointer similar to the HL or other register. We'll discuss indexing in the software chapter of this section.

The I and R registers are two special-purpose registers used for interrupts and memory refresh logic. The I register is used to allow up to 128 different *interrupts* to signal external conditions such as "keyboard character typed," "out of paper," or "house burning down." We will be using only one type of

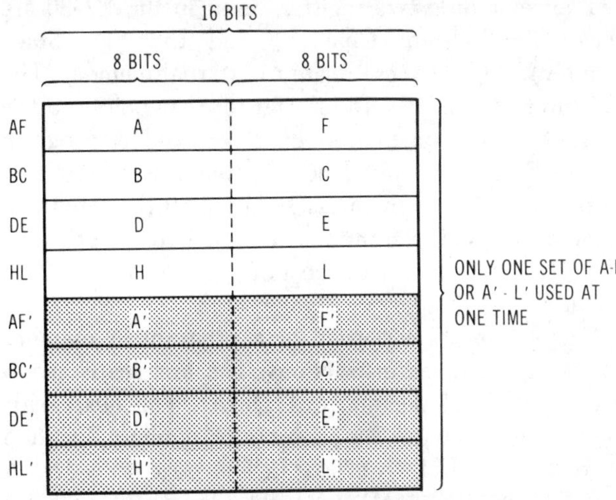

Fig. 2-7. Primed and unprimed registers.

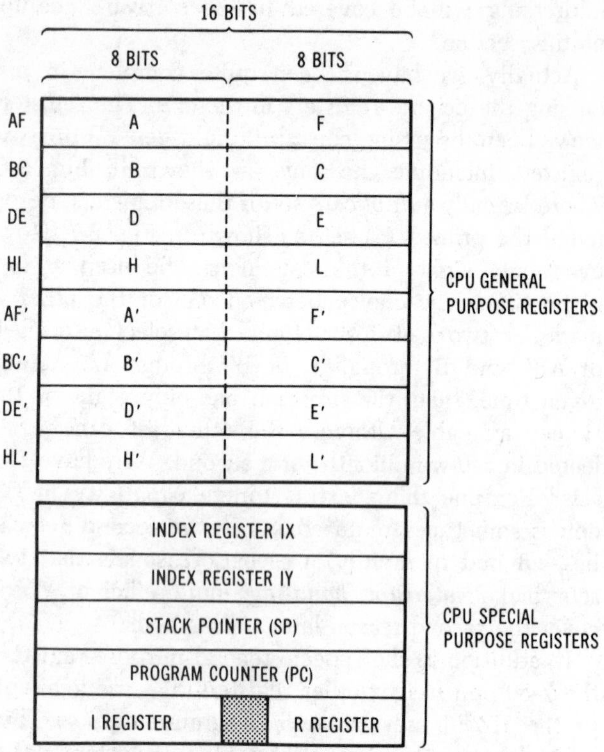

Fig. 2-8. Complete Z-80 register set.

interrupt, the *non-maskable interrupt,* for the EZ-80 so the I register will not be used in our design. The NMI (*non-maskable interrupt*) is discussed later in this section.

The R register is likewise not used for the EZ-80. The R(efresh) register is an 8-bit register that is used to provide a refresh address for a type of microcomputer memory called "dynamic" memory. As the memory used in the EZ-80 is "static" memory and does not need to be continually refreshed (or have data restored), the R register will not be discussed.

The remaining two registers used in the EZ-80 are the PC (*P*rogram *C*ounter) and the SP (*S*tack *P*ointer). Both of these relate to external memory. The program counter is a 16-bit register that points to the current instruction that is being executed. A program in the EZ-80 and any other computer is a string of instructions in the memory. In the Z-80 the length of each instruction is from one to four bytes. Let's look at a typical program to see how the PC in the Z-80 operates.

Fig. 2-9 shows a portion of a program in memory consisting of three instructions. The first loads the B register with 15 decimal (LD B,15). The next loads the A register with the contents of memory location 2048 decimal [LD A,(2048)]. The next adds the A and B registers (ADD A,B). The length of each instruction and its memory location are given on the

MEMORY LOCATION	LENGTH	PROGRAM	
512, 513	2	LD B,15	;15 TO B REGISTER
514, 515, 516	3	LD A,(2048)	;GET LOCATION 2048
517	1	ADD A,B	
518		(OTHER INSTRUCTIONS) ↓	

Fig. 2-9. Program counter use.

left side of the figure. The execution of these three instructions proceeds as follows:

1. PC initially set to 512 decimal.
2. First byte of LD B,15 instruction is loaded into cpu.
3. PC increments to 513.
4. Cpu recognizes that this is an LD B type instruction and knows that it must read in the contents of location 513.
5. Cpu reads in second byte of LD B,15 instruction.
6. PC incremented to 514.
7. Cpu *executes* LD B,15 by loading B register with 15.
8. First byte of LD A,(2048) instruction is loaded into cpu.
9. PC is incremented to 515.
10. Cpu recognizes that this is an LD A type instruction that will load from a memory location.
11. Cpu reads in next byte (first half of memory location).
12. PC is incremented to 516.
13. Cpu reads in next byte (second half of memory location).
14. PC is incremented to 517.
15. Cpu executes LD A,(2048) by reading contents of memory location 2048 and putting it into A register.
16. Cpu reads in first byte of ADD A,B instruction.
17. PC is incremented to 518.
18. Cpu recognizes that this is ADD A,B instruction and executes the instruction by adding contents of A register with contents of B register and putting result in the A register.

Notice that the PC is used to point to the next byte of each instruction. The cpu knows how long each instruction is by the first byte of the instruction. If the instruction is more than one byte long, additional reads of memory locations are made until the entire instruction is assembled in the cpu. This preliminary fetching of the bytes of the instruction is the *fetch* cycle. Once the instruction is assembled in the cpu, the cpu executes the instruction by performing the proper operation. In some cases this can be done with only data in the cpu (ADD A,B), while in other cases additional data must be retrieved from other memory locations *unrelated to the current location of the instruction.*

The PC is incremented by one for each new byte of the instruction read, but remains unaffected for other data read from memory during the execution portion of an instruction. The PC is exactly what the name implies; it points to or counts the location of the next instruction.

The program normally proceeds one instruction after another in sequence as in Fig. 2-9. However, the sequence of instructions can be altered from one instruction after another to a new path by a *jump* instruction. A jump instruction transfers control to a new set of instructions somewhere in memory. If the next instruction after the ones in Fig. 2-9 was a JP 636, the PC would be loaded with the value of 636, and the instructions starting at memory location 636 would be executed. In this way, a program may have literally thousands of paths, or branches, even in a program as short as 500 instructions. The program path is altered by jumps based on *conditions* such as zero result, minus, or equality or simply on *unconditional* jumps that always cause a jump to a new location.

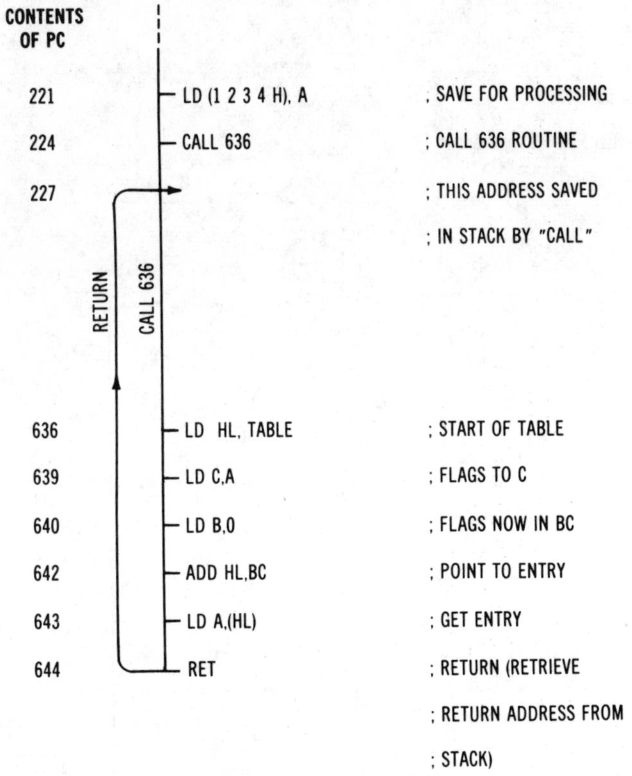

Fig. 2-10. Use of stack.

The SP (Stack Pointer) is another 16-bit register associated with memory. Whereas the PC always points to the location of the next byte of the current instruction, the SP points to the next *stack* location. The stack is an area of memory reserved for storage of certain types of data. The data may be stored in the stack in lieu of storing it in cpu registers or in another part of memory. Most significantly, the stack is used to save *addresses* for certain types of jump instructions.

When a "JP 636" is executed, the PC is loaded with 636 to start execution at memory location 636. The location of the instruction after the jump is not saved. The program does not know from which point the jump was made if location 636 is entered from several different points. However, executing a "CALL 636" *does* save the address after the CALL so that a return could be made at some later point as shown in Fig. 2-10. The return address is automatically saved in the stack area when the CALL is executed, and a subsequent RET(urn) instruction will retrieve the return address, load it into the PC, and cause a return to the next instruction after the CALL. We will learn more about the use of the stack for CALLs, temporary storage, and interrupts in a later chapter.

As both the PC and SP are 16 bits, along with the other register pairs and index registers used for addressing memory, the maximum memory address can be 1111 1111 1111 1111, or 65,535 decimal. Because of this 16-bit limitation, the maximum amount of external memory in any Z-80 system (without special *banking* schemes) can be 65,536 bytes (0–65,535).

In addition to the cpu registers discussed above, there are many other "invisible" registers used for holding the instruction to be decoded, holding the memory address for instruction execution, and other functions. As we're not concerned with *how* the instruction set is implemented in the Z-80 as much as how the Z-80 interacts with memory, i/o, and the rest of the system, we will not be discussing the remaining Z-80 registers.

Z-80 INPUT AND OUTPUT SIGNALS

Now that we've seen some of the internal architecture of the Z-80 as it relates to the external memory and i/o, let's talk about the electrical inputs and outputs of the Z-80 microprocessor. Fig. 2-11 shows the Z-80 as it is connected in the EZ-80.

The power supply inputs to the Z-80 are +5 volts dc and ground (pins 11 and 29 respectively). All signal inputs and outputs are *TTL compatible,* which

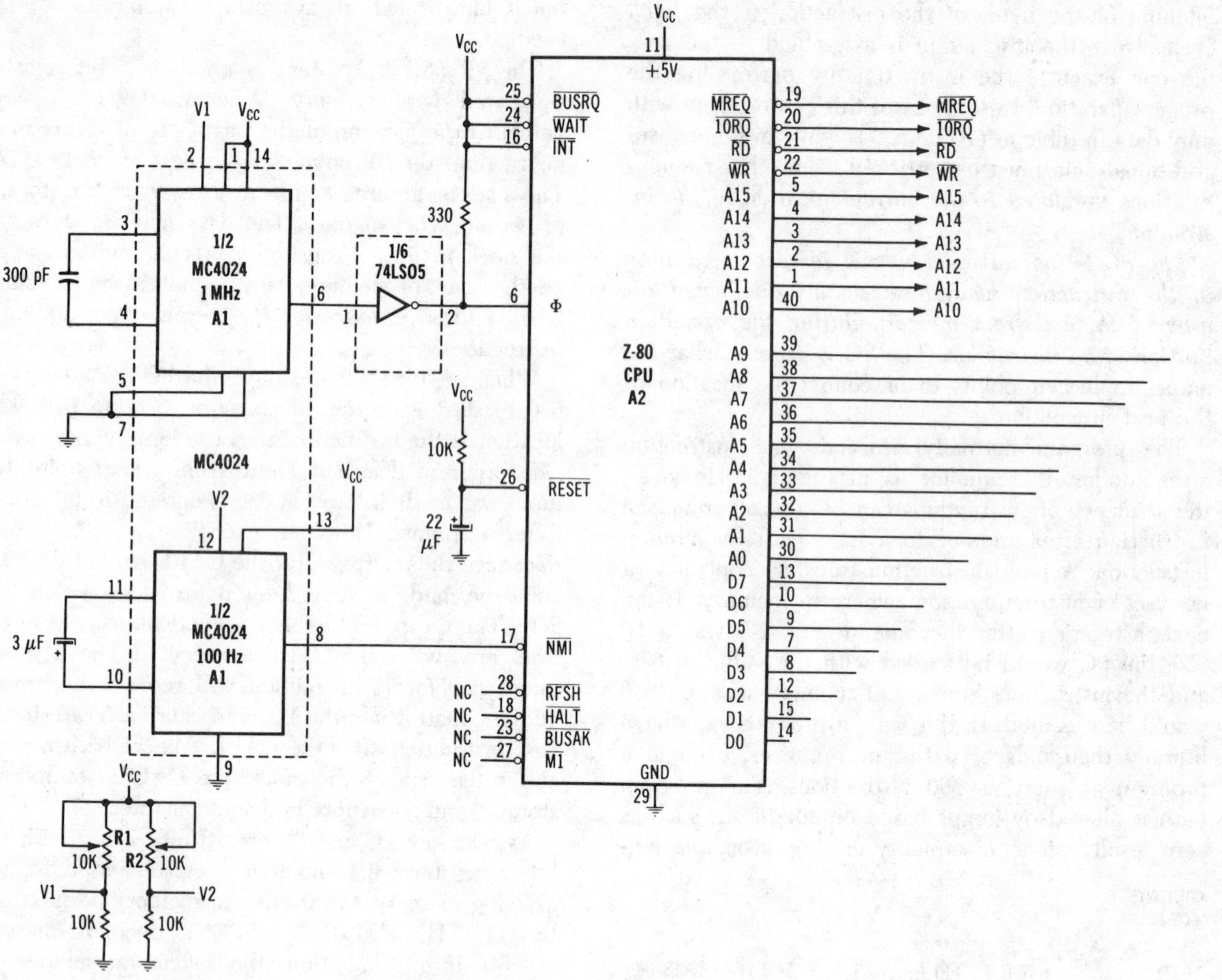

Fig. 2-11. The Z-80 IC in the EZ-80 system.

means that a logic 0 is approximately 0 volts and a logic 1 is 3.0 to 5 volts. The exception to this is the *clock input* at pin 6 which must be "pulled-up" by a 330-ohm resistor as shown.

The clock input is a simple square-wave input that appears as shown in Fig. 2-12. The frequency of the square wave is 1 megahertz (one million cycles per second) in the implementation of the EZ-80. This frequency was chosen for convenience and to give enough tolerance for the type of clock circuit chosen. The clock circuit shown in the figure is a *multivibrator* circuit contained in one-half of an MC4024 integrated circuit. This chip produces a square-wave output dependent upon the value of the capacitor and resistor attached to pins 3 and 4 of the chip. The value shown generates approximately 1 MHz. The output at pin 6 is buffered by an inverter (74LS05) which is an "open-collector" type that allows the square wave to approach 5 volts instead of a somewhat lower voltage.

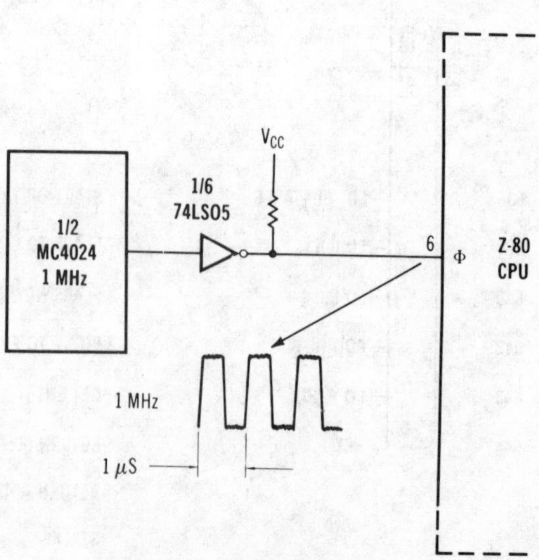

Fig. 2-12. Cpu clock.

The 0- to 5-volt swing fulfills the requirements of the Z-80 clock specification.

Every instruction executed within the Z-80 is divided up into *T cycles,* which are essentially clock cycles. Each *T* cycle is 1 microsecond (1 millionth of a second) long. The number of *T* cycles within an instruction varies from 4 to 23, making the execution time of instructions from 4 to 23 microseconds.

There are two main *buses* originating from the Z-80: the data bus and the address bus. A bus is simply a collection of lines. The data bus lines are D7 through D0, with D7 the most significant (highest binary weight of 128). All data that passes between the cpu and memory, and between the cpu and i/o, is transferred along the data bus. This includes all bytes read from memory for instructions, all operands that are transferred between cpu and memory, and all data that goes to or comes from external i/o. The data bus is byte-oriented, and all data is transferred 8 bits or one byte at a time.

The address bus is the second bus originating from the Z-80. It is made up of 16 lines, A15 through A0, with A15 the most significant. The address bus is used to address memory for fetches of instruction bytes and operand data.

Let's see how a typical instruction is executed. The instruction LD A,(1024) loads the cpu A register with the contents of memory location 1024 (see Fig. 2-13). The sequence is something like the following:

1. FETCH:
   (a) PC contents of 511 put on address bus.
   (b) Contents of memory location 511 transferred from memory along data bus to cpu.
   (c) PC is incremented by 1.
   (d) Cpu decodes the instruction as a "LD A, with memory location" type and knows it must fetch two more bytes for the memory address.
   (e) PC contents of 512 put on address bus.
   (f) Contents of memory location 512 transferred from memory along data bus to cpu.
   (g) PC is incremented by 1.
   (h) PC contents of 513 put on address bus.
   (i) Contents of memory location 513 transferred from memory along data bus to cpu.
   (j) PC is incremented by 1.
2. EXECUTION:
   (a) Cpu now has address for load (1024).
   (b) Address of 1024 put on address bus.
   (c) Contents of memory location 1024 transferred from memory along data bus to cpu register A.
3. FETCH:
   (a) Next instruction fetched.

. . . .

The address bus was used to hold both the address of the instruction being executed and the memory location to be loaded into the A register. The data bus transferred both the three bytes of the LD A,(1024) instruction and one byte of data from location 1024. During the fetch cycle the instruction bytes were transferred, while the operand byte was transferred during the execution cycle. Fetch and execution of all instructions proceeds in this fashion.

Associated with the read of memory data was a signal, $\overline{RD}$. $\overline{RD}$ serves to let the memory know whether data is to be read from or written to memory. In this case all memory accesses were read. The bar

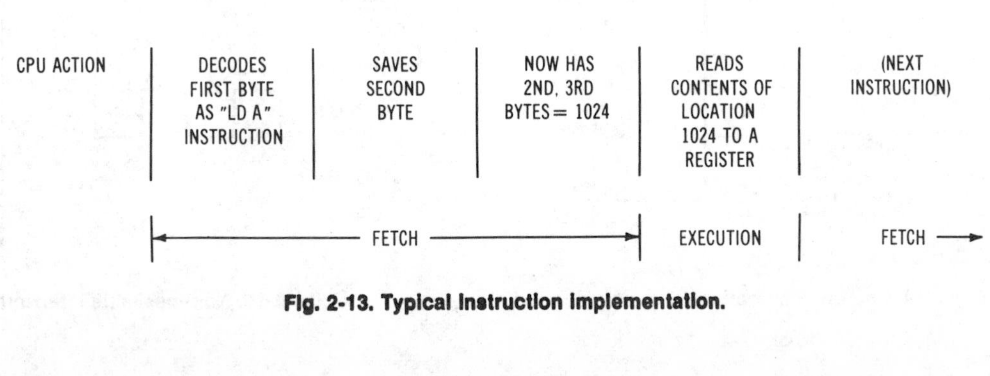

Fig. 2-13. Typical Instruction Implementation.

above the "RD" signifies that the signal is logically *false* when the condition is met. When signal $\overline{\text{RD}}$ is a zero (0 volts), then, a read is indicated.

Another signal, $\overline{\text{MREQ}}$, stands for *m*emory *req*uest. It is a zero only when a memory read or write is being performed. $\overline{\text{MREQ}}$ is *active* (0), then, four times in the above example—three times to fetch the LD A,(1024) bytes, and once to transfer the contents of memory location 1024.

The $\overline{\text{WR}}$ signal is active (0) when a write is being done to a memory location. Execution of LD (1024),A writes the contents of the cpu A register to memory location 1024 and $\overline{\text{WR}}$ (and $\overline{\text{MREQ}}$) is active during the write.

The last control signal associated with memory and i/o is $\overline{\text{IORQ}}$. $\overline{\text{IORQ}}$ stands for *I/O Req*uest and is used to signal external i/o logic that an i/o operation is being performed. In the case of the EZ-80 the i/o operation will transfer data between a cpu register and the 8255 programmable peripheral interface. $\overline{\text{IORQ}}$ is active (0) only when an i/o instruction is executed. When an RD (*ReaD*) instruction is performed, 8 bits of data are read from the PPI into the cpu A register and $\overline{\text{IORQ}}$ is active. The PPI also uses address lines A0 and A1 and transfers data over the data bus D7–D0. When a WR (*WRite*) instruction is performed, 8 bits of data are transferred from the cpu A register to the PPI, We'll discuss i/o in detail in the i/o chapter of this section.

Reading and writing to memory and i/o from the cpu, then, is handled by putting the address on the address bus *A15–A0,* activating the proper control signals of $\overline{\text{RD}}$ or $\overline{\text{WR}}$ and $\overline{\text{IORQ}}$ or $\overline{\text{MREQ}}$, and transferring the data along address bus D7–D0.

The Z-80 signals include other ones which are not used in the EZ-80. $\overline{\text{RFSH}}$ indicates that the refresh register R address is available on the address lines. As we do not have dynamic memories in the EZ-80, this signal is not required. $\overline{\text{M1}}$ indicates that a fetch cycle of an instruction is being executed in the cpu. This signal is not required in a small configuration. $\overline{\text{BUSRQ}}$ and $\overline{\text{BUSAK}}$ (*Bus Req*uest and *Bus Ack*nowledge) are used to implement transfer of data between i/o devices and memory without going through the cpu, in a *direct-memory-access* (dma) scheme. This is useful for large-scale systems and high-speed i/o devices. $\overline{\text{HALT}}$ indicates that a halt instruction has occurred. A halt instruction may be used for interrupts, but we will not use it in the EZ-80. $\overline{\text{WAIT}}$ is an input that allows the Z-80 to be used with memories (or i/o devices) that operate much more slowly than the cpu speeds. The EZ-80 matches the memory to cpu clock rates to make this unnecessary. $\overline{\text{INT}}$ (*Int*errupt) is an input that signals an external interrupt has occurred. In the EZ-80 we are using only the NMI, or *n*on-*m*askable *i*nterrupt, and no other external interrupt.

The $\overline{\text{RESET}}$ signal is an input signal to the Z-80 that indicates that power to the Z-80 has just been turned on, or that the cpu should be reset. Reset causes the Z-80 to clear the PC register, and, after a short pause, start execution from memory location 0. Certain other cpu functions are also initialized when $\overline{\text{RESET}}$ becomes active. An input like $\overline{\text{RESET}}$ is obviously necessary to allow the cpu to start from a known point. When power is first turned on, the voltage at pin 26 is near 0. It gradually builds up as the capacitor becomes fully charged. The voltage over time is shown in Fig. 2-14. This scheme is used to start from a time when the power supply voltage is a stable value.

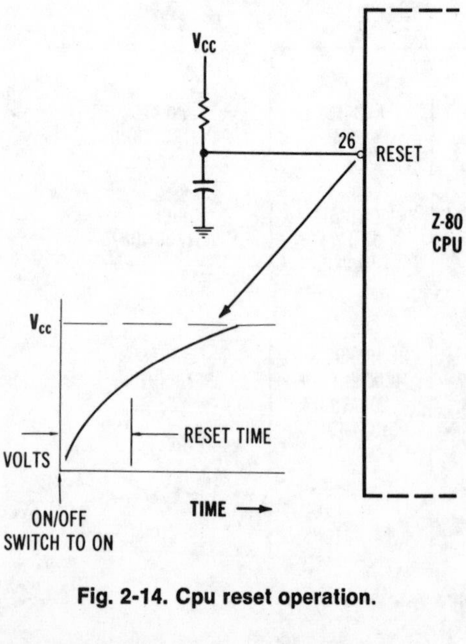

Fig. 2-14. Cpu reset operation.

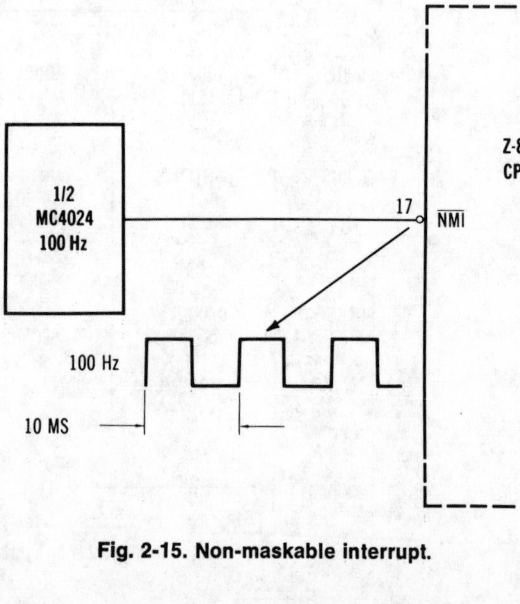

Fig. 2-15. Non-maskable interrupt.

The $\overline{\text{NMI}}$ signal is generated by the second half of the MC4024 chip. This signal is another square-wave signal that has a frequency of about 100 Hz (100 cycles per second). The $\overline{\text{NMI}}$ input causes a *n*on-*m*askable *i*nterrupt to occur every 1/100 of a second when the $\overline{\text{NMI}}$ square wave swings from high to low (see Fig. 2-15). A "non-maskable" interrupt simply means a signal that cannot be disabled or ignored. Every time the signal (high to low) occurs, it causes an interrupt to the cpu. The effect of the NMI interrupt is to cause the cpu to stop execution of the current instruction and jump to location 102 decimal. Why location 102? Only because location 102 has been defined as the NMI interrupt location (certain other locations lower than 102 are dedicated to other possible interrupts which are not implemented in the EZ-80).

Memory location 102, then, must provide an NMI interrupt handling routine, which is a series of instructions to process an NMI interrupt. What is the NMI for? Usually the NMI is used to handle catastrophic conditions in a microcomputer system, such as power failure. In the EZ-80 we are using it to count every pulse that occurs. By calibrating the pulse rate we can implement a *real-time clock* that provides a count proportional to elapsed time. This can then be used for time of day or other functions that require updates at periodic rates.

When an NMI comes in, the cpu stops execution of the current instruction, *stores the instruction location in the stack*, and transfers control to location 102. The program segment at 102 adds one count to the elapsed time, performs some other *overhead* chores, and returns to the interrupted instruction. We'll discuss the NMI interrupt further in the software chapter of this section.

CHAPTER 3

The Memory Section

We'll investigate the interaction of the memory and cpu in this chapter. The EZ-80 uses two types of memory: a 2758 erasable programmable read-only memory (EPROM) and a 6810 random-access memory (RAM). The sequence for reading and writing to memory is discussed in this chapter, along with the special requirements for programming and erasing EPROM.

EZ-80 MEMORY MAP

In Chapter 2 we discussed the address bus of the Z-80 and the inherent addressing limitations of a 16-line address bus microprocessor. As the memory bus has only 16 lines, only 65,536 memory locations can be addressed without special banking schemes or some other way to "switch" from one set of memory to another. As 65,536 bytes of memory will hold 30,000 instructions or so, the inherent limitation of a 16-line address bus is really not very limiting.

One of the chief design criteria in the EZ-80 was reasonable cost. To reduce the number of components used, memory was limited to 1024 bytes (optionally 2048) for the program and another 128 bytes for storage of data and stack area. The 1024 bytes are not an unreasonable amount of memory for a program area. An unlimited number of applications can be programmed in 1024 bytes or less. In addition, the design of the EZ-80 makes expansion to a 2716 EPROM chip possible, doubling the program storage area. This should not be necessary for most EZ-80 projects, and only one of the projects in this book (the Music Synthesizer) requires the larger (and slightly more expensive) chip.

The *memory map* of the EZ-80 is shown in Fig. 3-1. The unused locations in the 65,536 maximum memory size are shown in shaded areas. Locations 0 through 1023 are the memory locations of the 2758 EPROM chip. Above the 1024 locations for the 2758 are another 1024 locations for expansion to a 2716 EPROM chip. Locations 2048 through 2175 are memory locations of the 6810 RAM chip. The remaining locations are unused.

The locations designated are written both in decimal values and in *hexadecimal* form. Hexadecimal format is a shorthand way of writing binary numbers. Instead of writing 0000 0011 1111 1111 for memory location 1023, we've used the hexadecimal 03FF. To convert from binary to hexadecimal, group the binary digits into 4-bit groups. Now, each 4-bit group can be changed into a hexadecimal digit of 0, 1, 2, 3, 4, 5, 6, 7, 8, 9, A, B, C, D, E, or F. If the 4 bits are 0000 through 1001, substitute 1 through 9 for the binary value. If the 4 bits are 1010 through 1111, substitute the symbols A through F. Hexadecimal values can easily be converted into binary values by reversing the process (see Fig. 3-2).

Hexadecimal numbers are really numbers expressed in *base 16,* just as binary numbers were expressed in *base 2.* The same scheme of positional notation is used for hexadecimal as is used in decimal or binary, except that in *hex* the positions represent *powers of 16* (see Fig. 3-3). We'll be working with hex numbers throughout the book, but we'll refresh your memory about how to use them from time to time, so don't feel dismayed if you can't immediately convert from one system to another.

ADDRESSING MEMORY

How do the memory chips know when they are being addressed by the cpu? Refer to Fig. 3-4, which shows the cpu and memory connections. Let's consider the 2758 first. The 2758 has 10 address inputs, A9 through A0. This allows from 00 0000 0000 through 11 1111 1111 (hex 000 through 3FF) separate locations to be addressed, or a total of 1024. So it appears that to address any of the 1024 locations in the 2758, we need only to put the proper address on address lines A9 through A0 of the cpu address bus. That

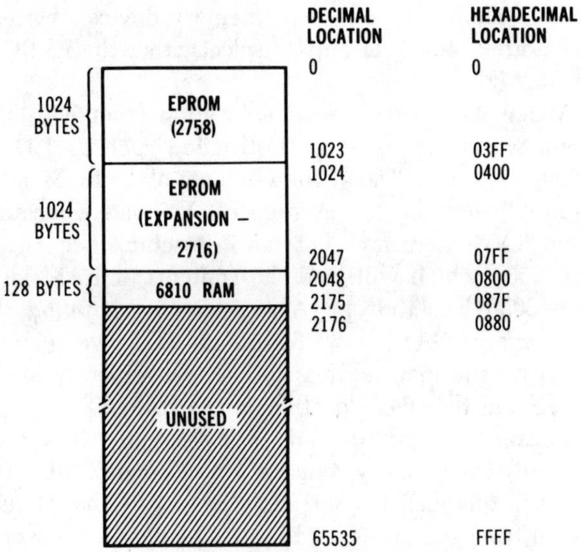

Fig. 3-1. EZ-80 memory map.

would be true if the 2758 were the only device in the system that was addressed by these lines. However, the 6810 RAM uses address lines A6 through A0 to address its 128 locations (000 0000 through 111 1111, 00 through 7F hex, or 0 through 127 decimal). If the cpu addressed memory location 100, both the EPROM and RAM would believe that their 101st (don't forget location 0) location were being addressed.

Because of this addressing conflict, we need some additional address lines to *select* either EPROM or RAM. The memory map of the system defines the EPROM area as locations 0 through 1023 (0 through

BINARY	DECIMAL	HEXIDECIMAL
0000	0	0
0001	1	1
0010	2	2
0011	3	3
0100	4	4
0101	5	5
0110	6	6
0111	7	7
1000	8	8
1001	9	9
1010	10	A
1011	11	B
1100	12	C
1101	13	D
1110	14	E
1111	15	F

1011 1001 0010 → BINARY
↓ ↓ ↓
B 9 2 → HEXADECIMAL

F 7 A → HEXADECIMAL
↓ ↓ ↓
1111 0111 1010 → BINARY

Fig. 3-2. Binary, hexadecimal, and decimal conversions.

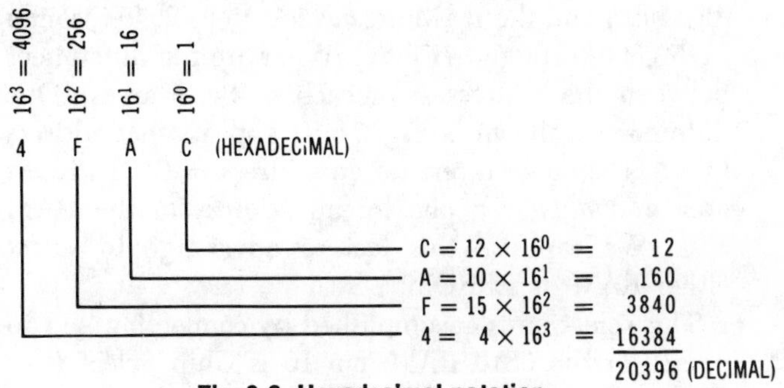

Fig. 3-3. Hexadecimal notation.

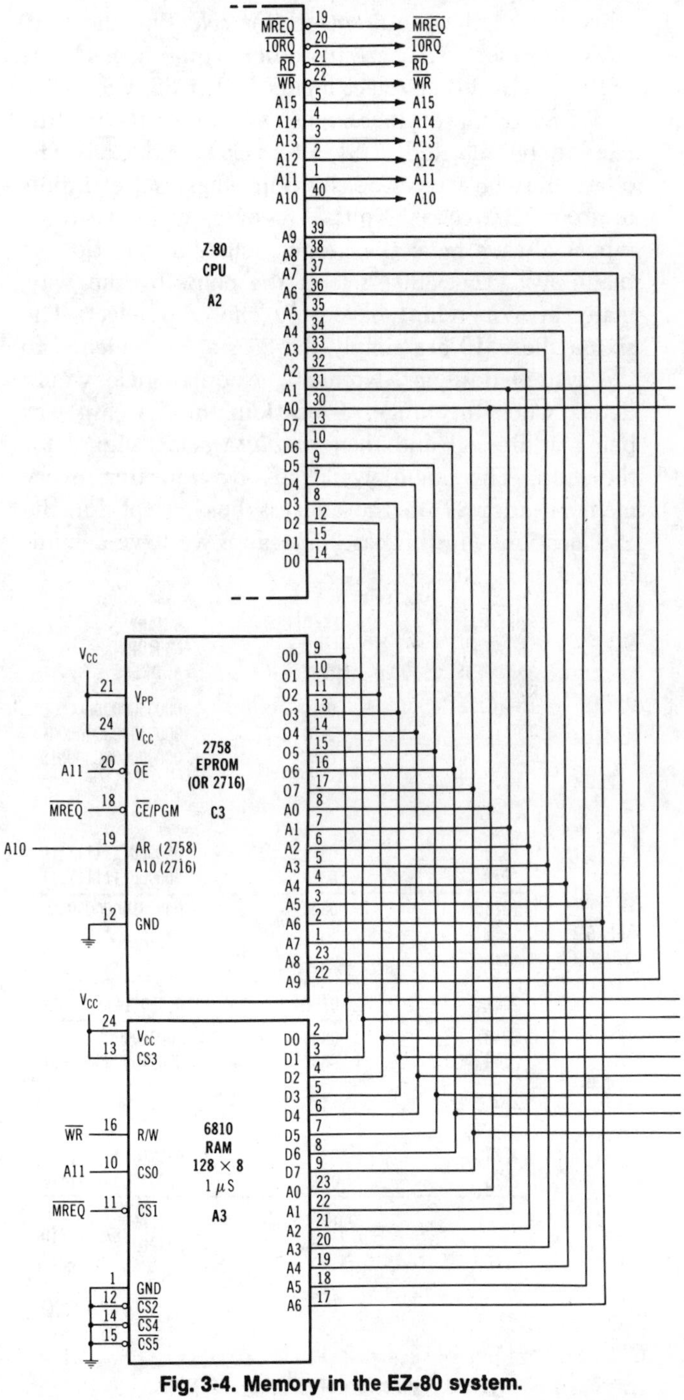

Fig. 3-4. Memory in the EZ-80 system.

3FF hex) and the RAM area as locations 2048 through 2175 (800 through 87F hex). What are the differences between the addresses for each of these areas? One difference is shown in Fig. 3-5. It appears that address line A11 is *never* a one for an address in the EPROM area and *always* a one for an address in the RAM area. We can use this fact to advantage to *select* either RAM or EPROM.

This selection is accomplished by connecting A11 to pin 10 of the 6810 RAM. Pin 10 is Chip Select *0* or CS0 on the 6810. Whenever the signal on pin 10 is true (1), part of the requirements for *selecting* the 6810 RAM are met. What are the other requirements? The 6810 has five other select inputs $\overline{CS1}$, $\overline{CS2}$, CS3, $\overline{CS4}$, and $\overline{CS5}$. Four of these must be false (0) for the chip to be selected: $\overline{CS1}$, $\overline{CS2}$, $\overline{CS4}$, and $\overline{CS5}$. The other must be true: CS3. By tying these select inputs to ground (0) or +5 volts (V_{CC} or 1) we make these inputs always have the proper state for selection so that only A11 (CS0) selects the chip. By the way, many memory chips have only *one* chip select. The six on the 6810 are simply there as a convenience to the system designer. Normally, external logic would detect when the range of locations for the chip was being addressed and then *enable* a select signal for the chip. This logic would involve rejecting every memory address on the address bus except for the 128 locations (in this case). Because we have a minimum system with only two memory devices, we can use address line A11 only to select either the EPROM or RAM.

	DECIMAL MEMORY ADDRESS	HEXADECIMAL MEMORY ADDRESS	BINARY MEMORY ADDRESS
EPROM	0	0000	0000000000000000
	1	0001	0000000000000001
	2	0002	0000000000000010
	•	•	•
	•	•	•
	•	•	•
	1022	03FE	0000001111111110
	1023	03FF	0000001111111111
EPROM XPANSION (2716)	1024	0400	0000010000000000
	•	•	•
	•	•	•
	•	•	•
	2047	07FF	0000011111111111
RAM	2048	0800	0000100000000000
	2049	0801	0000100000000001
	•	•	•
	•	•	•
	•	•	•
	2174	087E	0000100001111110
	2175	087F	0000100001111111
		ADDRESS LINES:	111111 9876543210 543210

↑ A11 = 0 FOR EPROM
1 FOR RAM

Fig. 3-5. Selection of RAM or EPROM.

When we want to read a location from EPROM, then, we can execute an instruction such as LD A,(200), which will load the contents of EPROM location 200 into the cpu A register. To read a location from RAM, we can execute an instruction such as LD A,(2050) which will load the contents of RAM location 2050 into the cpu A register. By *mapping* the locations of RAM as 2048 through 2175, we refer to them by the map address just as conveniently as by specifying the "64th location of the RAM."

Because the address bus A15 through A0 is used not only for memory, but for *i/o addresses,* we need another qualifier for selecting memory. The $\overline{MREQ}$ signal from the cpu goes to a 0 (0 volts) whenever a memory location is being read from or written into. To differentiate between an i/o address and a memory address (and prevent reading a memory location when we wanted data of an i/o device), $\overline{MREQ}$ is used to select the EPROM (pin 18) and RAM (pin 11).

Now every time we perform a *memory reference* instruction such as LD A,(128), we will get *only* a memory location and not an i/o device that has address 128. Conversely, if we perform an i/o instruction such as IN A,(128) we will read a byte from i/o device number 128 and not from *memory* location 128, as $\overline{MREQ}$ will remain true (1) during the entire execution portion of the IN(put) instruction.

DATA TO AND FROM MEMORY

The data bus, D7 through D0, is used to transfer data read from memory into the cpu. It is also used to write data into the 6810 RAM. Data can't be written into the 2758, of course (at least during program operation). The data bus is a *bidirectional* bus. Data flows both ways—*from* cpu and *to* cpu. The cpu always knows the direction of the flow. During an instruction fetch, for example, data is being read from memory into the cpu for instruction decoding. Once the cpu has read the one to four bytes of the instruction, it goes into the execute portion of the instruction and may read or write a byte (or two) to or from memory. Because the data bus is bidirectional, the cpu generates an $\overline{RD}$ (read) and $\overline{WR}$ (write) signal to signal memory and i/o devices whether a read or write is occurring. The $\overline{RD}$ and $\overline{WR}$, then, are other qualifiers that must be added to the memory logic.

The $\overline{WR}$ signal from the cpu goes into pin 16 of the 6810 RAM. The specifications of the 6810 are such that a write memory operation is a zero, and a read memory operation is a one. This fits in nicely with the state of the cpu WR signal, which is a zero any time a write is to be performed and a one otherwise.

The WR signal is not used in the 2758 EPROM. Neither is the cpu RD signal. The reason for this is that *every* time the EPROM is being addressed, the operation *must* be a read, as writing is impossible. Adding the qualification of a read or write signal for the 2758 EPROM would be an extraneous condition.

Z-80 READ AND WRITE CYCLES

Let's take a look at the sequence of read and write operations performed by the Z-80. Fig. 3-6 shows the read operation during the fetch of the first one or two of the instruction bytes. Each T period is 1 microsecond long, so the entire operation takes 4 microseconds. The first action taken by the cpu is to put the address (from the PC) onto the address bus lines A15–A0. (The $\overline{M1}$ signal indicates that this is the "op code" fetch, the first one or two bytes of the instruction.) The cpu then causes $\overline{MREQ}$ and $\overline{RD}$ to go to 0, indicating to external logic that a memory read is being made. From this point on, the memory being addressed has about 1½ *T states* to respond, or about 1½ microseconds.

The memory responds as follows: It knows by the $\overline{MREQ}$ that the cpu wants to read or write one byte of data via the data bus. If the memory is the 6810 RAM, it knows by the state of the $\overline{WR}$ signal whether a write ($\overline{WR} = 0$) or read ($\overline{WR} = 1$) is required. If A11 is true (if the cpu is reading an instruction byte from the 2048–2175 area), the 6810 RAM CS0 signal is true and the RAM is *selected.* If A11 is false, the $\overline{OE}$ signal of the 2758 is false and the EPROM is selected. (As it happens in the EZ-80, instruction bytes are *always* read from the EPROM, although in other systems they could be read from either EPROM or RAM.)

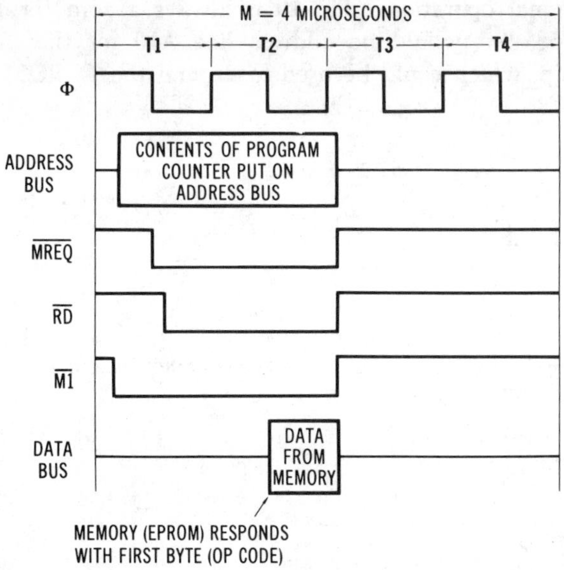

Fig. 3-6. Z-80 op-code fetch.

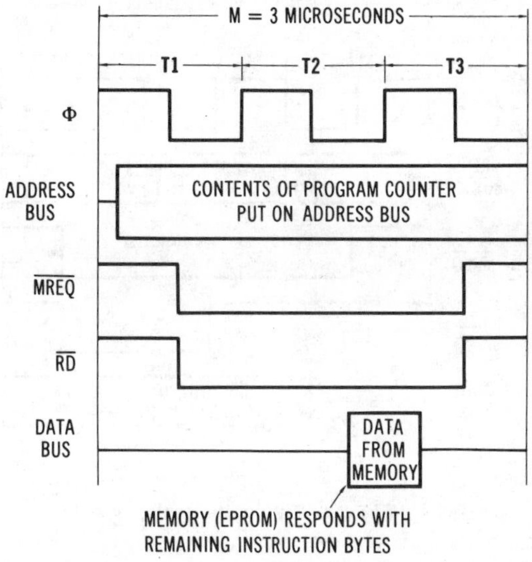

Fig. 3-7. Z-80 remainder of fetch cycle.

In the general case, if the chip is selected ($\overline{MREQ} = 0$ *and* A11 = 1 for the 6810, or $\overline{MREQ} = 0$ *and* A11 = 0 for the 2758), the memory chip looks at the address present on the address lines. If the chip selected is the 2758 or is the 6810 with a read, the 8 bits in the memory location specified on the address lines are *output* to the data lines D7 through D0. At the end of T2 the cpu reads the bits of the data lines into an internal register for decoding.

Subsequent reads of remaining instruction bytes are done in pretty much the same fashion, except that only three clock cycles are used, as shown in Fig. 3-7. (The "op code" fetch of the first one or two instruction bytes is longer to allow the R(efresh) register to be sent to system dynamic memories, if the system has any.) Reads of operands, such as in the instruction LD A,(2049), which loads the byte from memory location 2049 into the A register, are performed as shown in Fig. 3-7. In this case the address on the address bus represents not the PC, but the address of the operand from the instruction.

Writes to memory are done only during the execution portion of an instruction, so the "op code" fetch is not a consideration. The write cycle starts off similarly to the read, as shown in Fig. 3-8. The address of the memory location to be written into is put on the address bus A15–A0. Signal $\overline{MREQ}$ is activated (brought to zero). Shortly after, the cpu outputs the data to be written to memory onto the data bus

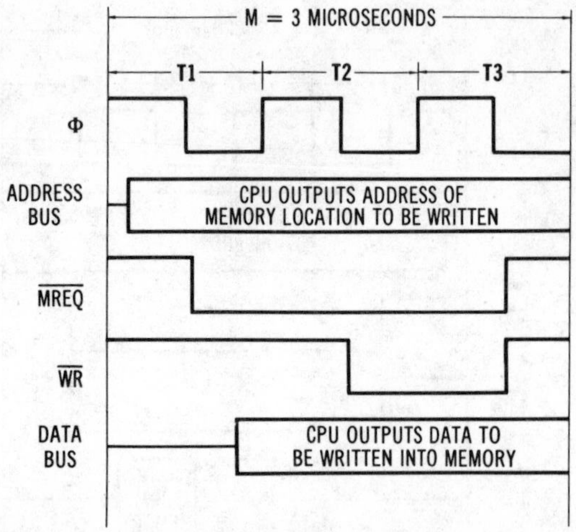

Fig. 3-8. Z-80 write cycle.

D7–D0. At this time the memory starts to actually do a *read* of the specified location. However, signal $\overline{WR}$ is brought to a zero, and the data on D7–D0 is written into the specified memory location instead, as the memory chip detects the transition of $\overline{WR}$ from a one to a zero.

Z-80 INSTRUCTION EXECUTION

The complete instruction execution is a combination of read and write cycles. The cycles for an "LD (2049),A" instruction are shown in Fig. 3-9. During the first read cycle the first byte of the "LD (2049),A" is read into the instruction decoding register of the cpu. The cpu recognizes that two additional bytes are to be read to complete the instruction. Two additional reads are done to get instruction bytes 2 and 3. The cpu now has the address 2049 of the instruction and writes the contents of the A register into location 2049 by performing a write cycle. The next instruction is then accessed. Note that in the first three reads the address on the address bus was the contents of the program counter. The PC was incremented by one for each read, to read in the next instruction byte. During the write cycle the address on the address bus was 2049 and the data transferred from the cpu was the contents of the cpu A register.

During program execution the address and data bus are very active with read cycles occurring for every byte of an instruction and write cycles occurring every time an operand is transferred from the cpu to a memory location. The rate of the cycles is hundreds of thousands of times per second.

THE 6810 VERSUS THE 2758

The 6810 RAM is somewhat more simple to understand than the 2758. If data is read from or written to the 2048–2175 (800–87F hex) area of memory, A11 is a 1, $\overline{MREQ} = 0$, and the 6810 reads or writes one byte from the location it finds on address lines A7–A0 (0–127 decimal, or 0–7F hex).

The 2758, however, has some complicating signals that are not on the RAM chip. Let's look at them in detail. As the data is only output (read) data, the data lines are designated O7–O0 for "output." Inputs A9–A0 are the address lines from the cpu.

During operation as a read-only-memory chip, pin 21 (V_{PP}) is +5 volts, as is the main power pin, pin 24 (V_{CC}). Pin 12 is always ground. During *programming*, however, pin 21 is connected to a higher voltage supply of +25 volts. This higher voltage is required to *write* data into the EPROM during the programming process.

Pins 18 and 20 are also "dual-purpose" pins and are used for different things during programming and normal operation. (Pin 19 is always a zero for the 2758, but would be address line A10 for the 2716 chip, which could be used to expand the EPROM to

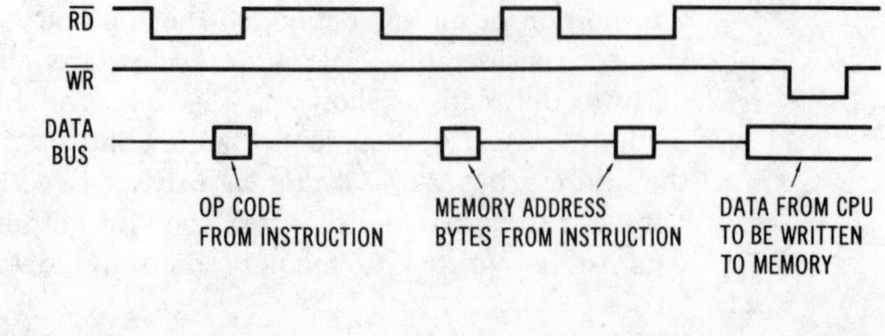

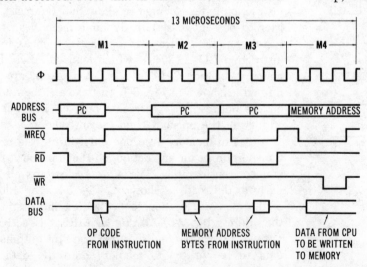

Fig. 3-9. Z-80 instruction execution.

double the size.) Pin 18 is zero for a read operation and can therefore be tied to the $\overline{MREQ}$ input which goes to a zero when a memory operation, which must be a read, is requested of the 2758. During programming, pin 18 is used to input a *pulse* that causes a memory location in the EPROM to be programmed. Pin 20 is a zero during a normal read, but may be a one (+5 V) during the program mode. Normal functions of the 2758 pins when the 2758 is installed in a circuit to act as read-only memory, then, are:

V_{PP} (21), V_{CC} (24), GND (12)	Power lines
OE (20)	Address line A11 to enable chip
$\overline{MREQ}$ (18)	Memory request to enable chip
AR (19)	Always 0

PROGRAMMING THE 2758

How does one program the 2758? A good question. First, we need a little history of EPROMs. The EPROM, which is an *e*rasable *p*rogrammable *r*ead-*o*nly *m*emory, was preceded by *ROMs* and *PROMs*.

A ROM is a *r*ead-*o*nly *m*emory. It is custom fabricated at a semiconductor manufacturer to hold programs or data or both. The initial cost to "design-in" the program or data is hundreds of dollars, but once the device has been designed, the individual chips are very inexpensive in quantity. The contents of the ROM can never be changed (unless a hammer is used) and ROMs are typically used for high-volume applications such as *hard-wired* electronic equipment or consumer electronic items (an example would be memory for a washing machine controller).

Because ROMs are suited for high-volume applications, there was and is a need for a memory device that could be programmed "in the field" without making up an expensive production run. The PROM (programmable read-only memory) fits this requirement. It can be electrically programmed to "burn-in" a set of instructions or data. Once burned-in, however, the contents are irreversible. A new PROM must be used in place of one with faulty data.

The EPROM (erasable programmable read-only memory) is (almost) the best of all worlds. Not only can it be field programmable, but it can be erased with ultraviolet light. If a user erroneously enters programs or data into an EPROM, he or she can erase it and start over, saving the cost of new PROMs. The EPROM is an ideal device for experimentation with programs or data that will not change too quickly.

Early EPROMs were difficult to program as they required that many hundreds of passes be made through each of the EPROM locations to burn-in data. As a result, *programmers,* which are devices to accomplish this were quite elaborate (typically a microcomputer may be used to *drive* the programmer through the hundreds of cycles). The 2758 and 2716 EPROMs, however, are much simpler to program. To change a location in the EPROM the following steps must be followed:

1. Put the address of the location on inputs A9–A0.
2. Put the data to be programmed on inputs D7–D0.
3. Put +25 volts on pin 21 (V_{PP}) and +5 volts or 0 volts on pins 24, 20, and 2.
4. *Pulse* pin 18 by a pulse that goes from 0 to +5 volts and back to 0 and lasts about 1/20 of a second (50 milliseconds).

This procedure is repeated for every location to be programmed. Because of the simple requirements for programming, a programmer for the 2758 and 2716 can be made very simply and inexpensively. Later in this book we will see how a programmer can be made and offer some alternatives to making a programmer for entering programs into the 2758 and 2716.

Erasing the 2758 or 2716 is accomplished by exposing the chip to strong ultraviolet light. Inexpensive ultraviolet lamps are available for this purpose. The erasing process is very simple and will be described under construction of the programmer.

CHAPTER 4

The I/O Section

The *interface* of the Z-80 microprocessor and 8255 programmable peripheral interface (PPI) is discussed in this chapter. In a sense the PPI is like a small microprocessor in itself. It accepts commands from the Z-80 and handles the tasks of inputting and outputting data from 24 i/o lines. The logic associated with the LED display, keyboard, input lines, and output lines is also discussed here.

THE 8255 PPI

Fig. 4-1 shows the i/o section of the EZ-80. The PPI acts as an intermediate *buffer* between the Z-80 cpu and the outside world of the LED display, keyboard, input lines, and output lines. The purpose of the PPI in the EZ-80 and in the general case is to buffer the i/o data to match the speed and signal characteristics of the outside world to the Z-80.

In the EZ-80 configuration the PPI consists of four *registers* similar to the registers in the Z-80 cpu. Each register is 8 bits wide. Three of the registers connect to three sets of eight input/output lines as shown in Fig. 4-2.

The cpu can read or write to each of the four registers in the PPI by an RD (read) or WR (write) instruction. Executing an RD A,(2) instruction, for example, reads register 2 of the PPI and transmits the 8 bits of data in the register to the A register of the Z-80. Executing a WR (0),A instruction writes the contents of the cpu A register into register 0 of the PPI.

The four registers are addressed by addresses of 00, 01, 10, and 11. Two address lines come into the PPI: A1 and A0; and these two lines are all that are required to hold the 2-bit address to specify the PPI register involved. Ordinarily, in a larger-configuration microcomputer there would be a conflict with this type of addressing scheme. The conflict would be of a nature similar to that of using the same address lines to select memory locations. A larger microcomputer would have several i/o devices and more than two address lines would be required to select the proper i/o device. In the EZ-80, however, the *only* i/o device is the PPI, and it is sufficient to use only A1 and A0 for addressing. Any time an i/o instruction (RD or WR) is executed, the program *must* be talking only to the PPI and no other device. To differentiate between memory and i/o communication the $\overline{\text{IORQ}}$ signal is connected to the PPI (pin 6). The $\overline{\text{IORQ}}$ is a zero only when an RD or WR is executed. The direction of transmission is decoded by the PPI from the $\overline{\text{WR}}$ and $\overline{\text{RD}}$ signals (pins 36 and 5).

Let's take a more detailed look at an i/o operation from the cpu signal viewpoint. The signals during an RD instruction are shown in Fig. 4-3. When an RD is executed, the cpu first puts the address of the i/o device on the address bus lines A7–A0. The format of the i/o instruction specifies only an 8-bit i/o address, so the number of devices that may be addressed are 0000 0000 through 1111 1111, or 256. In the EZ-80, only four addresses are used: 0, 1, 2, or 3.

Shortly after the address is put on the address bus the cpu "brings down" the $\overline{\text{IORQ}}$ and $\overline{\text{RD}}$ lines to zero (0 volts). This is interpreted by the PPI as an i/o operation in general and a read. The PPI looks at the two address lines of A1 and A0 to determine which one of the four registers is to be read. It then puts the contents of the selected register onto data bus lines D7 through D0. In the middle of the third T cycle, the cpu inputs the contents of the data bus into the A register. As in the case of memory, the time between the initial $\overline{\text{IORQ}}$ and $\overline{\text{RD}}$ and the *strobing* of the data into the A register is there for two reasons. First, the cpu needs the time to sequence through its internal operations. Second, the interval gives the external device time to respond. Even in the microprocessor world, events take discrete amounts of time.

A write operation for a WR instruction is similar (see Fig. 4-4). The address and $\overline{\text{IORQ}}$ are active as

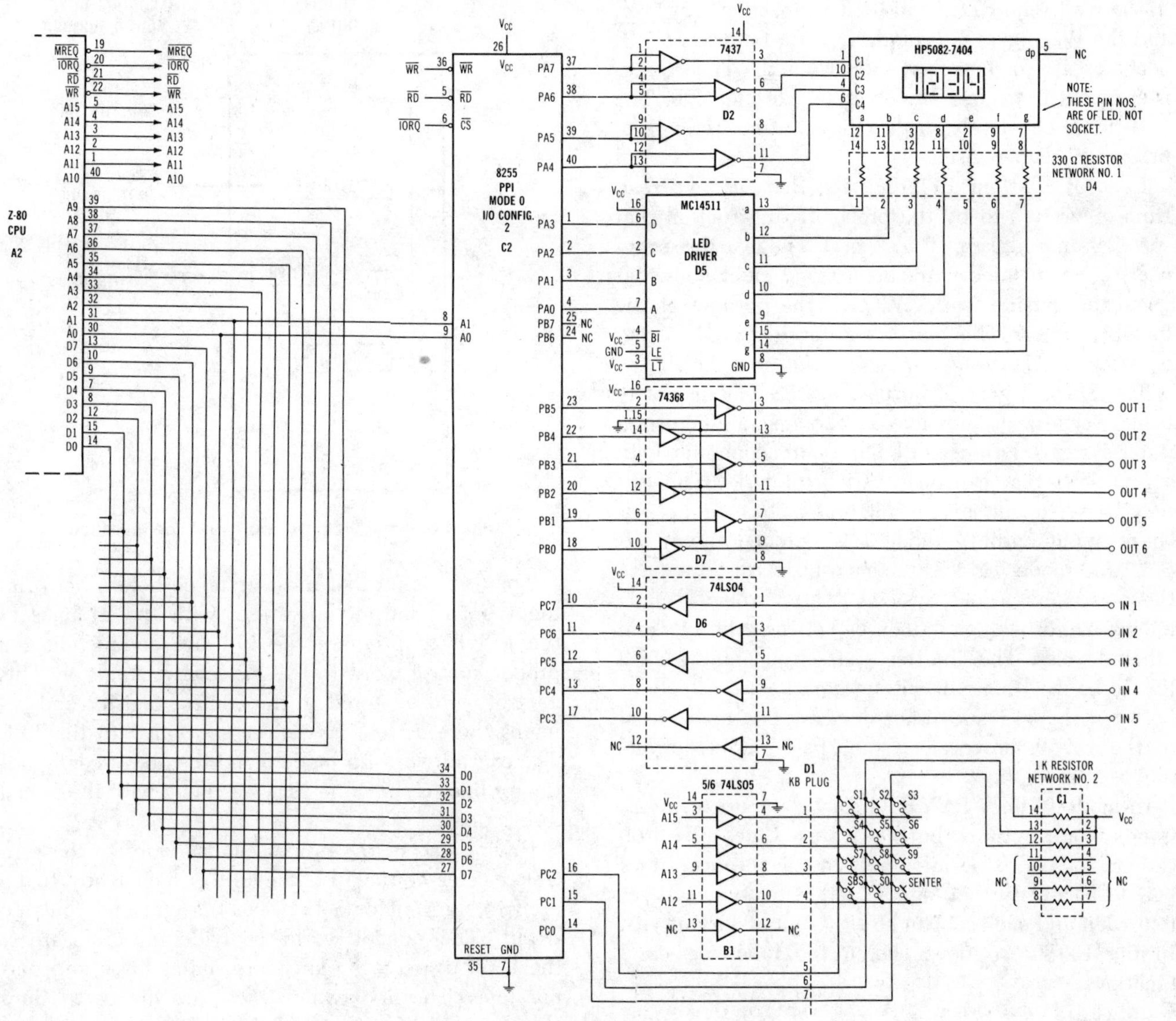

Fig. 4-1. Input/output in the EZ-80 system.

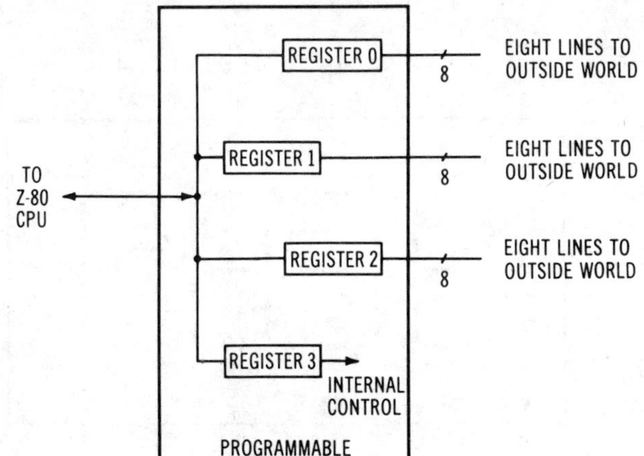

Fig. 4-2. PPI registers.

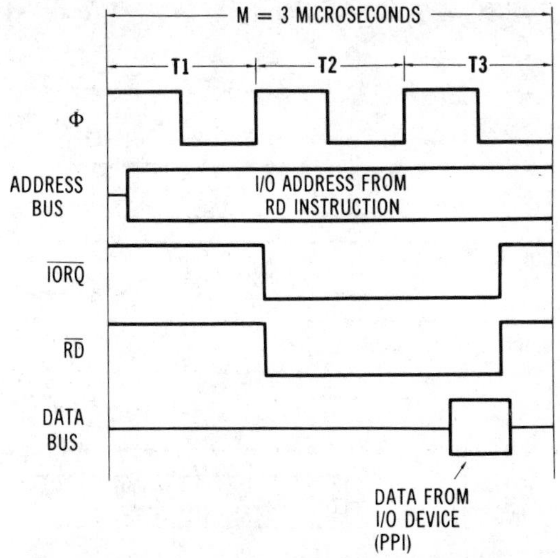

Fig. 4-3. Z-80 RD instruction cycle.

in the read. The RD signal remains inactive, however, and the WR signal is brought to zero. Before the WR becomes active, however, data from the cpu A register is put onto data bus lines D7 through D0. The WR signal effectively *strobes* the data into the appropriate PPI data register.

Each of the four PPI registers, then, can be read from or written to by the proper i/o instruction that specifies an address of 0, 1, 2, or 3. The first three registers are associated with three sets of eight lines that go to the outside world. What is the purpose of the fourth register? The fourth register is a control register that holds the *mode control byte* for the PPI.

The PPI is a general-purpose device. It is meant to be as versatile as possible in allowing a microcomputer systems designer to build a microcomputer with a few parts that can do a variety of tasks. The PPI may be set up in several different *modes*. Mode 0 is "basic input/output," mode 1 is "strobed input/output," and mode 2 is "bidirectional bus." All three have their uses in various systems. The "strobed" mode allows "handshaking" sequences between the PPI and other devices. The "bidirectional" mode allows each line to be used for transmitting data in two directions between the PPI and other devices. The mode used in the EZ-80, however, is the "basic input/output" mode, or mode 0.

In mode 0, lines PA7–PA0 can be set up to be all inputs or all outputs, but not a mix. Lines PB7–PB0 can be set up to be all inputs or all outputs. Lines PC7-PC0 are further subdivided into two sets of four each and each set can be either inputs or outputs. In the EZ-80 we have chosen the following combinations:

PA7–PA0	All Outputs	Address 0
PB7–PB0	All Outputs	Address 1
PC7–PC0	All Inputs	Address 2

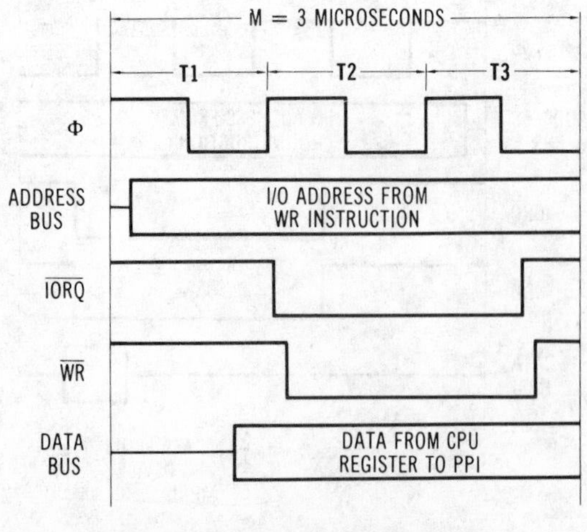

Fig. 4-4. Z-80 WR instruction cycle.

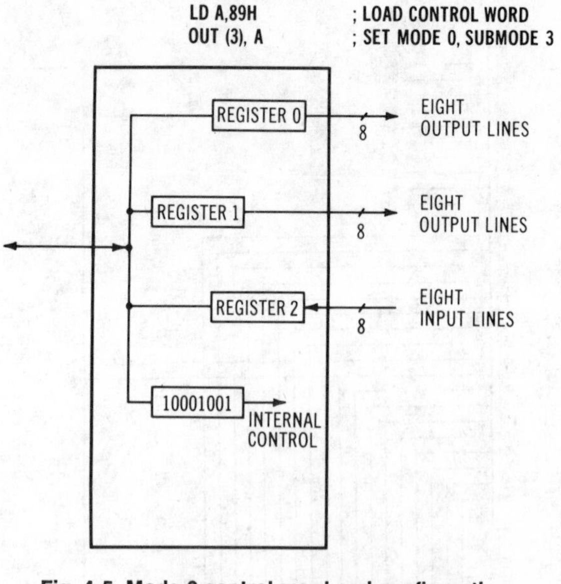

Fig. 4-5. Mode 0 control word and configuration.

The first action that must be taken before performing input or output operations with the 24 lines of the PPI is to *program* the PPI by sending out the proper control word to the PPI control register. This control word is stored in the control register and remains there as long as power is applied to the PPI. The control word for mode 0 and the above configuration of lines is shown in Fig. 4-5, along with the actual instructions.

Having output the proper control word to the control register of the PPI, the PPI is now ready to be used to transmit data between the cpu and "outside world." The "outside world" is divided into four areas: the LED display, the keyboard, input lines, and output lines. The first two of these are *dedicated* lines used for EZ-80 functions, while the latter two are used to enable the EZ-80 to perform useful tasks of a general nature.

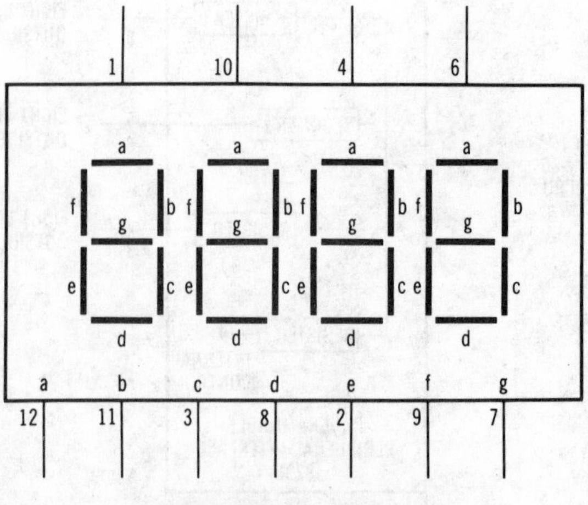

Fig. 4-6. EZ-80 LED display.

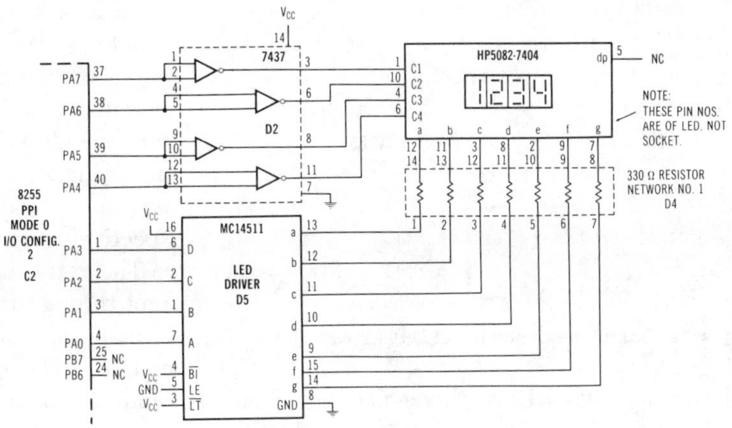

Fig. 4-7. LED circuitry.

THE LED DISPLAY

The LED display used in the EZ-80 is a garden variety four-digit display that can display four decimal digits from 0000 through 9999. Each digit of the LED display is made up of seven segments, as shown in Fig. 4-6. By lighting combinations of segments the numbers 0 through 9 can be displayed. The LED display used in the EZ-80 is a type of display called a *common-cathode* type. All segments of the four digits are connected in parallel and a common set of seven lines, one for each segment, come out of the chip on pins 12, 11, 3, 8, 2, 9, and 7.

The LED circuitry is shown in Fig. 4-7. The four lines labeled C1, C2, C3, and C4 connect to the *cathodes* of each of the digits. When *one* of these lines is at ground potential (0 volts) and at least one of the *anode* lines a–g is at +5 volts, current flows through the diode, which then emits red light. From one to seven of the anode lines can be at +5 volts during this condition, so all seven segments can be illuminated at one time (or only a portion), as shown in Fig. 4-8.

No more than one cathode line can be at 0 volts at one time, so that at any given time only one digit is displayed on the four-digit display in one position only. How, then, do we display all four digits at one time? By rapidly alternating between one digit position and the next. Every 1/100 of a second, a new set of inputs at a–g and a new cathode line is enabled. All four digits are displayed every 1/25 of a second. To the eye this *multiplexed* display appears to be a single display of four digits. Fig. 4-9 shows the signals required to display the number 1234 on the display.

Displaying any series of four digits on the LEDs, then, resolves down into rapidly switching inputs to the LED display. All that we must do with the PPI is to ensure that every 1/100 second a new cathode line (C1, C2, C3, or C4) is enabled in sequence and put out a new set of the seven segment lines at the same time.

Switching the cathode lines is easy. The four cathode lines are *driven* by the outputs of the 7437 chip. This chip is a *high-current inverter*. It takes the output of lines PA7–PA4 of the PPI and inverts them, changing a one to a zero and a zero to a one. The PPI alone could not handle the current through the LEDs, so the 7437 is used to provide more *current drive* capability. To output a zero to one of the cathode lines, *one* of the upper four bits in the first PPI register must be a one and the rest zeros. We can do this by performing an output instruction to the first (address 0) PPI register. First of all, the A register in the cpu is loaded with the proper configuration of ones and zeros. Next, a write instruction is executed to send the contents of A to the register in the PPI. In the

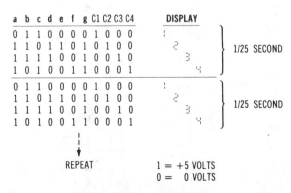

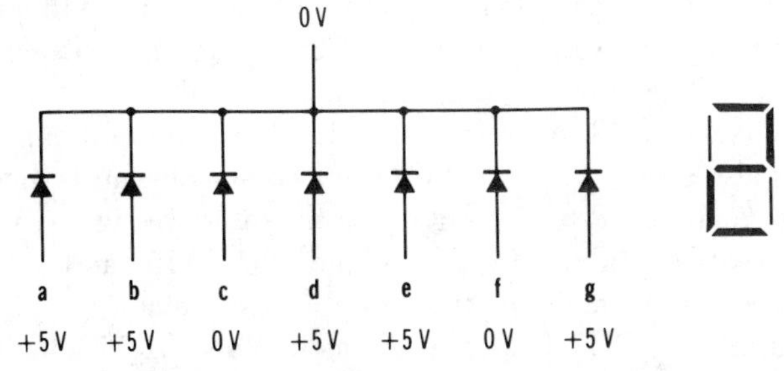

Fig. 4-8. LED operation.

a	b	c	d	e	f	g	C1	C2	C3	C4	DISPLAY	
0	1	1	0	0	0	0	1	0	0	0	1	1/25 SECOND
1	1	0	1	1	0	1	0	1	0	0	2	
1	1	1	1	0	0	1	0	0	1	0	3	
1	0	1	0	0	1	1	0	0	0	1	4	
0	1	1	0	0	0	0	1	0	0	0	1	1/25 SECOND
1	1	0	1	1	0	1	0	1	0	0	2	
1	1	1	1	0	0	1	0	0	1	0	3	
1	0	1	0	0	1	1	0	0	0	1	4	

REPEAT

1 = +5 VOLTS
0 = 0 VOLTS

Fig. 4-9. Sample display timing.

```
8 = DIGIT 1
4 = DIGIT 2
2 = DIGIT 3      ACTUAL DIGIT
1 = DIGIT 4      TO BE DISPLAYED

    LD   A,23H        ; OUTPUT 3 TO C3
    OUT  (0), A       ; LIGHT 3RD DIGIT
```

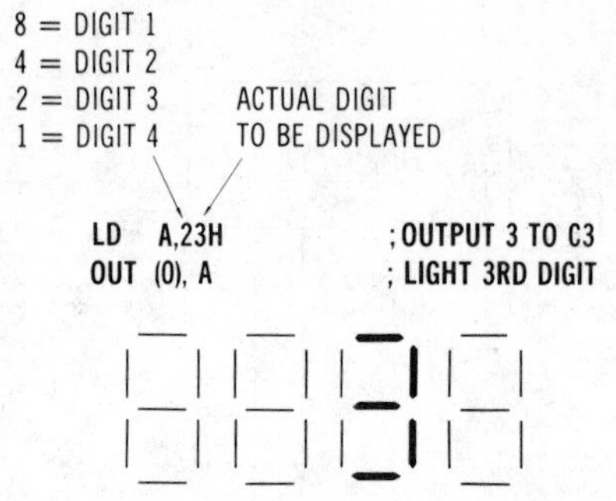

Fig. 4-10. Output sequence for LED display.

example shown in Fig. 4-10, cathode C3 has been enabled.

How do we enable the seven lines going to the segments of the display with only four lines from the PPI? And why not use seven lines from the PPI instead of four? The reason we avoid seven lines is simply that we have 24 lines to use on the PPI and would like to allocate them parsimoniously. The MC14511 gives us the capability to use only four output lines to generate the proper sequence of LED segments.

What the MC14511 does is to take four input (*output* from the 8255) lines, assume that they contain the binary equivalent of 0–9, and convert the input digit to the proper sequence of segments. The table for doing this is shown in Fig. 4-11. Note that the input values 1010, 1011, 1100, 1101, 1110, and 1111 are invalid inputs and produce no display at all. In addition to translating from binary into segments, the MC14511 provides additional drive current capability. The PPI by itself would not be able to meet the current requirements of the LED display segment inputs.

Several of the pins on the MC14511 are not used (see Fig. 4-7). \overline{LT} (pin 3) is a *lamp test* input that can be used to test the operation of all segments. \overline{LT} is active when it is a zero, and is therefore kept at a

logic 1 (V_{CC}) for the EZ-80. The blanking input (BI, pin 4) is used to blank or turn off the display and is kept inactive by tying it to a logic 1 (V_{CC}). The LE, or *latch enable* (pin 5), *latches* (stores) the input into the chip. LE in the EZ-80 is always active (zero or ground) and the segment outputs "follow" the inputs. Pins 16 and 8 are +5 volts and ground respectively.

The resistors in the resistor network limit the current through the LEDs. This is necessary because the circuit has very low resistance when a segment is enabled. The resistors limit the current to the proper value for adequate brightness.

THE KEYBOARD

The keyboard of the EZ-80 is a very simple affair to keep costs of the project low. The keyboard and associated circuitry is shown in Fig. 4-12. Pressing any key simply connects a row with a column. Let's see how this circuit works. When no key is pressed, the inputs to PPI register 2 on lines PC2, PC1, and PC0 are V_{CC} or about +5 volts, logic ones. When a key is pushed, two lines are connected and the *column* line associated with the key is connected to the *row* line associated with the key.

The column line goes to one of three inputs in the three lower bits of the PPI. The column line reflects the state of the connected row output from the 74LS05 chip. If the output of the inverter for the row is a zero (0 volts), then the input to the PPI will be zero; if the output of the inverter for the row is a one (+5 volts), then the input to the PPI will be a one. To detect a key depression, then, we can state that *if the* key is pushed *and* the inverter output is a zero, *then* the input to the PPI for the column associated with the key will be a zero. If we make certain that only one inverter output is zero at a time, then we can pinpoint the key by its row (inverter number) and column (bit position).

As an example of how this works, look at Fig. 4-13. Key S8 is depressed and the two contact points are connected. Assume that the key remains pressed for a long period. If we make A15 a one, and A14, A13, and A12 zeros, then only the output of the A15 inverter is a zero; the remaining inverter outputs are ones. The lines to the PPI connect only at S8, but since the A13 inverter output is a one, the PC1 input is also a one. PC0 and PC2 are also ones because they are connected to V_{CC} only (see the table in Fig. 4-13). Now we make A14 a one and A15, A13, and A12 zeros. The same situation applies as previously. The inputs on PC2–PC0 are all ones. Now A13 is made a one, and A15, A14, and A12 zeros. The output of

NUMBER	INPUT LINES TO MC14511				OUTPUT LINES FROM MC14511						
	D	C	B	A	a	b	c	d	e	f	g
0	0	0	0	0	1	1	1	1	1	1	0
1	0	0	0	1	0	1	1	0	0	0	0
2	0	0	1	0	1	1	0	1	1	0	1
3	0	0	1	1	1	1	1	1	0	0	1
4	0	1	0	0	0	1	1	0	0	1	1
5	0	1	0	1	1	0	1	1	0	1	1
6	0	1	1	0	0	0	1	1	1	1	1
7	0	1	1	1	1	1	1	0	0	0	0
8	1	0	0	0	1	1	1	1	1	1	1
9	1	0	0	1	1	1	1	0	0	1	1
(none)	1	0	1	0	0	0	0	0	0	0	0
	1	0	1	1	0	0	0	0	0	0	0
	1	1	0	0	0	0	0	0	0	0	0
	1	1	0	1	0	0	0	0	0	0	0
	1	1	1	0	0	0	0	0	0	0	0
	1	1	1	1	0	0	0	0	0	0	0

Fig. 4-11. MC14511 conversion.

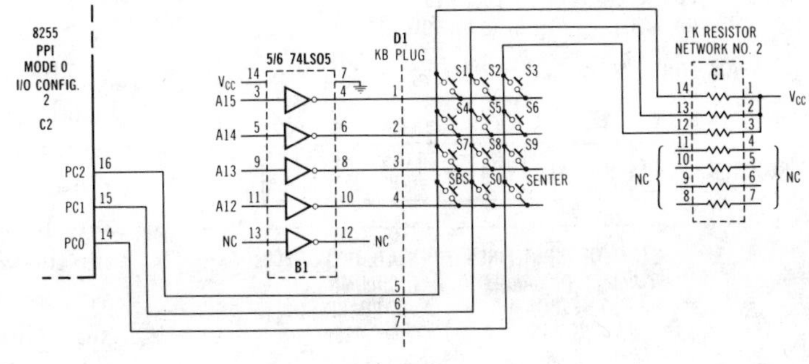

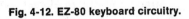

Fig. 4-12. EZ-80 keyboard circuitry.

the A13 inverter is a zero. PC2 and PC0 are ones as before, but S8 connects PC1 with the output of the A13 inverter and line PC1 becomes a zero input. Now A12 is made a one, and A15, A14, and A13 are made zeros. All ones are present on PC2–PC0.

The only time in the above sequence that PC1 was a zero was when A13 was a one. This approach holds true for all other keys pressed on the keyboard. There will be one and only one time that its PC input will be a zero—when its row inverter output is also a one. By continually sequencing A15, A14, A13, and A12 and observing the bits PC2–PC0, a key depression can be detected and the key number can be found by noting which of the bits is a zero and which of the four row inverter outputs was a one.

This process is called *keyboard scanning* and is a common technique for detecting and decoding keyboards. The reader can see that the principles can be applied to larger matrices than a four-by-three keyboard. Again, however, to reduce costs we have eliminated a larger keyboard in favor of a decimal keypad.

The scanning in the EZ-80 is implemented by simultaneously enabling one of the A15, A14, A13, or A12 address lines and reading in the state of PC2–PC0. If all three low-order bits in the PPI third register are

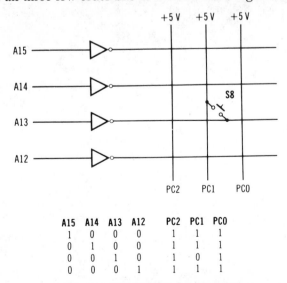

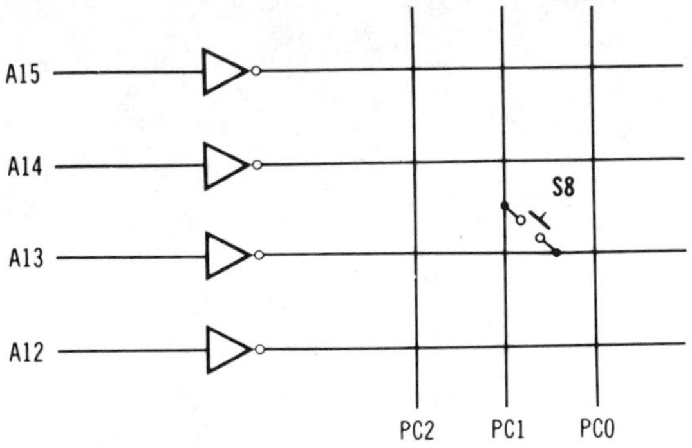

A15	A14	A13	A12	PC2	PC1	PC0
1	0	0	0	1	1	1
0	1	0	0	1	1	1
0	0	1	0	1	0	1
0	0	0	1	1	1	1

Fig. 4-13. Keyboard key press example.

ones, then no key has been pressed. In this case, the next address line is enabled and a new row is read. If one bit of the three is a zero, then there is a key depression and the key being pressed is found by looking at the column number by finding the zero bit of the three.

The key to the technique in the EZ-80 is that the RD (read) i/o instruction puts the contents of the cpu A register on address lines A15–A0 at the same time that the read is done of lines PC7–PC0. By putting the proper value in the upper four bits of the A register, we can select one address line of A15, A14, A13, and A12 at the same time that data is read in from PC2–PC0. The sequence for selecting A13 is shown in Fig. 4-14. First, the A register is loaded with 0010 0000. This value will go onto address lines A15–A8 when the read is performed. Next, an RD (read) is performed of PPI register 2 [RD A,(2)]. During the time that the address (2) goes out on the address lines A7–A0, the upper eight address lines A15–A8 hold 0010 0000 and A13 is enabled. If any of keys S7, S8, or S9 is pressed, the corresponding input bit will be a zero. This sequence is repeated rapidly for all four rows until a zero is found to indicate a key depression. The actual instructions used are discussed further in Section 3 of this book. They enable the entire set of 12 keys to be tested once every 300 microseconds or so.

OUTPUT LINES

The EZ-80 has six output lines that are not dedicated to any internal task. They are general-purpose lines used to provide an output of one or zero for the outside world. The six outputs can be used individually to control six on/off conditions such as relays or lights. They can also be used together to provide a 000000 to 111111 output, or 64 steps, each step with a meaning to the outside world. Not too impressive? We'll see how those six lines can do an amazing number of things in Section 3. The six outputs from the six low-order bits of the PPI register 2 are *buffered* by the inverters in the 74367 chip. This chip inverts

```
LD  A,20H      ; SELECT A13
RD  A,(2)      ; READ KB ROW A13
```

A NOW CONTAINS:

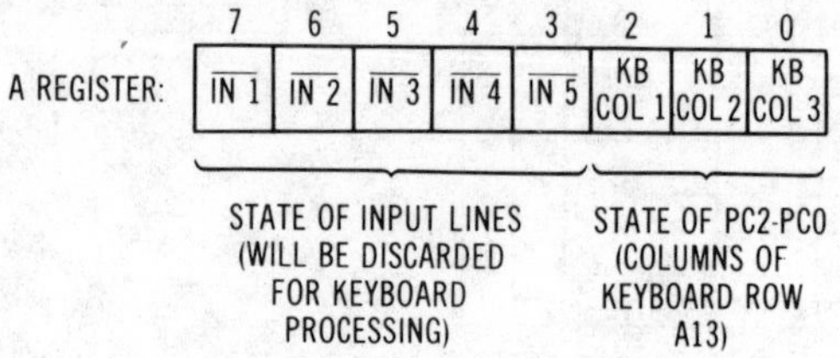

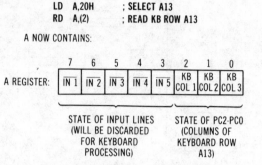

Fig. 4-14. Keyboard scan example.

the signal in the PPI register, but, more importantly, it provides higher current drive capability to drive external devices.

INPUT LINES

The top five bit positions of the PPI register 3 are used as input lines. External world inputs of on/off conditions can be scanned rapidly to detect switch closures or other applications. As in the case of the output lines, the inputs are *buffered* by six inverters on the 74LS04 chip. The main purpose of these inverters is not for current drive, but to prevent outside signals from destroying the relatively expensive 8255. (The 74LS04 chip is about 1/20 the cost of the 8255.) Section 3 of this book describes how the outside world may be interfaced to the EZ-80 via the five input lines.

CHAPTER 5

Z-80 Assembly Language Instruction Types

In the next two chapters we'll attempt to present enough software description on the Z-80 to enable the user to interpret the programs given in Section 3 of the book and to construct his or her own programs. This chapter will discuss what types of instructions are available in the Z-80. The next chapter will discuss some of the addressing variations of the instructions and how to interpret and assemble programs.

WHERE DO WE BEGIN?

One of the problems with the Z-80 instruction set is simply that there are too many instructions! There are too many ways to do the same thing. If there is one guiding principle to keep in mind in programming the Z-80, it is this: *There are many ways to program a task and few wrong ways.*

The Z-80 instruction set has well over 500 separate instructions. The instructions can be grouped into several sets, however, so the job of cataloging them becomes somewhat easier. Furthermore, any of the instructions of the same type differ only in the cpu register or bit position involved. In the following description we'll group the instruction set of the Z-80 into:

Loads
Arithmetic
Logical
Jumps, Calls, and Returns
Rotates and Shifts
Bit Set, Reset, and Tests
I/O
Miscellaneous

LOAD INSTRUCTIONS

Load instructions transfer 8 or 16 bits (one or two bytes) of data between memory and the cpu registers, or between cpu registers. We've already seen some of these in examples. Historically, a transfer of data into a cpu register was called a "load," while a transfer of data from cpu to memory was called a "store." In the Z-80, however, any movement of data between cpu and memory is called a *load*. The abbreviation or *mnemonic* of the load operation is "LD." Every time one sees an LD mnemonic, a transfer of data is involved. Transfers of data in an LD involve copying data into a cpu register or memory location. The original source of the data remains unchanged. As an example, suppose we load the cpu A register with the contents of the cpu D register, as shown in Fig. 5-1. After the LD the contents of D have been copied into A and the original contents of D are unchanged. In this example, D was the *source* register while A was the *destination* register.

The above example was a load between cpu registers. To load a cpu register with the contents of a memory location, a load such as the one in Fig. 5-2 can be done. This load loads the A register with the contents of location 2050 decimal (802H, where H stands for hexadecimal). Note the parentheses around the 2050. This is mandatory and indicates that the load will be done with the *contents* of location 2050. After the load, the contents of memory location 2050 remain unchanged. Notice that the order of the operands is DESTINATION, SOURCE, the same as in the previous example.

Now suppose that we want to transfer data the other way, from cpu register to a memory location. The example in Fig. 5-3 shows the transfer of the contents of the A register into memory location 2050 (802H). After the load, the contents of A remain unchanged. The order, again, is DESTINATION, SOURCE, with the destination in this case memory location 802H (2050 decimal).

In all of the above loads, the data transferred was eight bits, or one byte. One byte may be moved between any two cpu registers or between any cpu register and any memory location.

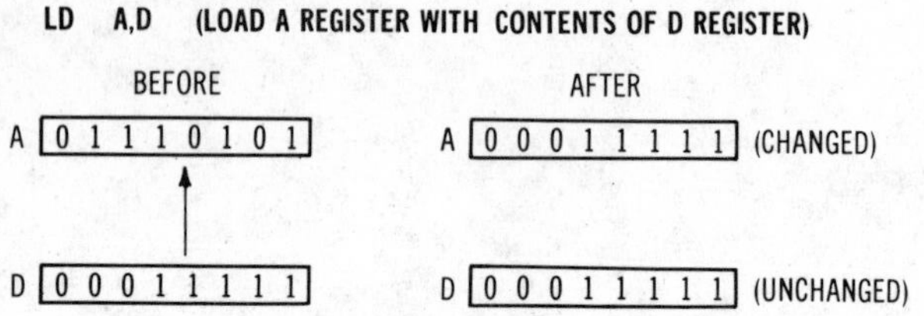

Fig. 5-1. Load from register example.

Another way to move data is with an *immediate* load. In all of the above examples, data was moved from one location to another. In the immediate load, data is moved from the instruction itself to a register or memory location. An example of this is shown in Fig. 5-4, which loads the A register with a decimal

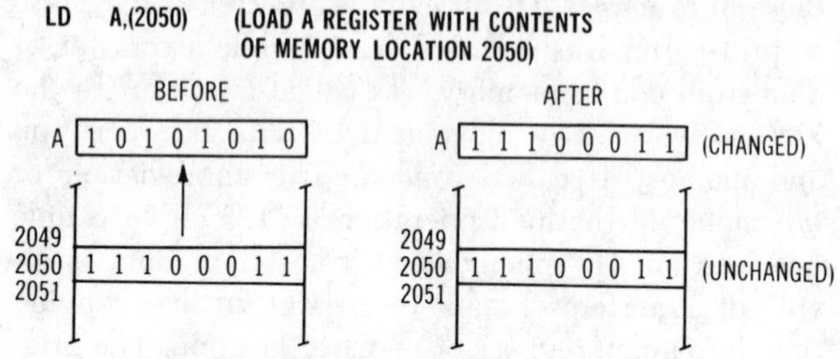

Fig. 5-2. Load from memory example.

32 (hexadecimal 20H). What is the difference between a move in which memory location 2050 holds 32 with an LD A,(2050) and a move of LD A,32? The difference is in instruction length, related speed, and ease of use.

The LD A,(2050) instruction is shown in Fig. 5-5. It is three bytes long. The first byte is the *operation code,* the encoded value that tells the cpu what type of an instruction this is, how long the instruction is, and so forth. The next two bytes are the 2050 address, 802H, *in reverse order* (we'll learn more about the format in the next section). To execute the instruction the cpu has to *fetch* the three bytes from memory (three cycles), and then use the 2050 (802H) address to load the contents of 2050 into A (another memory read cycle). The LD A,(2050) has taken three memory read cycles and three bytes of storage. The LD A,32 instruction, however, is two bytes long, as shown in

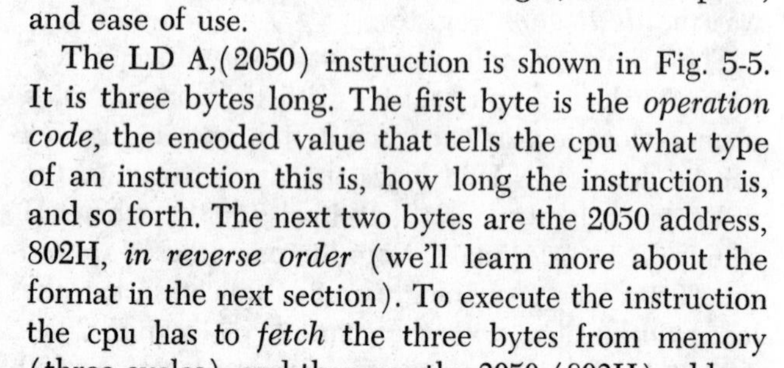

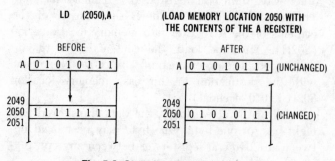

Fig. 5-3. Store to memory example.

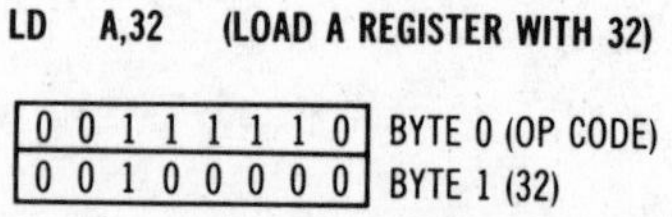

Fig. 5-4. Immediate load example.

Fig. 5-4. The cpu fetches the first two bytes, decodes the instruction as an immediate load, and stores the second byte into the A register. Two memory read cycles (for the instruction fetch) were expended and only two bytes of memory were used to store the instruction. The LD A,32 saves two memory read cycles and one byte of storage over the LD A,(2050). Is this significant? Not so much these days, when memory is inexpensive and cpu speeds are fast. But if nothing else, the programmer does not have to recall where the constant value of 32 was in memory. An

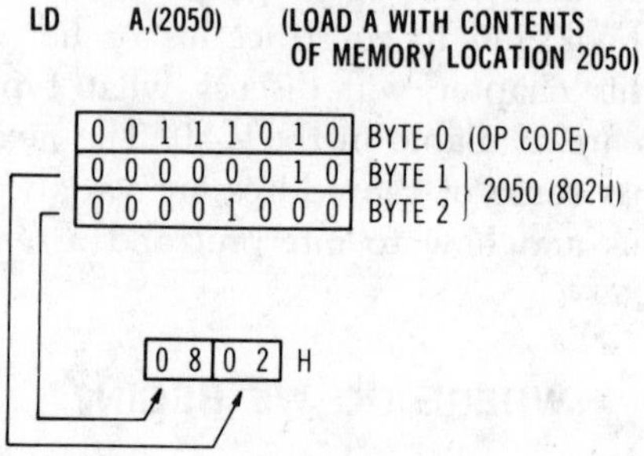

Fig. 5-5. Comparison of immediate and memory loads.

important format point: *Note that the immediate data is not enclosed by parentheses.* Every time the source data is in this format, the instruction uses immediate data.

All of the above loads involved 8 bits, or one byte of data. Sixteen-bit loads are also possible on the Z-80. These loads may be from a cpu register pair to two memory locations, from two memory locations to a cpu register pair, or from *immediate data* to a cpu register pair. Let's consider the latter case, the case in which a register pair is loaded with immediate data.

The register pairs, to refresh the reader's memory, are AF, BC, DE, and HL. As the IX, IY, and SP registers are the same width, 16 bits, as the other register pairs, they too fall in this category. The instruction LD HL,2050 will load the HL register pair with 2050 decimal (802H), as shown in Fig. 5-6. An example of an immediate load of the IX register is shown in the same figure. LD IX,FFH loads the IX register with the immediate value of FFH, or 255 decimal. Note that in both cases no parentheses were used around the immediate data.

Register pairs may also be loaded from memory or stored to memory. When a register pair is loaded or stored, two memory locations are involved, as 16 bits of data must be transferred. The instruction shown

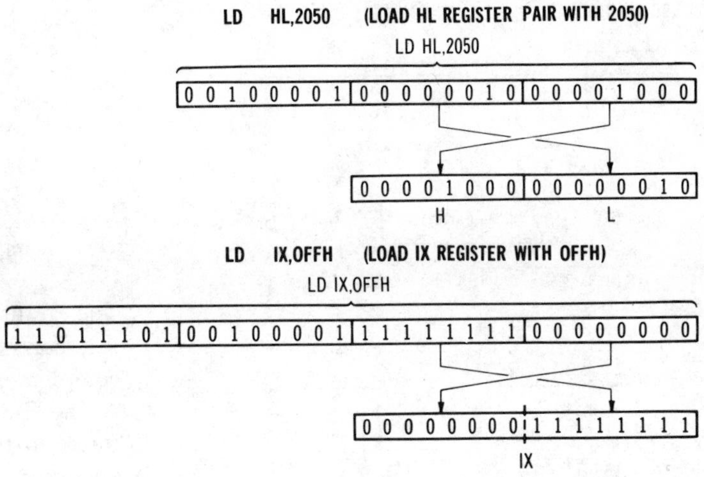

Fig. 5-6. Immediate loads of 16 bits.

in Fig. 5-7, LD BC,(860H), transfers the two bytes from memory locations 860H (2144 decimal) and 861H into register pair BC. Note that the instruction specifies the first memory location and that this location plus the next higher is used in the transfer. The same figure shows the inverse instruction LD (860H), BC, which stores the contents of register pair BC into memory locations 860H and 861H.

ARITHMETIC

Arithmetic and logical instructions are the cornerstone of all computer instructions, for they allow processing of data. These instructions allow addition, subtraction, and comparisons of two operands, and also allow *logical* types of operations.

Both 8- and 16-bit adds and subtracts may be done in the Z-80. Adds are done by using the A register in the 8-bit case; the A is always the *destination* register. The instruction in Fig. 5-8 adds the contents of the L register to the contents of the A register and puts the result in A. A second example adds the contents of memory location (802H) with A and puts

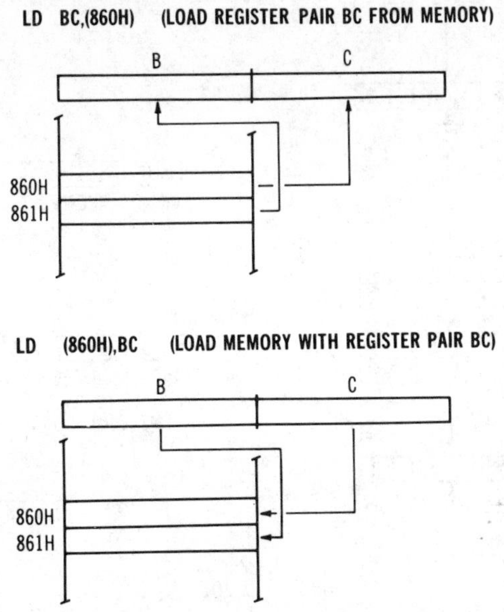

Fig. 5-7. Sixteen-bit loads and stores.

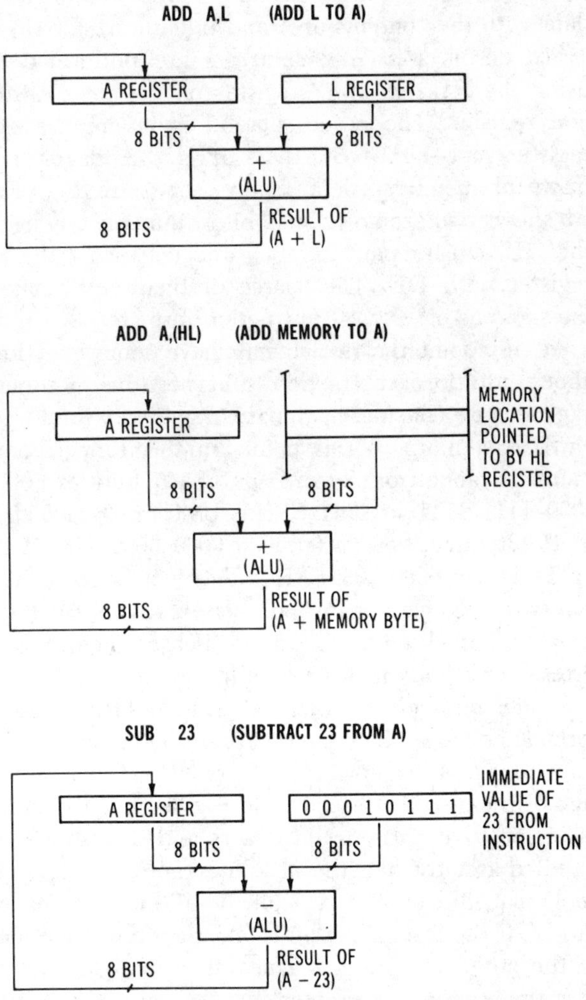

Fig. 5-8. Eight-bit arithmetic operations.

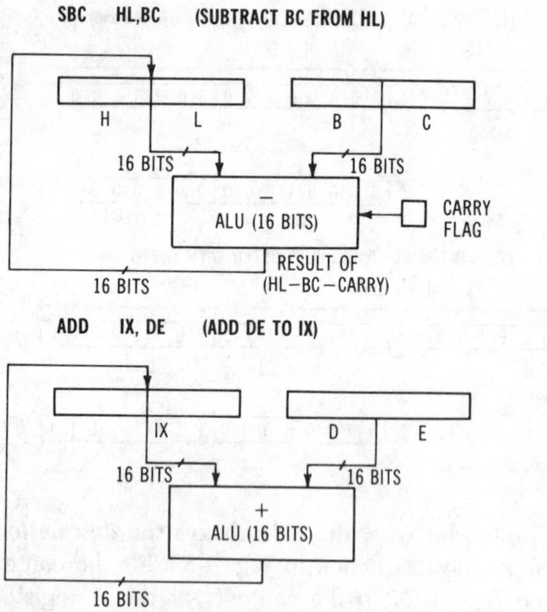

Fig. 5-9. Sixteen-bit arithmetic operations.

the result in A. A third example subtracts *immediate* data with the contents of A and puts the results in A.

Sixteen-bit adds and subtracts are performed by using the HL, IX, or IY register pair as the destination register. The other operand is in another cpu register pair—either BC, DE, or HL. Adds or subtracts of memory operands are not permitted. Fig. 5-9 shows two examples of 16-bit arithmetic, one using the HL register pair and BC, and one using the IX register with DE. The source–destination format is the same as other Z-80 instruction formats.

At this point the reader may have some questions about addition, subtraction, and negative numbers. We've been considering binary numbers without regard to sign up to this point. In this form, binary numbers range from 0 to 255 in 8-bit quantities (0000 0000–1111 1111 or 00H–FFH), or from 0 to 65,535 in 16-bit quantities (0000 0000 0000 0000–1111 1111 1111 1111 or 0000H-FFFFH). This is a perfectly fine way to work with many numbers in the Z-80. Such *unsigned* or absolute quantities such as memory addresses or counts may be handled in this fashion.

Signed numbers are handled in a slightly different format, however. In signed 8- or 16-bit numbers, the first bit (most significant) is used to represent the sign of the number, as shown in Fig. 5-10. If the number is positive, the sign bit is zero and the number is handled exactly like the absolute representation except that it becomes a 7-bit or 15-bit number as shown. If the first (sign) bit is one, then the remainder of the number represents a negative number. In this case the number represented may be found by *changing all zeros to ones, all ones to zeros, and adding 1.*

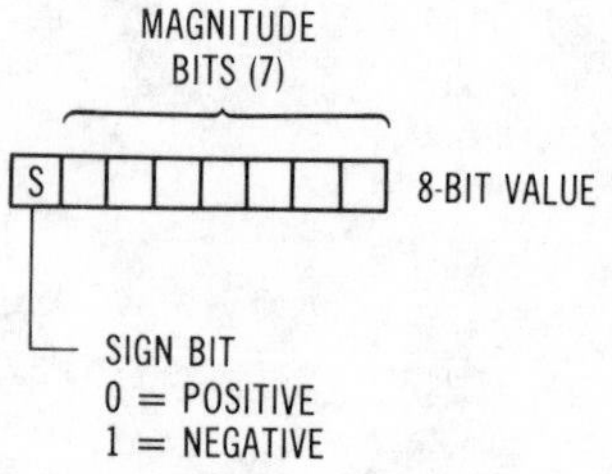

Fig. 5-10. Twos complement representation.

The result is the *magnitude* of the negative number. Fig. 5-11 shows the ranges and examples of this twos complement representation.

The Z-80 performs all 8- or 16-bit adds and subtracts in twos complement fashion. The programmer does not have to be concerned with testing for the sign of the number, performing the add or subtract, and then changing the result to the proper sign. Adding +120 and −53 is done by simply performing the ADD; the result is +67 as shown in Fig. 5-12. As in the case of unsigned numbers, however, the 8-bit and 16-bit registers and memory cells have a definite limit on the sizes of numbers that can be held. The smallest number that can be held in 8 bits, for example, is −128, and the largest that can be held in 16 bits is +32,767.

What happens when +127 is added to +100? The result of +227 is too large to fit in 8 bits. As a matter of fact, the result looks like the negative number −29, which is incorrect (see Fig. 5-13). The Z-80 (and other computers) *flags* this *overflow* condition by the overflow flag. The overflow (P/V) flag can be tested by a conditional jump, which we'll discuss shortly. The overflow and other flags are grouped together,

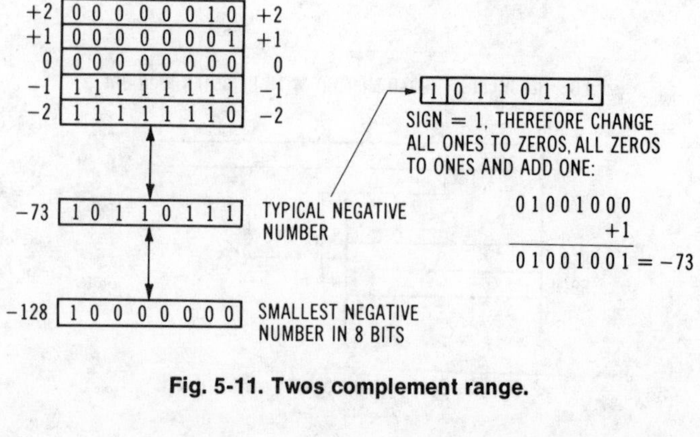

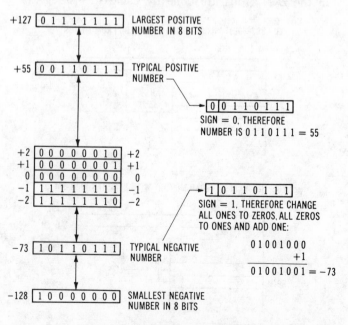

Fig. 5-11. Twos complement range.

```
ADD  +120  AND  -53

  0 1 1 1 1 0 0 0   +120

  1 1 0 0 1 0 1 1   - 53
  ---------------
  0 1 0 0 0 0 1 1   +67
```

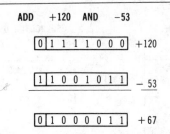

Fig. 5-12. Twos complement: example.

as the reader will recall, into a flag register as shown in Fig. 5-14. Other flags affected by arithmetic operations are the Z flag, which is set (1) if the result is zero, the S flag which is set (1) if the sign is negative, and the C flag, which is set (1) if there is a carry out of the high-order bit position. The flags are not always set after an instruction, but are set only for certain operations. Arithmetic instructions almost always set the flags. The complete flag actions are listed in the Z-80 instructions in Appendix D.

The last type of arithmetic instruction is the *compare*. Compares are permitted only with 8-bit operands. A compare is identical with the 8-bit SUB(tract) except for one difference: The result *only* affects the flags (zero, sign, carry, overflow) and does not replace the A register contents. It is useful when a test

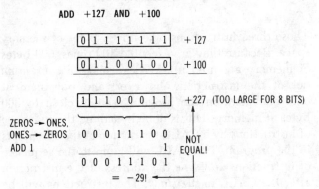

```
ADD  +127  AND  +100

                 0 1 1 1 1 1 1 1   + 127
                 0 1 1 0 0 1 0 0   + 100
                 ---------------
                 1 1 1 0 0 0 1 1   +227 (TOO LARGE FOR 8 BITS)
ZEROS→ONES,
ONES→ZEROS       0 0 0 1 1 1 0 0       NOT
ADD 1                          1       EQUAL!
                 ---------------
                 0 0 0 1 1 1 0 1
                     = -29!
```

Fig. 5-13. Overflow example.

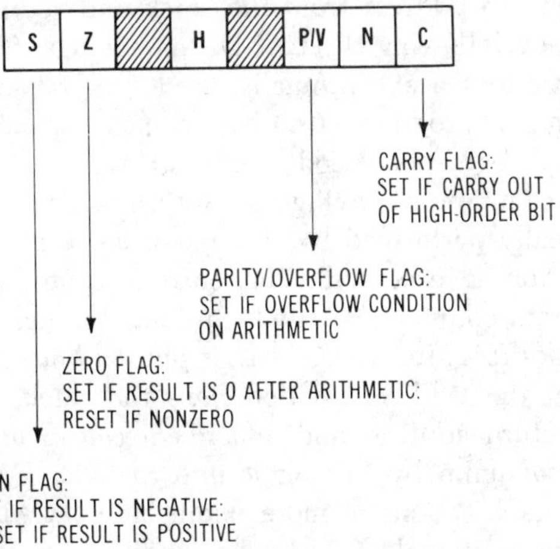

Fig. 5-14. Arithmetic flag actions.

must be made of the operand in the A register without destroying the contents of A.

LOGICAL INSTRUCTIONS

The logical instructions are instructions that can be used only with 8-bit operands. Here again, as in the case of the arithmetic instructions, the A register is used as the destination for the result. There are three types of logical instructions: ANDs, ORs, and exclusive ORs (XORs).

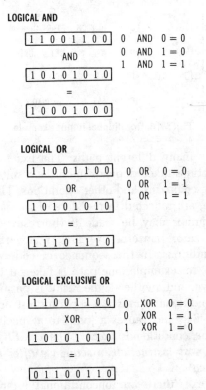

```
LOGICAL AND

1 1 0 0 1 1 0 0     0 AND 0 = 0
      AND           0 AND 1 = 0
                    1 AND 1 = 1
1 0 1 0 1 0 1 0
       =
1 0 0 0 1 0 0 0

LOGICAL OR

1 1 0 0 1 1 0 0     0 OR 0 = 0
      OR            0 OR 1 = 1
                    1 OR 1 = 1
1 0 1 0 1 0 1 0
       =
1 1 1 0 1 1 1 0

LOGICAL EXCLUSIVE OR

1 1 0 0 1 1 0 0     0 XOR 0 = 0
      XOR           0 XOR 1 = 1
                    1 XOR 1 = 0
1 0 1 0 1 0 1 0
       =
0 1 1 0 0 1 1 0
```

Fig. 5-15. Logical operations.

The AND, OR, and XOR are shown in Fig. 5-15. The AND operation puts a one bit in the result if both the bits in each operand are a one. If both bits are not ones, a zero goes into the result bit position. Each bit position is considered by itself. The OR operation puts a one bit in the result if *either* (or) bit of the operands is a one. The XOR puts a one bit in the result if *one but not both* bits are a one. ANDs and ORs are used quite extensively in Z-80 programs to manipulate data bits. Many examples will be found in the software descriptions.

JUMPS, CALLS, AND RETURNS

Up to this point we've talked a little bit about sequences of instructions and conditional and unconditional branches. The typical program was described

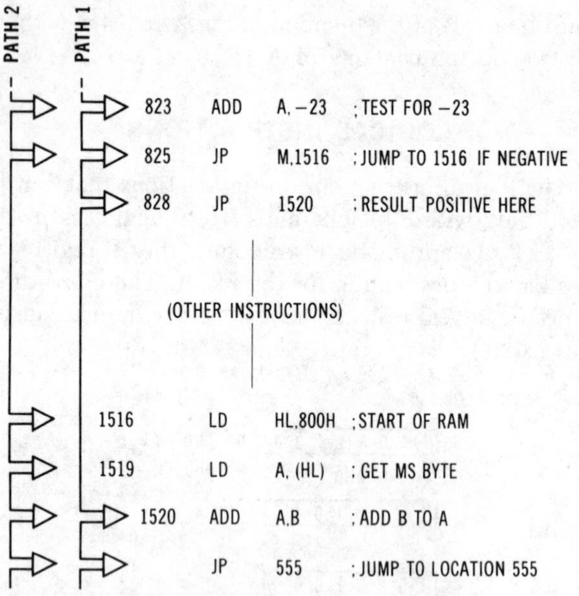

Fig. 5-16. Conditional jump: example.

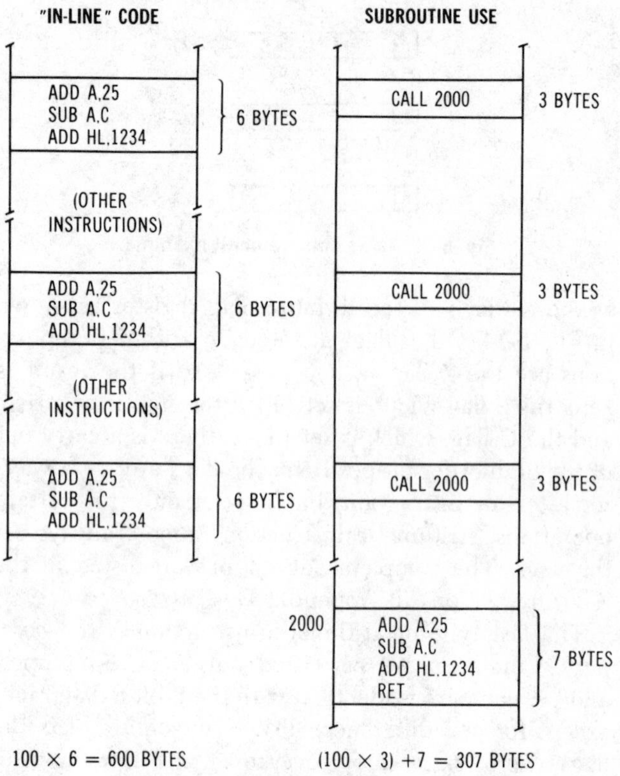

Fig. 5-17. Subroutine use.

as having many different paths. The exact sequence of instructions taken depends upon the results of adds, subtracts, compares, and other operations. The results, of course, are reflected in the state of the *flags*. Conditional jumps may be made if the result is minus, positive, zero, nonzero, overflow, nonoverflow, and other conditions. In the sequence of code shown in Fig. 5-16, for example, one path is taken if the result is negative, and another if the result is positive. Each of the conditional jumps is a separate instruction that tests one flag and causes a jump to a specified location if the condition is met. *If the condition is not met, the next instruction in sequence after the jump is executed.*

Of course, there are unconditional jumps in the Z-80, also. The JP instruction *always* jumps to the specified location. Unconditional jumps are necessary because the flow of the program occasionally has to be altered to get around blocks of data, or because a set of instructions has to be entered again. The last instruction shown in Fig. 5-16 will always jump to location 555 after the preceding instructions have been executed.

As mentioned earlier, performing an unconditional or conditional jump does not *save* the location of the jump. If we want to come back to the same location, the programmer must include the address of the location and specifically put it in the program. However, there are instructions in the Z-80 (and in other computers) that do save the *return address*. Let's look at the reason for having such a set of instructions.

Suppose that at 100 different points in the program we had to execute the instructions of "ADD A,25," "SUB A,C," and "ADD HL,1234" (see Fig. 5-17). Those three instructions take up six bytes of memory space. Because they are executed 100 times, 600 bytes of memory are used up. We can make a *subroutine* out of the instructions, however, and put them at only *one* point in the program, saving close to 300 bytes of memory. This is done by calling the sequence of instructions by a CALL instruction at the 100 points in the program. The CALL will jump to the sequence of instructions and *save* the address of the instruction after the CALL in the *stack*. The instructions will be executed, and a RET(urn) instruction will retrieve the return address from the stack and return to the location following the CALL. Net savings: 293 bytes. Subroutines are continually used in Z-80 and other computer programs to save memory space for repeated segments of code such as this.

The action of saving the return address is automatically performed by the cpu when the CALL instruction is executed. The current contents of the program counter (PC), which holds the next instruction address after the CALL, is *pushed* onto the stack. Later, the RET instruction *pops* the stack, retrieves the return address, and *effectively causes an unconditional* jump by forcing it into the PC. (We'll discuss stack actions in more detail later.) CALLs may be unconditional (CALL) or conditional upon the Z flag, P/V flag, and other cpu flags. RETurns may also be conditional or unconditional. All in all, there are quite a few ways to alter the sequence of instructions by jumps, calls, and returns.

STACK OPERATIONS

The memory stack may be thought of as building down in memory, as shown in Fig. 5-18. Each time a CALL is made, another address is put on the stack. Each address consists of two bytes. The stack pointer (SP) register is adjusted to point to the next stack location for every byte *pushed* onto the stack. The current location in the SP represents the *location of the last byte pushed onto the stack.* Whenever a RET(urn) instruction is executed, two bytes are retrieved (popped) from the stack and the SP is adjusted by two to point to a *higher* memory location. The stack area is initially set by *loading* the SP register with the first location to be used for the stack +1. As the stack builds downward, it is advisable to locate it in the highest memory location. In EZ-80 programs the stack area is initialized at 87FH (2175 decimal), the very top byte of the RAM memory area.

In addition to addresses being pushed onto the stack, register pairs may be pushed onto the stack for temporary storage. The instruction that pushes a register pair onto the stack is PUSH and the instruction that pops the register pair from the stack is POP. Fig. 5-19 shows a PUSH of register pair BC and a POP into the IX register (in effect, a load of IX with BC).

As CALLs may be *nested* (a CALL within a CALL within a CALL within . . .) and any number of PUSHes may be used to store data, the stack area may rapidly build downward. However, each PUSH must have a POP and each CALL a RET(urn) so that

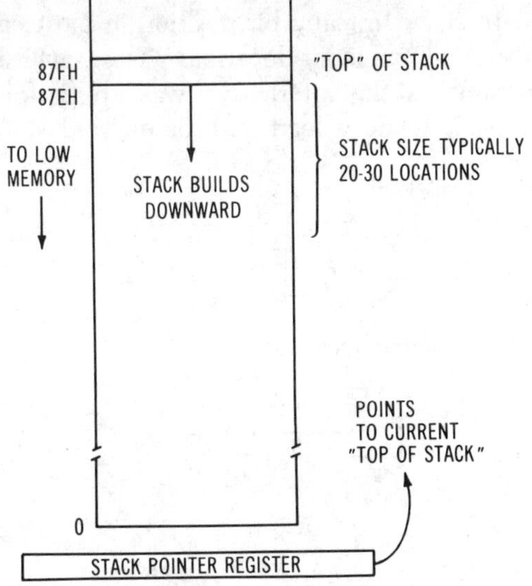

Fig. 5-18. Stack use.

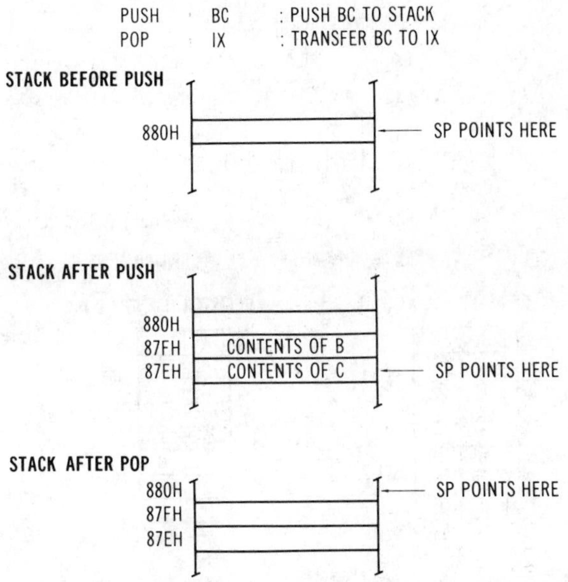

Fig. 5-19. PUSHes and POPs.

a practical stack area is probably less than 30 bytes for most programs.

A third use of the stack area in the EZ-80 and other Z-80 microcomputers is for storage of the return address for *interrupts.* Interrupts signal external events that require action and may come at any time; they are *asynchronous* events not related to cpu timing.

The only interrupt used in the EZ-80 is the NMI interrupt, the *n*on-*m*askable *i*nterrupt, which occurs every 1/100 of a second so that the EZ-80 can keep track of *real time.* When the NMI occurs, the program may be executing virtually any instruction. Because the interrupt requires a jump to an NMI routine, the address of the interrupted instruction must be saved for a subsequent return to the interrupted point. The NMI action causes the cpu to automatically save the return address in the stack. After the NMI interrupt has been *processed,* an RETI instruction pops the stack, loads the PC with the return address, and causes a return to the interrupted location.

As the NMI processing requires use of the cpu registers and flags, they must somehow be kept intact for the return. This may be done by temporarily saving them in the stack and restoring them just before the return. In the EZ-80, however, the primed registers are used instead. In effect, the nonprimed registers are used for all processing except the NMI processing; the primed registers are used for NMI processing. The switch is made by EX AF,AF′ and EXX upon entering the NMI processing routine, which makes the primed registers active.

These two instructions simply switch each set of eight cpu registers, making the active set inactive and the inactive set active. Immediately before the RETI,

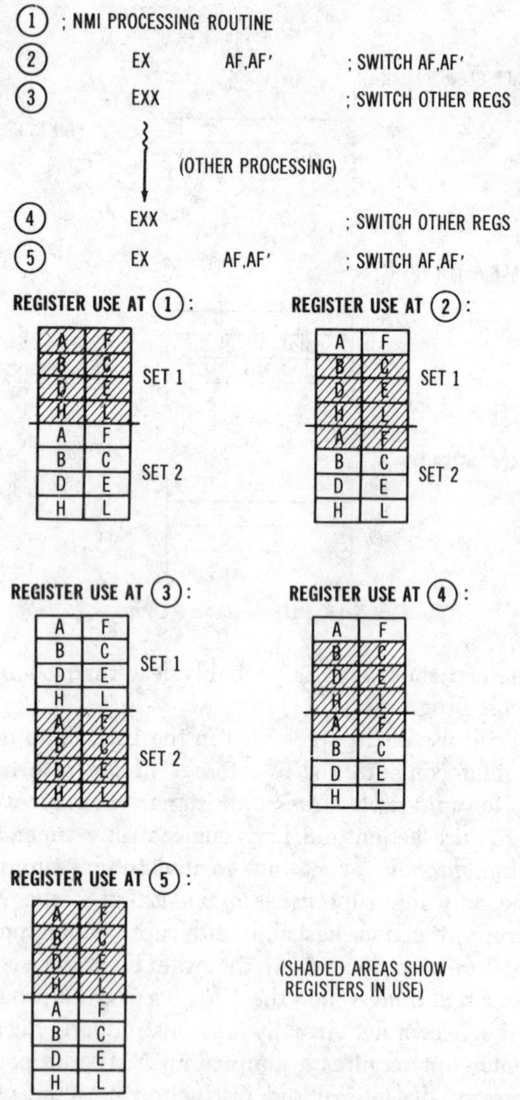

Fig. 5-20. General register exchanges.

the registers are switched again (see Fig. 5-20). In this way the nonprimed registers are kept intact.

ROTATES AND SHIFTS

The rotate and shift instructions in the Z-80 operate upon cpu registers, and, in some cases, memory locations.

The rotate instructions rotate 8 or 9 bits to the right or left one bit position, as shown in Fig. 5-21. The bit rotated out of the left or right end of the cpu register or memory location replaces the bit on the opposite end for an 8-bit rotate. At the same time, the bit goes into the carry flag. The bit "shifted out" can then be tested for a one or zero by a conditional jump such as JP NC, JumP if No Carry. Nine-bit rotates operate in the same manner except that the bit shifted out replaces the previous contents of the carry

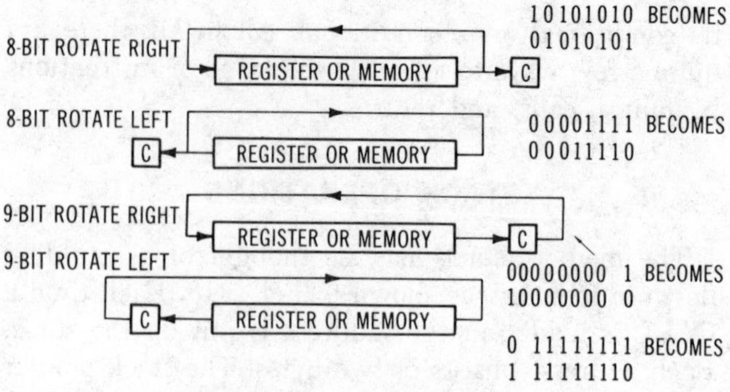

Fig. 5-21. Rotate operations.

flag. The previous contents of the carry goes into the opposite end of the register or memory location. Both 8- and 9-bit rotates find use in Z-80 programs, many times shifting cpu registers rather than memory locations.

Shifts in the Z-80 fall into two categories, *logical* shifts and *arithmetic* shifts (see Fig. 5-22). Logical shifts shift one bit position at a time right or left with a zero filling in the vacated bit position. The arithmetic shift (SRA) shifts a cpu register or memory location one bit position right. The sign bit duplicates itself as the shift is made. This has the effect of *extending* the sign bit as the number in the operand is shifted. Both logical and arithmetic shifts are used in Z-80 programs. The logical shift finds more extensive use than the arithmetic, however. (A logical shift left multiples by a power of two, while a logical shift right divides by a power of two.) Both types of shifts set the carry flag to the value of the bit shifted out of the register.

BIT SET, RESET, AND TEST

The instructions in this group allow a programmer to set, reset, or test any bit position in most cpu registers and all memory locations. This saves several instructions as the alternative way to perform this operation is to do a load, AND or OR, and store. The

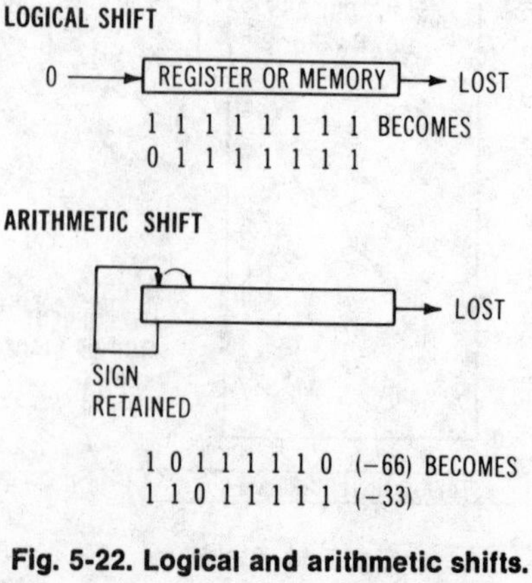

Fig. 5-22. Logical and arithmetic shifts.

SET 5,B (SET BIT 5 OF B)

	7	6	5	4	3	2	1	0
B REGISTER BEFORE	1	1	0	1	1	1	1	1
B REGISTER AFTER	1	1	1	1	1	1	1	1

RESET 5,B (RESET BIT 5 OF B)

	7	6	5	4	3	2	1	0
B REGISTER BEFORE	1	1	1	1	1	1	1	1
B REGISTER AFTER	1	1	0	1	1	1	1	1

BIT 5,B (TEST BIT 5 OF B)

	7	6	5	4	3	2	1	0	
B REGISTER BEFORE	0	1	1	0	0	1	1	0	
CARRY BEFORE	0								
B REGISTER AFTER	0	1	1	0	0	1	1	0	(UNCHANGED)
CARRY AFTER	1								

Fig. 5-23. Bit instruction operation.

bit instruction performs the same operation with one instruction. Fig. 5-23 shows an example of each of the three types operating on the cpu B register. The format of this type of instruction includes a "bit" specifier that defines which bit of the cpu register or memory location is to be acted upon. Bit positions in the Z-80 are numbered 7–0 from left to right, each number corresponding to the power of two that is represented, as shown in Fig. 5-24.

I/O OPERATIONS

Input/output instructions have been discussed in preceding chapters in relation to the architecture of the EZ-80. There are two basic i/o instructions: read (RD) and write (WR). The two instructions we will use in the EZ-80 use the A register for both input and output, although another type uses a slightly different scheme (see Appendix D).

The format of the read instruction is RD A,(NN),

	2^7	2^6	2^5	2^4	2^3	2^2	2^1	2^0
BIT NUMBER	7	6	5	4	3	2	1	0

(REGISTER OR MEMORY LOCATION)

Fig. 5-24. Bit position numbering.

where NN is an i/o address of 0 to 255. The valid i/o read address in the EZ-80 is 2, and refers to the 8255 PPI input register. When data is being read from the keyboard (when the keyboard is being scanned), the A register must contain an address of 80H, 40H, 20H, or 10H before the read to scan the appropriate row bit. When data is being read from the input lines IN1–IN5, the A register address is not required.

The format of the write instruction is WR (NN),A, where NN is an i/o address of 0 to 255. Valid i/o addresses in the EZ-80 are 0 and 1. A WR (0),A outputs data in the A register to the LED display. A WR (1),A outputs data in the A register to the output lines OUT1–OUT6.

MISCELLANEOUS INSTRUCTIONS

The preceding discussion briefly describes 90 percent of the instructions used in typical programs written for the EZ-80 and for most other Z-80 programs. There are many other instructions that are not used as frequently in Z-80 programs. Some of them are very simple, such as NEG, which negates the value in the A register, and some of them are very complex, such as LDIR, which moves an entire block of memory from one area in memory to another. Instructions not described above will be discussed as they appear in the application programs for the EZ-80, and they are also described fully in Appendix D.

CHAPTER 6

Z-80 Assembly Language—Addressing and Formats

This chapter discusses the several addressing types available in the Z-80 instruction set. Some Z-80 instructions have *no* addressing variations, while others offer several variations to address either cpu registers or memory locations. Once the instruction and addressing possibilities are known, a set of instructions for an EZ-80 program can be either hand assembled or assembled automatically. If the reader does not want to create his or her own programs for the EZ-80, he or she may want to scan the applications programs and investigate their approach to solving applications problems.

ADDRESSING MODES OF THE Z-80

What are addressing modes and why are they necessary? Some instructions perform a specific predefined set of actions. No variations are possible. An example of this type of instruction is the CPL instruction. The CPL always operates on the A register, changing all ones to zeros and all zeros to ones (*Com*-*PL*ement Accumulator). This action cannot be performed on any other cpu register. We could use this scheme of unique instructions and create hundreds of predefined instructions in the Z-80 or another microprocessor. However, this approach is somewhat limiting. Do we only permit an add of the B register to the A register? Or do we allow all registers to be added? Do we allow only cpu registers to be added, or do we allow memory locations? The reader can see that it is useful to take a generic instruction such as an ADD and allow variations on the source operand. This generic approach is used on many instructions in the Z-80 to create a general-purpose instruction set.

Another reason for having different addressing modes for instructions in the Z-80 relates to the antecedents of the Z-80. Its grandfather, the 8008, had a limited way of addressing memory. Its father, the 8080, had incorporated these methods and added more powerful addressing capability. The Z-80 expanded even further on this addressing capability, *while retaining all of the 8008 and 8080 instruction types and addressing modes.*

The basic addressing types in the Z-80 instruction set are:

Implied Addressing
Immediate Addressing
Register Addressing
Register Indirect Addressing
Extended Addressing
Page 0 Addressing
Relative Addressing
Indexed Addressing
Bit Addressing

IMPLIED ADDRESSING

Implied addressing is the case mentioned above, a specific predefined set of operations for an instruction. Some implied instructions are NEG (*Neg*ate Accumulator), SCF (*S*et *C*arry *F*lag), and NOP (*N*o *Op*eration). These and other instructions perform simple operations, or are limited to operations on the A register. Format examples are shown in Fig. 6-1.

IMMEDIATE ADDRESSING

We've already mentioned immediate addressing, but let's discuss it a bit more. In immediate addressing the *operand* is in the second or second and third bytes (in most cases) of the instruction. The *immediate* data may be either an 8-bit value or a 16-bit value. The first byte of the instruction is an *op code,* or operation code that defines the instruction type and which the cpu uses in decoding the instruction.

An example of an 8-bit immediate instruction is shown in Fig. 6-2, which shows the ADD A,N instruction. The first byte is 11000110 (C6H) and is fixed. This is the op code for the ADD A,N. The second byte

NEG (NEGATE)

1 1 1 0 1 1 0 1	BYTE 0	(EDH)
0 1 0 0 0 1 0 0	BYTE 1	(44H)

SCF (SET CARRY FLAG)

0 0 1 1 0 1 1 1	BYTE 0	(37H)

NOP (NO OPERATION)

0 0 0 0 0 0 0 0	BYTE 0	(00H)

Fig. 6-1. Implied addressing examples.

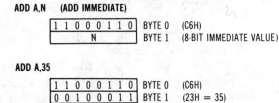

ADD A,N (ADD IMMEDIATE)

1 1 0 0 0 1 1 0	BYTE 0	(C6H)
N	BYTE 1	(8-BIT IMMEDIATE VALUE)

ADD A,35

1 1 0 0 0 1 1 0	BYTE 0	(C6H)
0 0 1 0 0 0 1 1	BYTE 1	(23H = 35)

Fig. 6-2. Eight-bit immediate addressing example.

is "N." N stands for an 8-bit operand from 0 to +127, or from −1 to −128 (twos complement form). The instruction ADD A,35, for example, has a 35 decimal (23H) in the second byte. When the instruction is executed, 35 will be added to the contents of the A register and the result will be put into the A register. The flags will also be affected. Eight-bit immediate instructions are found for loads (LD B,38), arithmetic instructions (ADD A,0FEH), logical instructions (OR 59), and others. In the instruction format the immediate data never has parentheses around it.

An example of a 16-bit immediate instruction is shown in Fig. 6-3. The instruction is LD HL,NN. The first byte of the instruction is the op code 0010 0001 (21H) and is fixed. The second and third bytes are the immediate operand NN. NN stands for a 16-bit operand from 0 to +32,767, or from −1 to −32,768 (twos complement). As an example of a specific immediate load, look at LD HL,1000 in the same figure. LD HL,1000 will load the decimal value 1000 into the HL register pair. Decimal 1000 is 3E8 in hexadecimal or 0000 0011 1110 1000 in binary. Note that the second byte holds the low-order 8 bits of 1110 1000 while the third byte holds the high-order 8 bits

LD HL,NN (LOAD HL IMMEDIATE)

0 0 1 0 0 0 0 1	BYTE 0	(21H)
N	BYTE 1	(16-BIT IMMEDIATE VALUE)
N	BYTE 2	

LD HL,1000

0 0 1 0 0 0 0 1	BYTE 0	(21H)
1 1 1 0 1 0 0 0	BYTE 1	(1000)
0 0 0 0 0 0 1 1	BYTE 2	

Fig. 6-3. Sixteen-bit immediate addressing example.

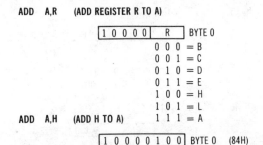

ADD A,R (ADD REGISTER R TO A)

1 0 0 0 0	R	BYTE 0

R	Register
0 0 0	B
0 0 1	C
0 1 0	D
0 1 1	E
1 0 0	H
1 0 1	L
1 1 1	A

ADD A,H (ADD H TO A)

1 0 0 0 0 1 0 0	BYTE 0	(84H)

Fig. 6-4. Single register addressing format.

of 0000 0011. This somewhat strange orientation holds throughout all Z-80 instruction and data formats. *The high-order byte is always first (low memory address) followed by the low-order byte (high memory address).* Sixteen-bit immediate addressing is used for immediate loads of register pairs and 16-bit registers in the Z-80.

REGISTER ADDRESSING

Register addressing is easily understood. We could say that we had seven separate instructions for an ADD of a cpu register to the A register: ADD A,B; ADD A,C; ADD A,D; and so forth. Instead, we put the instruction in general form and say that we have a register *field,* as shown in Fig. 6-4. Here the 10,000 bits are fixed, but the low-order three bits are used to specify a cpu register. Thus 000 stands for B, 001 for C, and so forth, as shown in the figure. This same type of general approach is used in other instructions. The ADD HL,SS instruction adds a specified register pair to HL. The "SS" is a two-bit field as shown in Fig. 6-5, and specifies either BC (00), DE (01), HL (10), or SP (11). Here again, there could have been four "implied" instruction types, but to save time and space the ADD HL,SS format was used. The "field" concept is used in many instructions in the Z-80. Depending upon the instruction, different codes are used for the registers. A cpu register is always specified by a three-bit field with the coding shown in Fig. 6-4. Register pair codes vary with the instruction type as shown in Fig. 6-5. These codes are repeated to avoid confusion in Appendix E, "Z-80 Operation Code Listings." Most instructions of this type are one byte long.

REGISTER INDIRECT ADDRESSING

Register indirect addressing is a carryover from the 8008 instruction set. In the 8008 a single register pair, HL, was used to address memory operands for every instruction that used a memory operand. The HL register pair had to be loaded with a memory address before the memory reference instruction was executed.

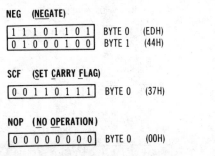

ADD HL,SS (ADD REGISTER PAIR SS TO HL)

0 0 S S 1 0 0 1	BYTE 0

0 0 = BC
0 1 = DE
1 0 = HL
1 1 = SP

ADD HL,HL (ADD HL TO HL)

0 0 1 0 1 0 0 1	BYTE 0	(29H)

ADD IX,PP (ADD REGISTER PAIR PP TO IX)

1 1 0 1 1 1 0 1	BYTE 0	(DDH)
0 0 P P 1 0 0 1	BYTE 1	

0 0 = BC
0 1 = DE
1 0 = IX
1 1 = SP

ADD IX,SP (ADD SP TO IX)

1 1 0 1 1 1 0 1	BYTE 0	(DDH)
0 0 1 1 1 0 0 1	BYTE 1	(39H)

Fig. 6-5. Register pair field coding.

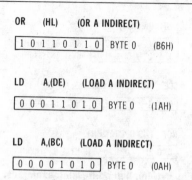

Fig. 6-6 shows this sequence. First the HL register is loaded with 803H, the RAM memory address. Next, the ADD A,(HL) instruction is executed. The ADD A,(HL) finds the second operand for the ADD by using HL as a *register pointer* to memory address 803H. The contents of 803H is read and added to the A register with the result going to the A register.

The 8080 expanded upon this concept by allowing BC and DE to be used as register pointers in identical fashion. The disadvantage of this method is that the memory operand cannot be referenced directly. Every time an instruction uses the form (HL), (DE), or (BC) as the source (rightmost) operand, this register indirect form of addressing is being used. Examples of this are shown in Fig. 6-7. This is not necessarily a bad way to access memory operands, but it *does* have an historical basis. Instructions using this type of addressing are loads, arithmetic, logical, increments, decrements, bit instructions, and others. All instructions of this type are one-byte instructions.

LD	HL,803H	LOAD POINTER REGISTER
ADD	A, (HL)	ADD CONTENTS OF 803H

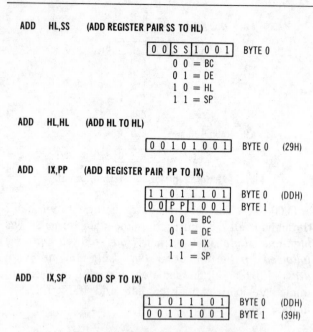

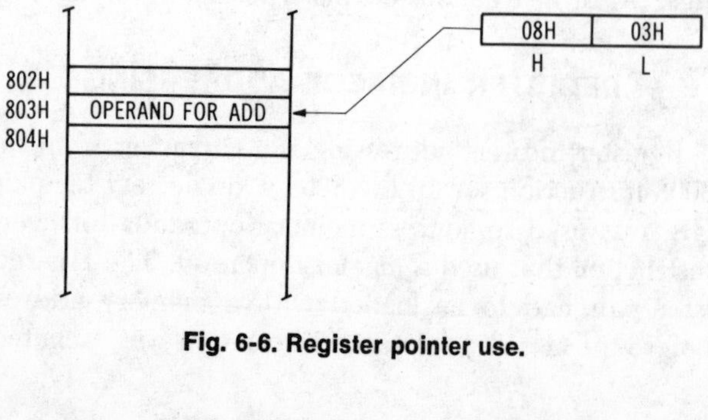

Fig. 6-6. Register pointer use.

OR (HL) (OR A INDIRECT)

1 0 1 1 0 1 1 0	BYTE 0	(B6H)

LD A,(DE) (LOAD A INDIRECT)

0 0 0 1 1 0 1 0	BYTE 0	(1AH)

LD A,(BC) (LOAD A INDIRECT)

0 0 0 0 1 0 1 0	BYTE 0	(0AH)

Fig. 6-7. Register indirect addressing examples.

EXTENDED ADDRESSING

This form of addressing was added in the 8080 and is powerful. Here the memory operand address does not first have to be put into a register pair to be used as an indirect printer. The memory operand can be referenced directly, as in LD A,(803H) which loads the A register with the *contents* of memory location 803H, or LD HL,(803H), which loads the HL register pair with the contents of 803H (to L) and 804H (to H) (see Fig. 6-8). This form of addressing is used only for loading the A register or register pairs, for a comparable store operation, for jumps, or for calls.

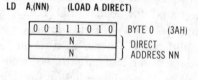

LD A,(NN) (LOAD A DIRECT)

0 0 1 1 1 0 1 0	BYTE 0	(3AH)
N	DIRECT ADDRESS NN	
N		

LD A,(803H)

0 0 1 1 1 0 1 0	BYTE 0
0 0 0 0 0 0 1 1	BYTE 1 : LS BYTE OF ADDRESS
0 0 0 0 1 0 0 0	BYTE 2 : MS BYTE OF ADDRESS

Fig. 6-8. Extended addressing examples.

When extended addressing is used, the memory address in the instruction is in the second and third bytes, and is in reverse format. The low-order byte of the address (0000 0011 in this case) is in the second byte, and the high-order byte (1000 0000) is in the third byte. Extended addressing instructions are usually three-byte instructions, with the first byte representing the *op code.*

PAGE 0 ADDRESSING

Page 0 addressing is only used for eight instructions, the restart (RST) instructions. The RSTs are one-byte instructions that are equivalent to a CALL. Recall that the CALL jumped to a subroutine and stored the return address in the stack. The CALL is a three-byte extended addressing type of instruction that

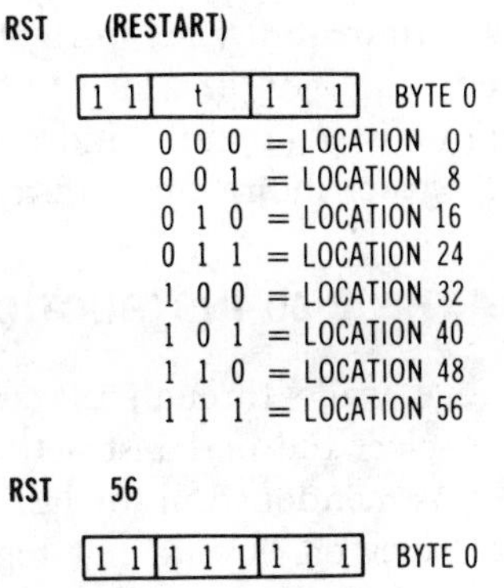

Fig. 6-9. RST vs. CALLs.

specifies the jump address in the second and third bytes of the instruction, as shown in Fig. 6-9. The RST performs exactly the same function as the CALL. It jumps to a subroutine location and stores the return address in the stack. The RST, however, can only jump to one of eight locations: 0, 8, 16, 24, 32, 40, 48, or 56 in page 0 (locations 0–255). The location for the CALL is encoded in a 3-bit field in the RST as shown in Fig. 6-9. The RST is used for commonly used subroutines called many times in the program.

RELATIVE ADDRESSING

Relative addressing is used only for certain types of two-byte jumps. Let's compare the two types of addressing used in jumps. In a three-byte JP the first byte is the op code, and the second and third are the address in reverse format. The address specified is an *absolute* address that refers to a specific memory location. In a two-byte JR the first byte is the op code and the second byte is a relative address. Relative to what? Relative to the current contents of the program counter, PC. But the PC points to the next instruction after the JR! That's correct. The relative jump finds the location for the jump by adding the contents of the PC with the displacement field in the second byte of the JR. As this may be 0 to +127, or −1 to −128, the JR may cause a jump up to 127 locations forward or up to 128 locations back from the location of the instruction. If the JR were located at location 100H, and a jump to 110H was required (see Fig. 6-10), then the displacement value in the second byte of the instruction would be (110H–102H), or EH or 14 decimal. The value 102H was used because the PC really points to the location after the JR; the JR starts at 100H, but the PC points to 102H.

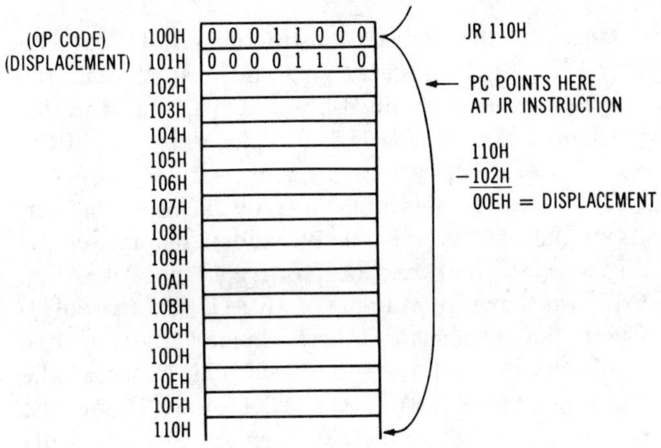

Fig. 6-10. Relative jump example.

Relative jumps save one byte in length over a direct jump. Furthermore, because they do not specify an absolute address, they are *relocatable*—they can be moved anywhere in memory and still jump *n* number of bytes forward or back from the JR instruction. When a relocatable JR is combined with other relocatable instructions, a *relocatable code segment* is defined which does not have to be redefined (reassembled) for different locations in memory.

INDEXED ADDRESSING

The most complex form of addressing in the Z-80 is indexed addressing. In indexed addressing the contents of one of the two index registers IX or IY is added with a twos complement displacement byte in the instruction, as shown in Fig. 6-11. The result of this add is the address used to read the operand of the instruction.

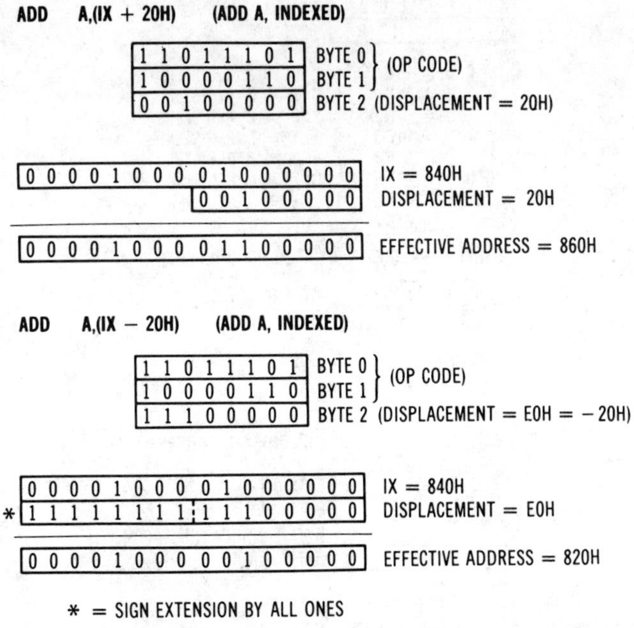

Fig. 6-11. Indexed addressing operation.

Consider the indexed instruction ADD A,(IX+20H). If the IX register contained 840H, then the *effective address* obtained by adding IX and the displacement byte of 20H is 860H. The add will add the contents of memory location 860H with the contents of the A register and put the result in the A register. As in the case of the relative addressing mode, the displacement byte can be positive or negative. Fig. 6-11 also shows an example of an ADD A,(IX−20H), where the displacement byte contains the negative displacement E0H (−20H or −32). In this case the effective address is 840H + (−20H) or 820H, and the add will use the contents of memory location 820H for the operand to be added to A.

Indexed addressing can be used to good advantage in accessing *tables* of data. The index register, IX or IY, is set to the beginning of the table and data can be read by changing the displacement value in the instruction.

All indexed instructions use two bytes for the op code. The only effect of this is to make instruction execution somewhat longer (and to generate two M1 cycles—see Chapter 2).

BIT ADDRESSING

The last instruction addressing type is bit addressing. Bit addressing is used only for the bit set, reset, and test instructions. These instructions may use register, register indirect, or indexed addressing and the bit addressing really refers to the field in all of these

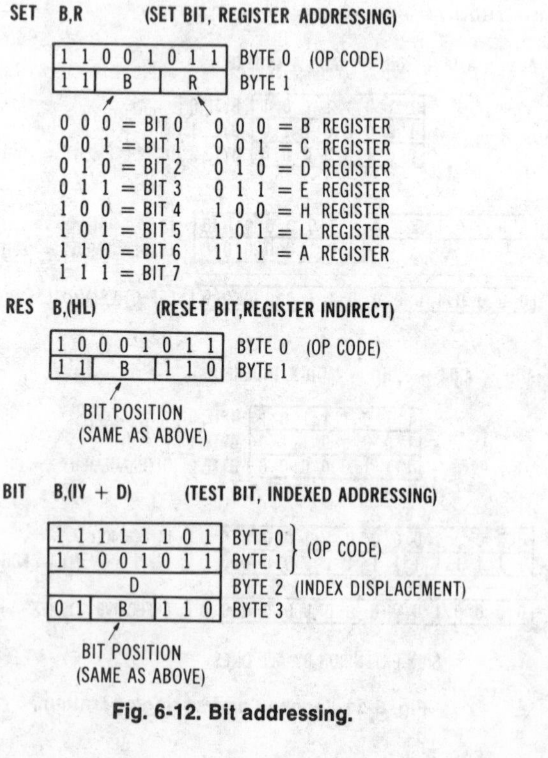

Fig. 6-12. Bit addressing.

instruction types that specify the bit to be used in the instruction, as shown in Fig. 6-12. The bit field specifies which bit 7 through 0 (left to right) is to be set, reset, or tested. The byte in which the bit is located is either a cpu register (register addressing) or memory location (register indirect or indexed addressing).

USING THE Z-80 INSTRUCTION SET

How does one wade through the swamp of Z-80 instructions to select the best instructions to perform a certain task? As mentioned in the last chapter, there are no precise rules on how to put together instructions into a program. Because the execution speeds are very fast—hundreds of thousands of instructions per second—even an inefficient program will probably be fine for a particular task.

To illustrate this idea let's discuss a typical problem and write several programs to solve it. The problem is this:

PROBLEM

Find the smallest of 16 positive numbers. The numbers are located from 810H through 81FH in EZ-80 memory, as shown in Fig. 6-13.

In the solutions to this problem, we'll refer to Appendix D, the instruction set of the Z-80 grouped in a functional basis, and Appendix E, a detailed description of the Z-80 instruction set.

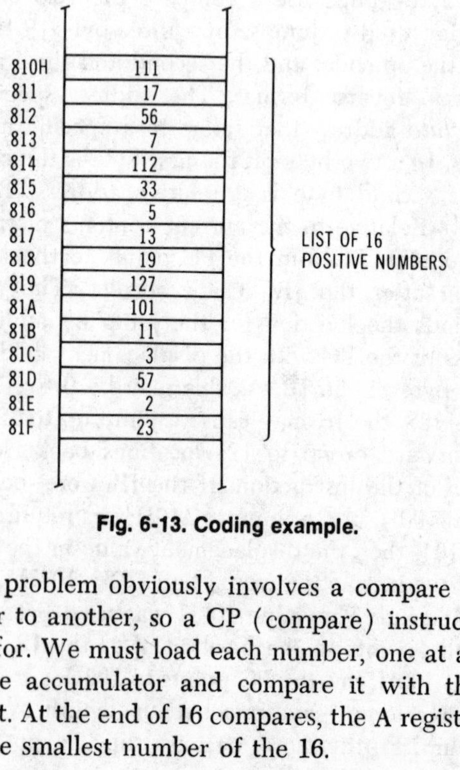

Fig. 6-13. Coding example.

This problem obviously involves a compare of one number to another, so a CP (compare) instruction is called for. We must load each number, one at a time, into the accumulator and compare it with the last smallest. At the end of 16 compares, the A register will hold the smallest number of the 16.

Solution 1

The *code* below shows one solution to the problem. Register B holds the smallest number throughout for comparison with the next number in A. At the end the smallest number in B is transferred to A. Each number is loaded into A by an extended addressing load, the compare is done, and if the new number is smaller than the old, it replaces the old as the smallest number up to that point. Initially, B is loaded with +127 to ensure that *some* number is smaller (or that all numbers are +127).

```
        LD B,127        Smallest number
        LD A,(810H)     Load first number
        CP B            Compare A to B (A—B)
        JP P,NEXT1      Jump if A—B is positive
        LD B,A          New smallest
NEXT1   LD A,(811H)     Load second number
        CP B            Compare A to B
        JP P,NEXT2      Jump if A—B is positive
        LD B,A          New smallest
NEXT2   .
        .
        .
NEXT15  LD A,(81FH)     Load sixteenth number
        CP B            Compare A to B
        JP P,NEXT16     Jump if A—B is positive
        LD B,A          New smallest
NEXT16  LD A,B          A now has smallest
```

The instructions above repeat the same operation 16 times. (The dots indicate similar operations not listed.) The next number is loaded, compared, and put into B if it is smaller than the current smallest. The JP P,NEXTX jumps around the transfer if the new number is not smaller. (The *label* NEXTX is used to indicate where the jump will be. In fact, this will be replaced by numeric value in the instruction, but for now it serves to represent the actual numeric location. The "P" in the "JP P, . . ." represents the conditional jump, *Jump* if *Positive*. This program will work but is quite long. If we had to compare hundreds of numbers, the program would be quite unwieldy.

Solution 2

One way to shorten the program would be to make a subroutine out of the instructions CP, JP, and LD, which are repeated 16 times. This could be done by:

```
        LD B,127        Smallest number
        LD A,(810H)     Load first number
        CALL COMP       Compare and switch
        LD A,(811H)     Load second number
        CALL COMP       Compare and switch
        .
        .
        .
        LD A,(81FH)     Load sixteenth number
        CALL COMP       Compare and switch
        LD A,B          A now has smallest
        .
COMP    CP B            Compare A to B (A—B)
        JP P,NEXT       Jump if A—B is positive
        LD B,A          New smallest
NEXT    RET             Return
```

The subroutine designated COMP performs the three operations and can be CALLed from 16 points in the program. It returns to the return address by the RET instruction. The label COMP in the CALL instruction is a *symbolic* representation of the actual numeric value that will be used in the code for the CALL.

Solution 3

The code above is shorter (38 instructions instead of 66), but still not too efficient. Let's use the register indirect capability to load each of the 16 data values.

```
        LD C,16         Count of 16
        LD HL,810H      Load pointer
        LD B,127        Smallest number
LOOP    LD A,(HL)       Get next number
        CP B            Compare A to B (A—B)
        JP P,NEXT       Jump if A—B is positive
        LD B,A          New smallest
NEXT    INC HL          810, 811, 812, 813, . . . , etc.
        DEC C           Count —1
        JP NZ,LOOP      Jump if count not zero
        LD A,B          A now has smallest
```

This program is quite short. The key to its operation is a *loop*. Instead of making 16 loads of LD A,(810H), LD A,(811H), etc., the program loops back 16 times to location LOOP. Each time it loops back HL points to a new location. HL initially starts off at 810H, but is *incremented* by one in the INC HL instruction. A *count* of 16 in the C register is *decremented* by the DEC C instruction. This count varies from 16, 15, 14, . . . , and so on down to 0. When it reaches zero, the *zero flag* is set and the conditional branch JP NZ,LOOP is not made—the LD A,B is executed instead. The concept of the loop is very powerful and used extensively in programs.

```
LOCATION  LENGTH
   0        2          LD    C,16
            3          LD    HL,810H
            2          LD    B,127
            1   LOOP   LD    A,(HL)
            1          CP    B
            3          JP    P,NEXT
            1          LD    B,A
            1   NEXT   INC   HL
            1          DEC   C
            3          JP    NZ,LOOP
            1          LD    A,B
```

Fig. 6-14. Assembling example 1.

ASSEMBLING THE PROGRAM

Now that the program has been defined, let's generate the code used by the Z-80. The EZ-80 uses the EPROM area to hold programs, so we'll use the EPROM locations starting from memory location zero. The numbers on the extreme left represent the locations that will hold the code. First of all, we must know how long each instruction is. We can find this out by reference to Appendix E, which gives the length in bytes. Write down the lengths before each instruction, as shown in Fig. 6-14.

Now we can assign a location to each instruction by adding the length in bytes to the last location, as shown in Fig. 6-15. These will be *hexadecimal* locations. Conversion from decimal to hex can be done by reference to Appendix B.

```
LOCATION  LENGTH
   0        2         LD    C,16
   2        3         LD    HL,810H
   5        2         LD    B,127
   7        1  LOOP   LD    A,(HL)
   8        1         CP    B
   9        3         JP    P,NEXT
   C        1         LD    B,A
   D        1  NEXT   INC   HL
   E        1         DEC   C
   F        3         JP    NZ,LOOP
  12        1         LD    A,B
```

Fig. 6-15. Assembling example 2.

Now we can construct each byte of the instruction, based on the number of bytes in the instruction. Draw a line for each byte required, as shown in Fig. 6-16. By reference to Appendix E we can now fill in the op codes and operands of each instruction. The LD C,16, for example, is two bytes long with an op code of 00001110 or 0EH. (The code in the C register 001 has been included.) The immediate value of 16 goes in the second byte as 10H. Some of the operands are memory addresses. Location LOOP is actually numeric location 0007H, for example. A reference to this location is made in JP NZ,LOOP, and the second and third bytes of the instruction are filled in with the *reverse form* of the memory address. In this manner the entire program can be hand assembled. The result is shown in Fig. 6-16.

The hand assembly process at first seems very difficult. There are many hobbyists doing exactly this, however, and the reader will find that after a while the process goes very rapidly and mechanically.

Is there an easier way to *assemble* a program? Yes, there is, but the reader must have access to a microcomputer built around the Z-80, such as a Radio Shack TRS-80 or similar personal computer. These microcomputers enable automatic assembly of a program by a program called an *assembler*. All of the programs in this book have been automatically assembled by an assembler running on a TRS-80 and we will take a look at the *format* of such an assembly. (The author has also done his share of hand assembly, and assures you it is quite feasible!)

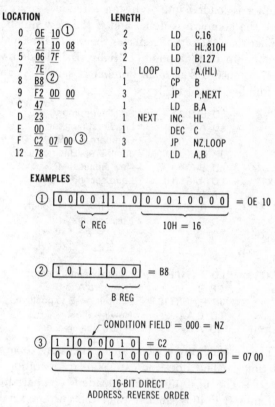

```
LOCATION              LENGTH
   0  0E 10 (1)         2          LD    C,16
   2  21 10 08          3          LD    HL,810H
   5  06 7F             2          LD    B,127
   7  7E                1   LOOP   LD    A,(HL)
   8  B8 (2)            1          CP    B
   9  F2 0D 00          3          JP    P,NEXT
   C  47                1          LD    B,A
   D  23                1   NEXT   INC   HL
   E  0D                1          DEC   C
   F  C2 07 00 (3)      3          JP    NZ,LOOP
  12  78                1          LD    A,B

EXAMPLES

(1) | 0 0 | 0 0 1 | 1 1 0 | 0 0 0 1 0 0 0 0 | = 0E 10
           C REG               10H = 16

(2) | 1 0 1 1 1 | 0 0 0 | = B8
                  B REG

                 CONDITION FIELD = 000 = NZ
(3) | 1 1 | 0 0 0 | 0 1 0 | = C2
    | 0 0 0 0 0 1 1 0 | 0 0 0 0 0 0 0 0 | = 07 00
            16-BIT DIRECT
        ADDRESS, REVERSE ORDER
```

Fig. 6-16. Assembling example 3.

The format of program listings in this book is shown in Fig. 6-17. The right-hand two-thirds of a listing represents the *source* program that was written down by the programmer. The left-hand one-third represents the automatic *assembly* of the program. The extreme left-hand column is the memory location of the first byte of the instruction. The next column is the hexadecimal representation of the one to four bytes of the instruction (each byte consists of two hex digits). The third column is the *line number* of the instruction. These are arbitrary ascending numbers used only for reference purposes.

There are certain other assembler-related operations that replace the operation code mnemonic. These will be described in Section 3 of the book as the applications programs for the EZ-80 are described. This chapter was meant to give the reader some feeling for the operations involved in programming and assembling programs for the EZ-80. If you do not want to program your own applications, you can get by quite nicely using the applications programs provided.

ASSEMBLY **SOURCE PROGRAM**

```
0049 C24900   00620 RAM10   JP     NZ,RAM10       ;LOOP HERE ON ERROR
004C 2F       00630         CPL                   ;-1 TO A
004D 320208   00640         LD     (802H),A       ;STORE -1
0050 3A0208   00650         LD     A,(802H)       ;GET CONTENTS
0053 3C       00660         INC    A              ;TEST FOR ALL ONES
0054 C25400   00670 RAM20   JP     NZ,RAM20       ;LOOP HERE ON ERROR
0057 21FFFF   00680         LD     HL,-1          ;FOR DELAY CNT
005A 01FFFF   00690         LD     BC,-1          ;FOR DELAY DECREMENT
005D 09       00700 RAM30   ADD    HL,BC              ;DECREMENT COUNT
005E DA5D00   00710         JP     C,RAM30            ;LOOP IF NOT 64K
              00720 ;
              00730 ;TEST 2:SHORT RAM MEMORY TEST
              00740 ;
0061 3E12     00750 MEMTST  LD     A,12H          ;FOR TEST 2
0063 1804     00770         JR     69H            ;BYPASS NMI VECTOR
              00780 ;
              00790 ;NM INTERRUPT VECTOR
              00800 ;
0066          00810         ORG    66H
0066 C36101   00820         JP     NMIHAN         ;GO TO PROCESS NMI
0069          00830         ORG    69H
0069 D300     00835         OUT    (0),A          ;OUTPUT TO LEDS
006B 210208   00840         LD     HL,802H        ;START OF RAM
006E 067C     00850         LD     B,124          ;SIZE OF RAM -WORKING
0070 AF       00860         XOR    A                  ;0 TO A
0071 77       00870 MEM10   LD     (HL),A             ;STORE ALL ZEROES
0072 7E       00880         LD     A,(HL)             ;GET STORED VALUE
0073 FE00     00890         CP     0                  ;IS IT ZERO?
0075 C27500   00900 MEM20   JP     NZ,MEM20           ;LOOP HERE ON ERROR
0078 2F       00910         CPL                       ;-1 TO A
0079 77       00920         LD     (HL),A             ;STORE ALL ONES
007A 7E       00930         LD     A,(HL)             ;GET STORED VALUE
007B 3C       00940         INC    A                  ;IS IT -1
007C C27C00   00950 MEM30   JP     NZ,MEM30           ;LOOP HERE ON ERROR
007F 23       00955         INC    HL                 ;BUMP POINTER
0080 10EF     00960         DJNZ   MEM10              ;CONTINUE HERE FOR 128
0082 21FFFF   00970         LD     HL,-1          ;FOR DELAY CNT
0085 01FFFF   00980         LD     BC,-1          ;FOR DELAY INC
0088 09       00990 MEM40   ADD    HL,BC              ;DECREMENT COUNT
0089 DA8800   01000         JP     C,MEM40            ;LOOP HERE IF NOT 64K
              01010 ;
              01020 ;TEST3:NMI/CLK FREQUENCY TEST
              01030 ;
008C 3E13     01040 NMICLK  LD     A,13H          ;FOR TEST 3
008E D300     01050         OUT    (0),A          ;OUTPUT TO LEDS
0090 213075   01060         LD     HL,30000       ;30 SEC DELAY AT 1 MHZ
0093 CD5301   01070         CALL   DELAY
0096 AF       01080         XOR    A              ;0 TO A
0097 D300     01090         OUT    (0),A          ;CLEAR LEDS
0099 211027   01100         LD     HL,10000       ;10 SEC DELAY
009C CD5301   01110         CALL   DELAY
009F 2138FC   01120         LD     HL,0FC38H      ;FINAGLE FACTOR FOR 10
00A2 220008   01130         LD     (TIME),HL      ;INITIALIZE RTC CNT
00A5 3E13     01140         LD     A,13H          ;SECOND PART OF TEST 3
```

Fig. 6-17. Program listing format.

However, if you *do* choose to learn assembly-language programming, you may want to study the programs in detail and try your hand at many different applications that can be performed on the EZ-80.

For the more serious reader, Sams publication *The Z-80 Microcomputer Handbook* by this writer may be consulted for additional information on Z-80 programming and hardware aspects.

SECTION 2

EZ-80 Construction

CHAPTER 7

Construction of the EZ-80

This chapter describes the construction of the EZ-80 microcomputer. The EZ-80 consists of five parts: the power supply, keyboard, microcomputer board, applications area, and optional large-digit display, as shown in Fig. 7-1. The cabinetry containing the EZ-80 may be as elaborate as the reader desires. The chassis used in the examples of this book is a relatively inexpensive slope-front chassis measuring 9 inches deep by 7 inches wide by 3 inches high or 22.86 by 17.78 by 7.62 cm (see Fig. 7-2). It nicely accommodates the microcomputer board and power supply and provides a convenient mounting for the 12-key keypad and LED display. This cabinetry is an embellishment and the EZ-80 can be just as easily used in a more simple chassis.

The EZ-80 was designed to utilize inexpensive computer components. Obtaining all of the parts should be no problem in a metropolitan area. For those not near the computer stores and electronic parts suppliers of a larger town, all of the parts are offered through numerous mail order parts distributors that advertise in magazines such as *Kilobaud Microcomputing, Popular Electronics,* and *Radio Electronics.* Chart 7-1 lists all parts required for the EZ-80.

Two basic types of construction are possible for the microcomputer board: wire-wrap and printed-circuit construction. Both types are explained in detail in this chapter. The wire-wrap technique requires some inexpensive wire-wrap tools and a little more patience than the printed-circuit board construction. A complete set of printed-circuit board layouts is shown in Appendix F for those who have the facilities to etch the board, the description of which is beyond the scope of this book. Another alternative is a complete kit of parts that includes a double-sided printed-circuit board. Information about the kit may be obtained by writing:

Micro Applications
P. O. Box 3568
Mission Viejo, CA 92692

WIRE-WRAPPING THE MICROCOMPUTER BOARD

The wire-wrap technique of building the EZ-80 microcomputer board is shown in Fig. 7-3. A phenolic "perfboard" measuring approximately 4 by 8 inches (10.16 by 20.32 cm) is predrilled with a matrix of 0.042-inch (0.1 cm) holes with spacing of 0.1 inch (0.25 cm). This hole spacing matches the spacing on *wire-wrap* sockets shown in the figure. The wire-wrap sockets are semiconductor chip sockets with long square pins. Once all the sockets have been mounted, connections are made between pins by wrapping a thin 30-gauge solid wire around a pin, running the wire to the required connecting pin, and wrapping the wire again. Multiple connections can be made to a single pin.

The wire-wrapping technique offers several advantages. Sockets can be put quite closely together, making a very "dense" board. Fabrication of a printed-circuit board is not necessary. The wire-wrap connections can be made easily and efficiently. The disadvantages are increased susceptibility to noise from close proximity of several types of signals and longer construction times.

The wire-wrap technique is perfectly fine for a small microcomputer such as the EZ-80. The reader should experience no difficulty in constructing the microcomputer board if he or she follows the suggested layout and carefully follows the *wire-wrap list* of connections.

A completed wire-wrap version of the EZ-80 is shown in Fig. 7-4. The board was constructed by using a DIP plugboard (Vector Electronics 3677). This plugboard has the same hole size and spacing as a bare plugboard. It also has a ground and +5 V *etch* that is interleaved on the board. This etch allows easy connections of the ground and +5-volt power connections to the sockets. The reader is urged to use this board, or a similar type of board, to mount the

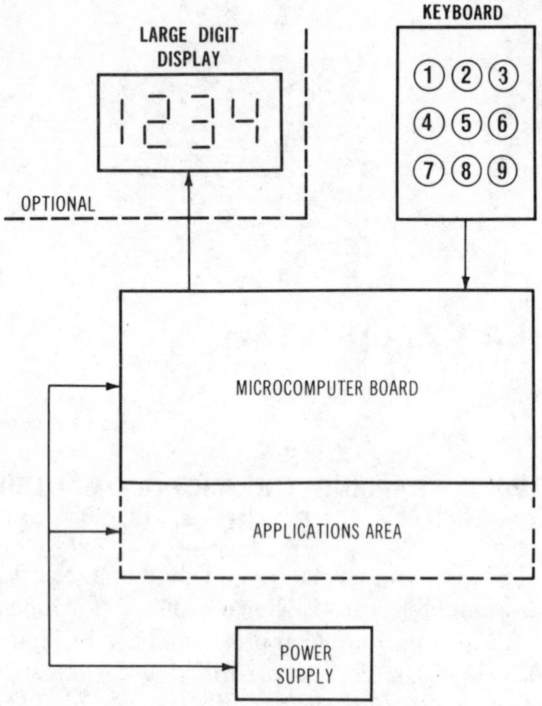

Fig. 7-1. Physical parts of the EZ-80.

sockets. A bare board *may* be used, but care must be taken in using heavy wire for power connections with soldered connections rather than wire-wrapping. The bare board approach is recommended for experienced builders of electronic projects only.

WIRE-WRAP: TOOLS

The only tool necessary for wire-wrapping is some kind of manual wire-wrap tool, a wire-wrap "pencil," or a wire-wrap *gun* (see Fig. 7-5). The manual wire-wrap tool is available for a few dollars, while a good quality wire-wrap gun is available for $30 to $40.

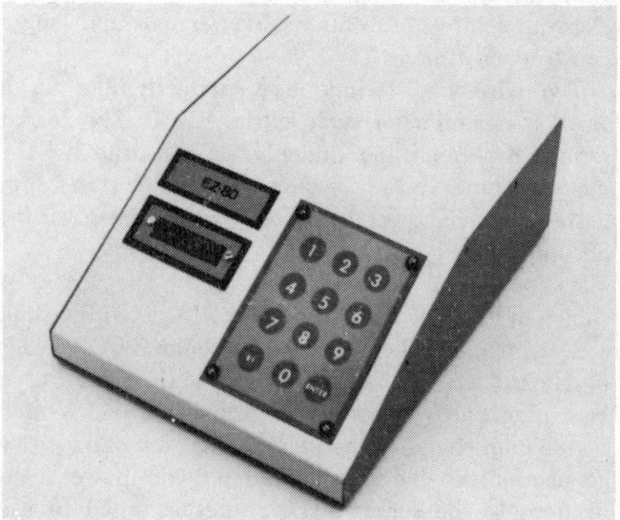

Fig. 7-2. The EZ-80 microcomputer.

Chart 7-1. EZ-80 Parts List

Prototype Board	
1	DIP Prototype board (Vector Electronics)
Power Supply Section	
1	LM340-5 or 7805 regulator
1	Full-wave bridge rectifier
1	Electrolytic capacitor, 1 μF, 5 V
1	Electrolytic capacitor, 1000 μF, 25 V
1	Cable clamp (optional)
1	6-32 machine screw and nut
1	Heat sink to fit 340-5 regulator
	Bare and insulated wire
Semiconductor Integrated Circuits	
1	MCM6810 random-access memory (RAM) (Motorola)
1	2758 erasable programmable read-only memory (or 2716 EPROM)
1	Z-80 microprocessor (2 or 4 megahertz)
1	8255 programmable peripheral interface (PPI)
1	MC14511 display driver
1	4-segment LED display (or 4 LED displays)
1	74368 IC
1	74LS04 IC
1	7437 IC
1	74LS05 IC
1	MC4042 IC (Motorola)
2	DIP plug, 14-pin
1	1-kΩ resistor pack (14-pin, 7 resistors)
1	330-Ω resistor pack (14 pin, 7 resistors)
Sockets	
2	24-pin wire-wrap
2	40-pin wire-wrap
8	14-pin wire-wrap
2	16-pin wire-wrap
Resistors/Capacitors	
5	0.1-μF disc capacitors
1	300-pF, 10-V capacitor
1	3.3-μF, 10-V electrolytic capacitor
1	22-μF, 10-V electrolytic capacitor
1	330-Ω, 1/4-W resistor
3	10-kΩ, 1/4-W resistors
2	10-kΩ, mini pc board potentiometers
Chassis, Transformer	
1	Slope-front chassis (optional)
1	8–12.6 Vac, 2–3-A filament (or doorbell) transformer
1	Fuseholder
1	1/4-A fuse
1	spst toggle switch
1	6-32 machine screws and nuts
Miscellaneous	
1	Wire-wrap wire
1	Plastic sheet or bristol board
1	Copper adhesive sheet

Wire-wrap wire is inexpensive (about 25 feet per dollar) and available in all Radio Shack or other electronic parts stores.

The technique of wire-wrapping is very simple. Strip about one inch of insulation off the wire using wire strippers or the built-in stripper on some wire-wrap wire dispensers. Insert the stripped wire into the end of the wire-wrap tool. Insert the tool over the

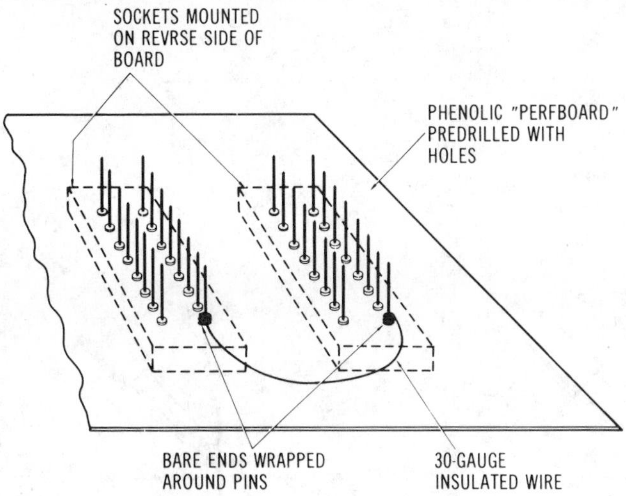

Fig. 7-3. Wire-wrap construction.

pin to be wrapped. (Don't press down too hard.) Press the trigger of the gun or rotate the manual tool to wrap the pin. The process and the completed wrap are shown in Fig. 7-6. The completed wrap should have adjacent wraps close together with no gap, but wraps should not be bunched, as shown in the figure. Up to three levels of wraps may be used on one pin. Perfect your technique by wrapping a dozen pins or so before starting assembly.

Unwrapping is done by a manual unwrap tool or by brute force. A pair of long-nosed tweezers may be used to advantage in both unwrapping and "mucking about" in the nest of wire-wraps.

Another tool required in construction is a small soldering iron for making power and component connections. A 30-watt iron will do nicely. Soldering is also an easy process but requires a little practice. Make certain the iron is hot. *Tin* the iron by melting solder over the tip and then wiping the tip on a moist sponge. The tip should be shiny when properly tinned. When soldering connections, use the minimum of heat

Fig. 7-4. Wire-wrapped EZ-80 board.

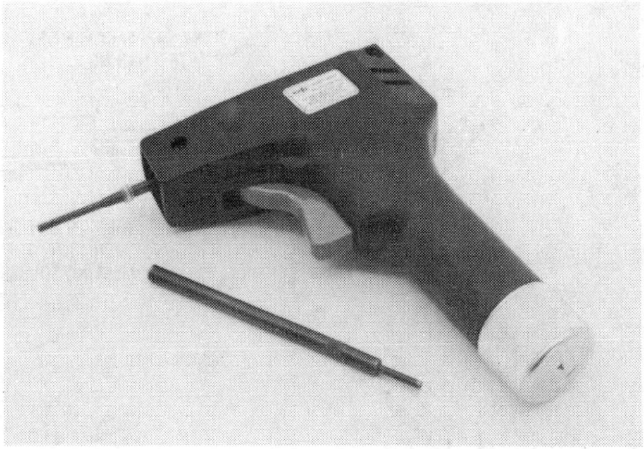

Fig. 7-5. Wire-wrapping tools.

and allow the solder to flow freely around the pin or lead. A properly soldered connection will have a somewhat shiny appearance with no large clumps of solder (see Fig. 7-7).

WIRE-WRAP: MOUNTING THE SOCKETS AND PARTS

The following steps should be followed to mount the semiconductor wire-wrap sockets. Refer to Chart 7-1, the parts list for the EZ-80.

1. Mount the 14 wire-wrap sockets on the board in the positions shown in Fig. 7-8. If a bare board is used, the sockets may be glued or epoxyed. If

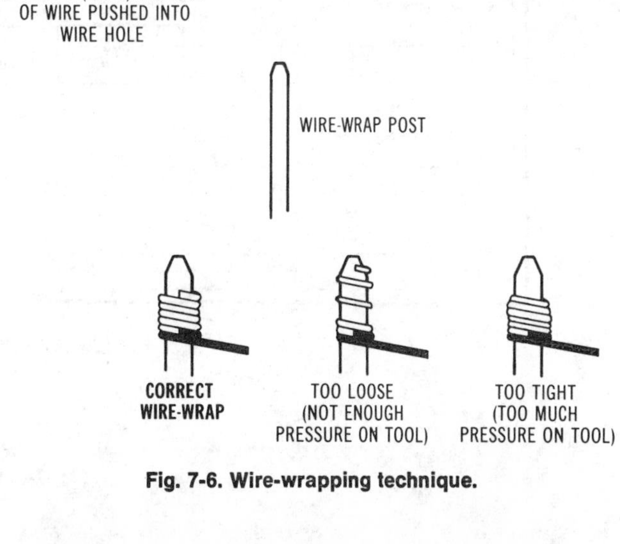

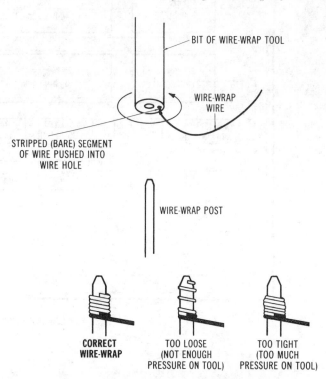

Fig. 7-6. Wire-wrapping technique.

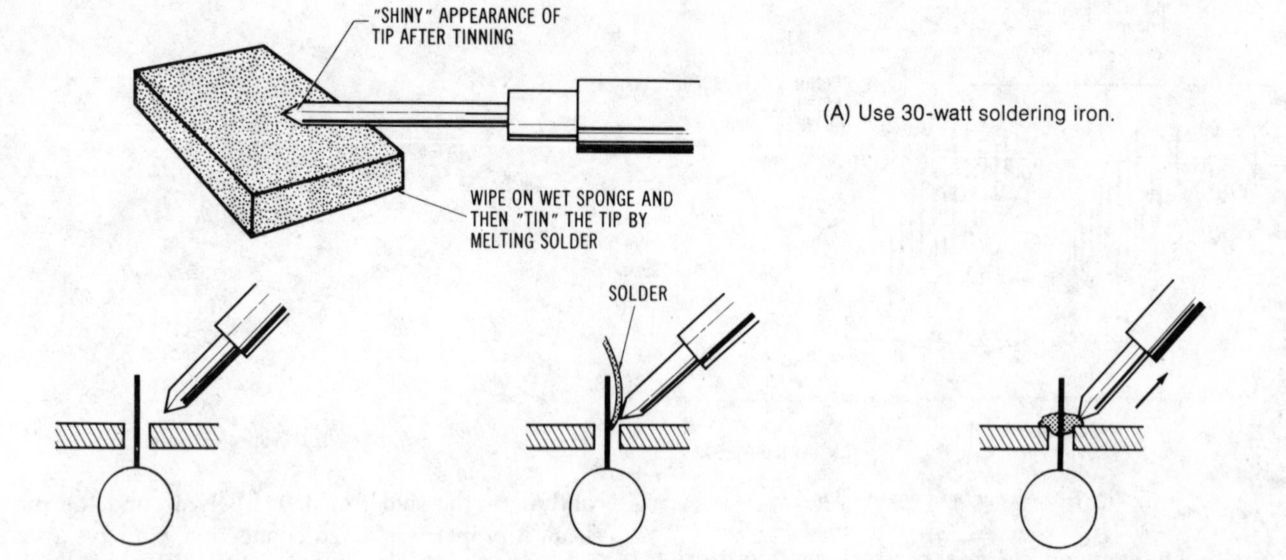

(A) Use 30-watt soldering iron.

(B) Heat the component lead to be soldered briefly (2 seconds).

(C) Apply thin *rosin-core* solder to junction. Ideally solder is melted by lead to be soldered.

(D) Use solder and heat sparingly—just enough solder for positive connection. Final joint should be shiny.

Fig. 7-7. Soldering technique.

a plugboard is used, secure each chip by soldering the two opposing pins to the printed-circuit "pads," as shown in Fig. 7-9, or if no pad is present, by a short wire-wrapping of the pin.

2. Mount the two potentiometers R1 and R2, as shown in Fig. 7-10. These two potentiometers should be as close to the MC4024 at A1 as possible.

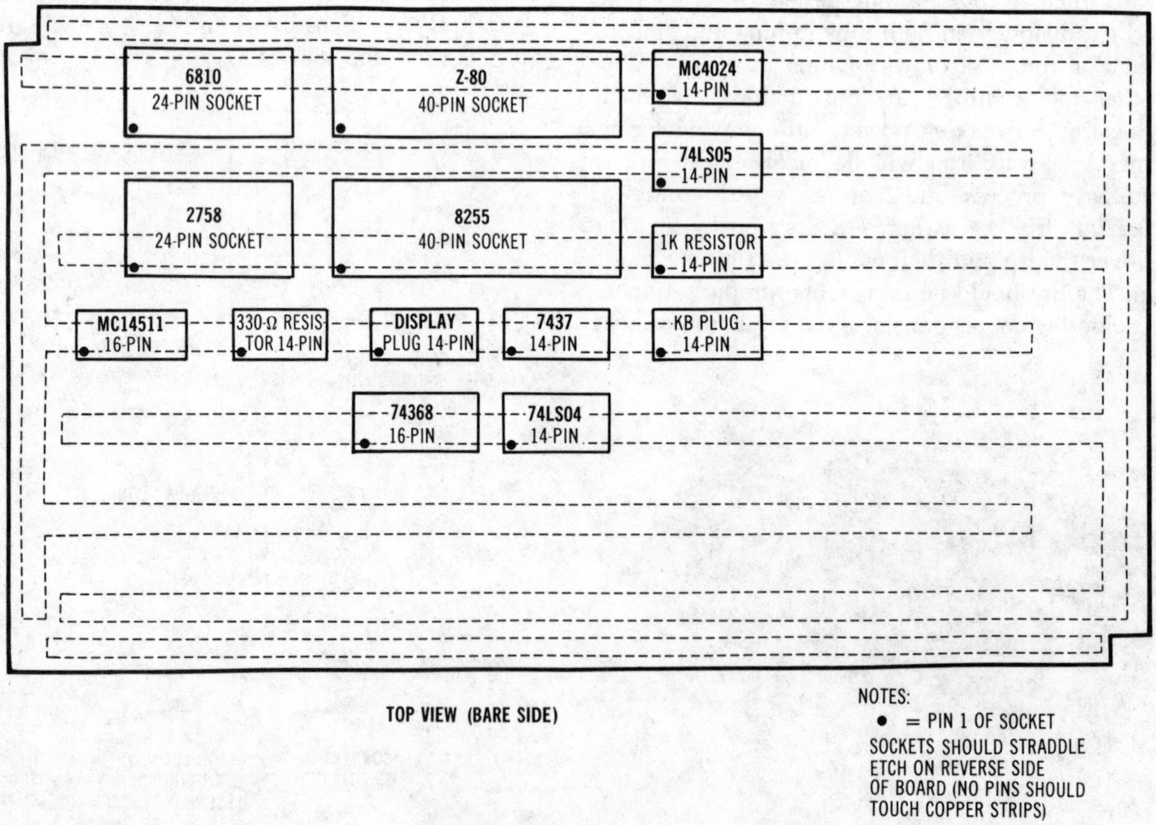

Fig. 7-8. Socket layout.

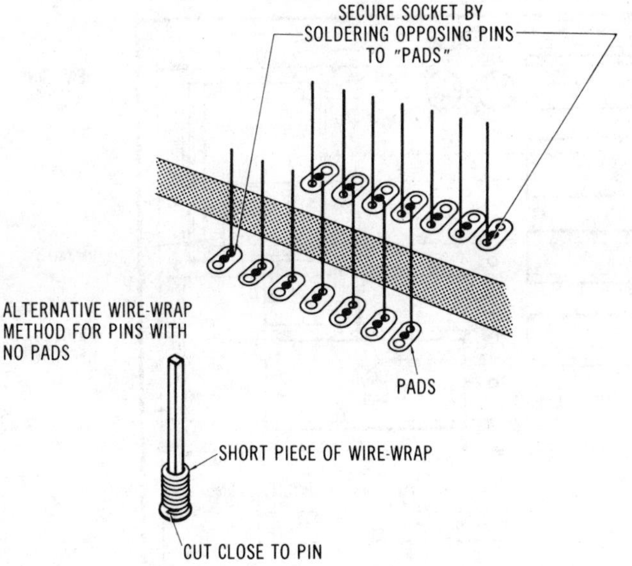

Fig. 7-9. Securing the sockets.

3. Mount the power supply components as shown in Fig. 7-11.
4. Using short medium-gauge wires (No. 22), solder the following pins to the *ground* bus of the board, as shown in Figs. 7-12 and 7-13.

A1-5	C2-7
A1-7	C3-12
A1-9	D2-7
A2-29	D5-8
A3-1	E1-7
B1-7	E2-8

5. Using short medium-gauge wires (No. 22), solder the following pins to the +5-volt (V_{CC}) bus of the board, as shown in Fig. 7-14.

A1-1	C3-24
A1-14	D2-14
A2-11	D5-16
A3-24	E1-14
B1-14	E2-16
C2-26	

WIRE-WRAP: WRAPPING THE SOCKETS

At this point all connections have been made except for the wire-wrap connections and several small components which will be soldered later. The next step is to wire-wrap all required connections. The wire-wrap list given in Table 7-1 shows all necessary wire-wrap connections (there are 128). To make the connections, use as short a length of wire-wrap wire as possible and follow the previous instructions on wire-wrapping techniques. Take care to wrap the right pins. The pins are oriented as shown in Fig.

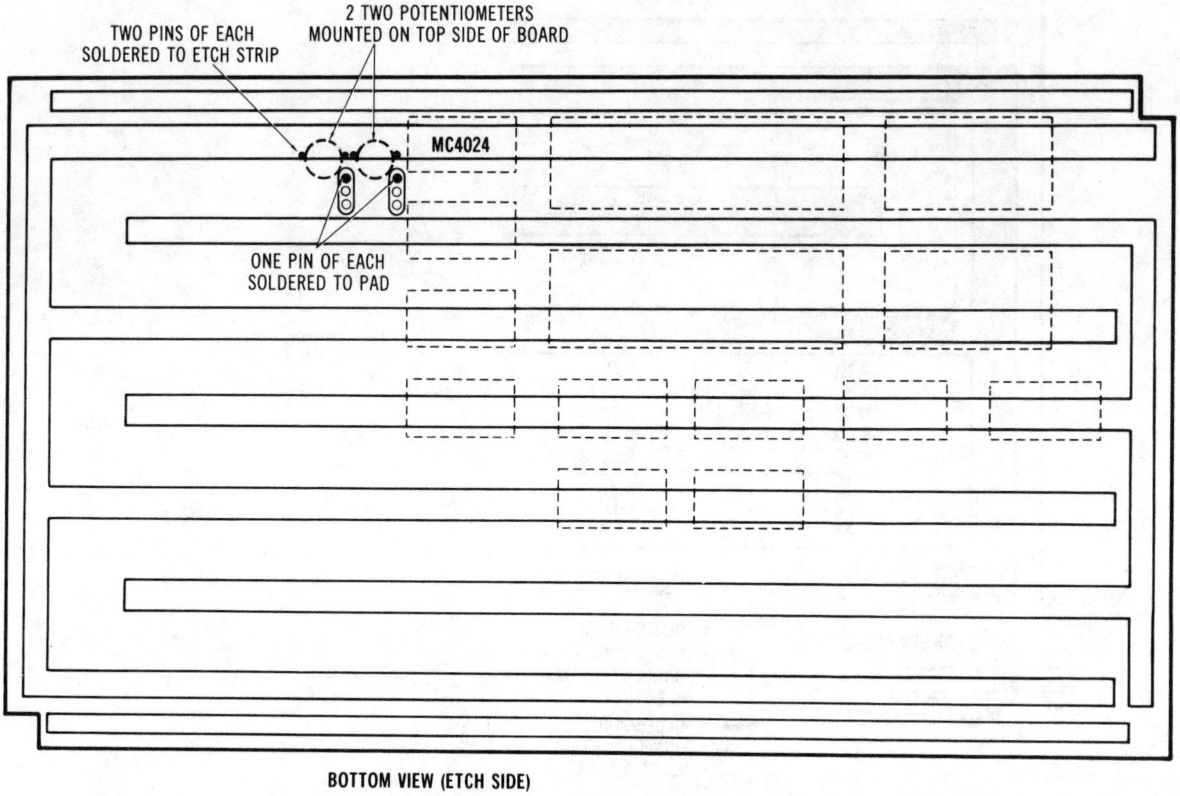

Fig. 7-10. Potentiometer mounting.

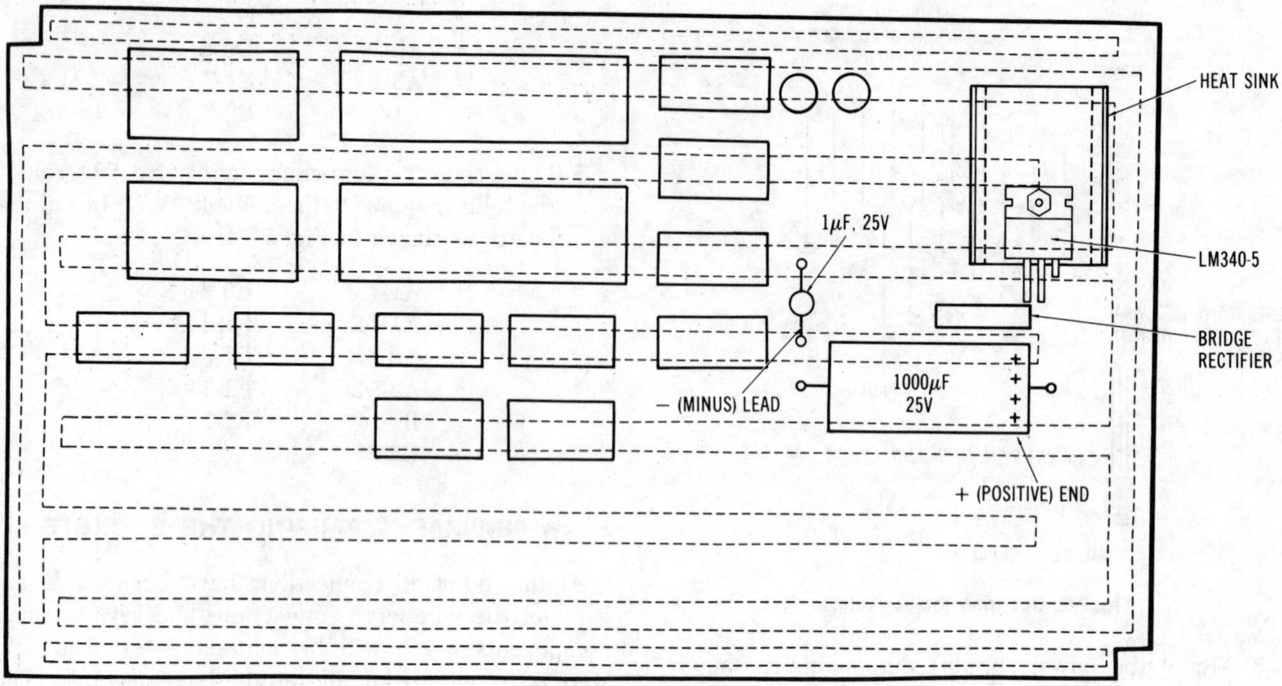

(A) Top view (bare side).

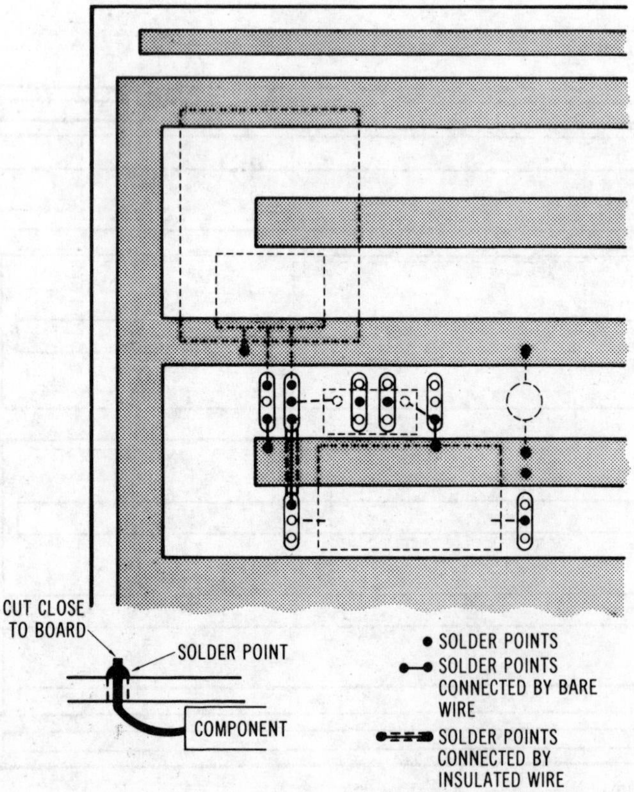

(B) Bottom view (etch side).

Fig. 7-11. Power supply component mounting.

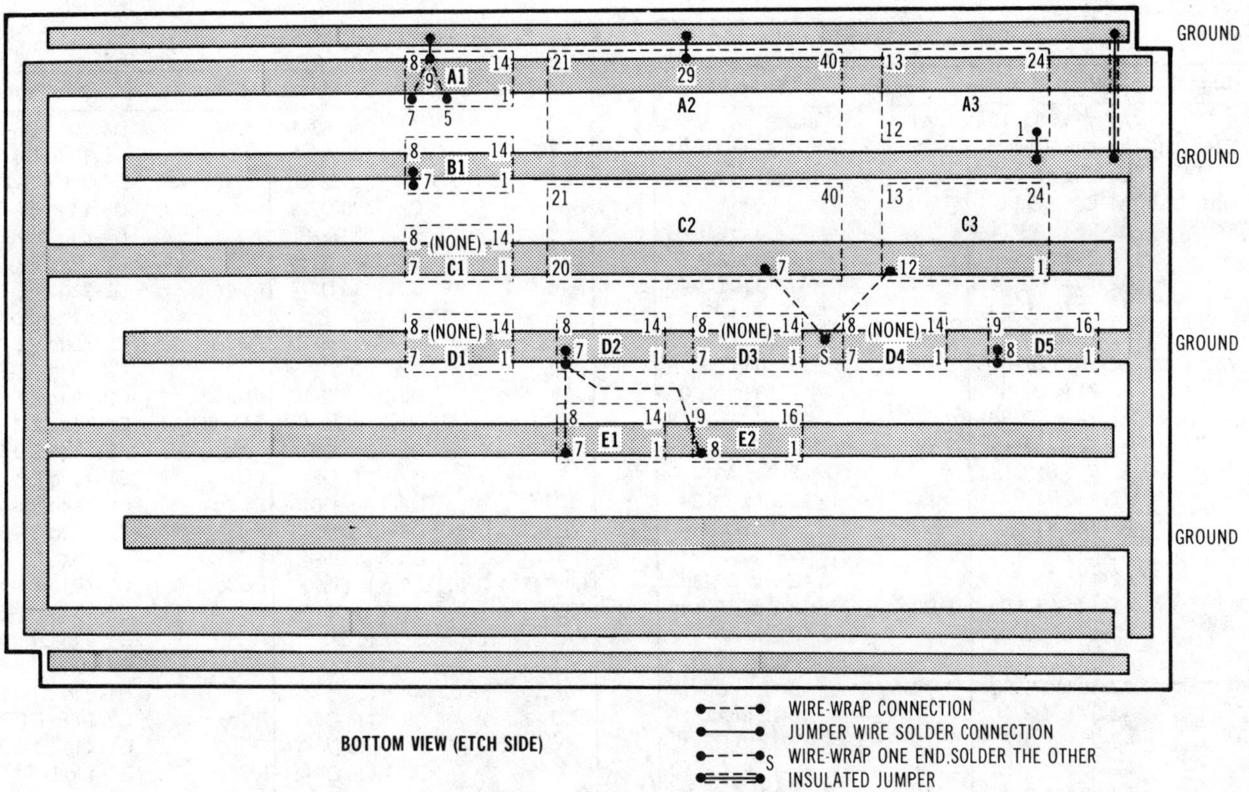

Fig. 7-12. Socket ground connections.

7-12. Note the ground and V_{CC} connections that already exist.

WIRE-WRAP: CHECKING THE CONNECTIONS

At this point all wire-wrap connections have been made. Each pin of every socket should now be checked for the proper number of wraps: none, 1, 2, or 3, as shown in Table 7-2. These numbers are exclusive of ground or V_{CC} connections. If the proper number of wraps do not match the actual number on the pin, review Table 7-1 to correct the connections.

The next step is to verify that all wire-wrap connections have been properly made by "buzzing out" the connections from the socket side of the board. Make a continuity tester as shown in Fig. 7-15, or use a vom (volt-ohmmeter) or other device to check continuity (inexpensive "continuity testers" are sold at many electronic parts stores). Go down the list of Table 7-1 again, checking each connection for con-

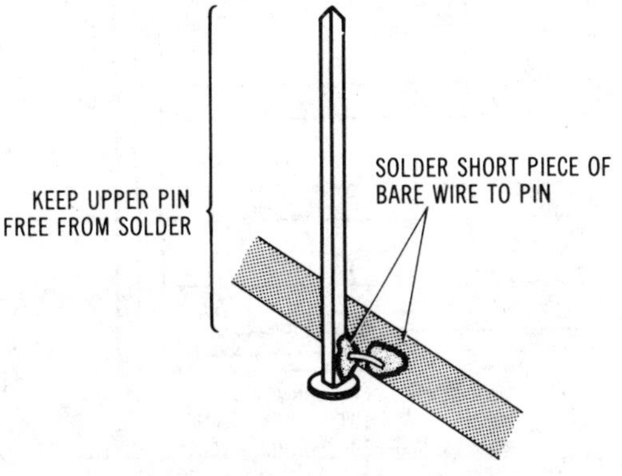

Fig. 7-13. Pin to etch connections.

Chart 7-2. EZ-80 V_{CC}/GND Pins

Grounds	V_{CC}
A1-5	A1-1
-7	-13
-9	-14
A2-29	A2-11
A3-1	-16
-12	-24
-15	-25
-10	A3-13
B1-7	-24
C2-7	B1-14
-35	C1-1
C3-12	-2
D2-7	-3
D5-5	C2-26
-8	C3-21
E1-7	-24
E2-1	D2-14
E2-8	D5-3
-15	-4
	-16
	E1-14
	E2-16

Table 7-1. EZ-80 Wire-Wrap List

Signal	Wrap Pins	Signal	Wrap Pins
4024 V_{CC}	A1-13 to A1-1	A1	A2-31 to C3-7
1 MHz CLK	A1-6 to B1-1		A2-31 to A3-22
	B1-2 to A2-6		A2-31 to C2-8
100 Hz $\overline{NMI}$	A1-8 to A2-17	A0	A2-30 to C3-8
Z80 V_{CC}	A2-25 to A2-11		A2-30 to A3-23
	A2-24 to A2-25		A2-30 to C2-9
	A2-16 to A2-24	D7	A2-13 to C3-17
$\overline{MREQ}$	A2-19 to C3-18		A2-13 to A3-9
	A2-19 to A3-11		A2-13 to C2-27
$\overline{IORQ}$	A2-20 to C2-6	D6	A2-10 to C3-16
$\overline{RD}$	A2-21 to C2-5		A2-10 to A3-8
$\overline{WR}$	A2-22 to C2-36		A2-10 to C2-28
	A2-22 to A3-16	D5	A2-9 to C3-15
A15	A2-5 to B1-3		A2-9 to A3-7
A14	A2-4 to B1-5		A2-9 to C2-29
A13	A2-3 to B1-9	D4	A2-7 to C3-14
A12	A2-2 to B1-11		A2-7 to A3-6
A11	A2-1 to C3-20		A2-7 to C2-30
	A2-1 to A3-10	D3	A2-8 to C3-13
A10	A2-40 to C3-19		A2-8 to A3-5
A9	A2-39 to C3-22		A2-8 to C2-31
A8	A2-38 to C3-23	D2	A2-12 to C3-11
A7	A2-37 to C3-1		A2-12 to A3-4
A6	A2-36 to C3-2		A2-12 to C2-32
	A2-36 to A3-17	D1	A2-15 to C3-10
A5	A2-35 to C3-3		A2-15 to A3-3
	A2-35 to A3-18		A2-15 to C2-33
A4	A2-34 to C3-4	D0	A2-14 to C3-9
	A2-34 to A3-19		A2-14 to A3-2
A3	A2-33 to C3-5		A2-14 to C2-34
	A2-33 to A3-20	2758 V_{CC}	C3-24 to C3-21
A2	A2-32 to C3-6	6810 V_{CC}	A3-24 to A3-13
	A2-32 to A3-21	6810 GND	A3-1 to A3-12

Signal	Wrap Pins	Signal	Wrap Pins
	A3-12 to A3-14		D4-10 to D3-2
	A3-14 to A3-15		D5-15 to D4-6
8255 GND	C2-7 to C2-35		D4-9 to D3-11
PA7	C2-37 to D2-1		D5-14 to D4-7
	D2-1 to D2-2		D4-8 to D3-9
	D2-3 to D3-1	PB5	C2-23 to E2-2
PA6	C2-38 to D2-4	PB4	C2-22 to E2-14
	D2-4 to D2-5	PB3	C2-21 to E2-4
	D2-6 to D3-12	PB2	C2-20 to E2-12
PA5	C2-39 to D2-9	PB1	C2-19 to E2-6
	D2-9 to D2-10	PB0	C2-18 to E2-10
	D2-8 to D3-4	74368GND	E2-8 to E2-1
PA4	C2-40 to D2-12		E2-1 to E2-15
	D2-12 to D2-13	PC7	C2-10 to E1-2
	D2-11 to D3-6	PC6	C2-11 to E1-4
MC14511 V_{CC}	D5-16 to D5-3	PC5	C2-12 to E1-6
	D5-3 to D5-4	PC4	C2-13 to E1-8
MC14511 GND	D5-5 to D5-8	PC3	C2-17 to E1-10
PA3	C2-1 to D5-6	PC2	C2-16 to D1-5
PA2	C2-2 to D5-2		D1-5 to C1-14
PA1	C2-3 to D5-1	PC1	C2-15 to D1-6
PA0	C2-4 to D5-7		D1-6 to C1-13
LED Anodes	D5-13 to D4-1	PC0	C2-14 to D1-7
	D4-14 to D3-14		D1-7 to C1-12
	D5-12 to D4-2	KB Address	B1-4 to D1-1
	D4-13 to D3-13		B1-6 to D1-2
	D5-11 to D4-3		B1-8 to D1-3
	D4-12 to D3-3		B1-10 to D1-4
	D5-10 to D4-4	KB Resistors	C1-1 to B1-14
	D4-11 to D3-10		C1-2 to C1-1
	D5-9 to D4-5		C1-3 to C1-2

128 total wraps

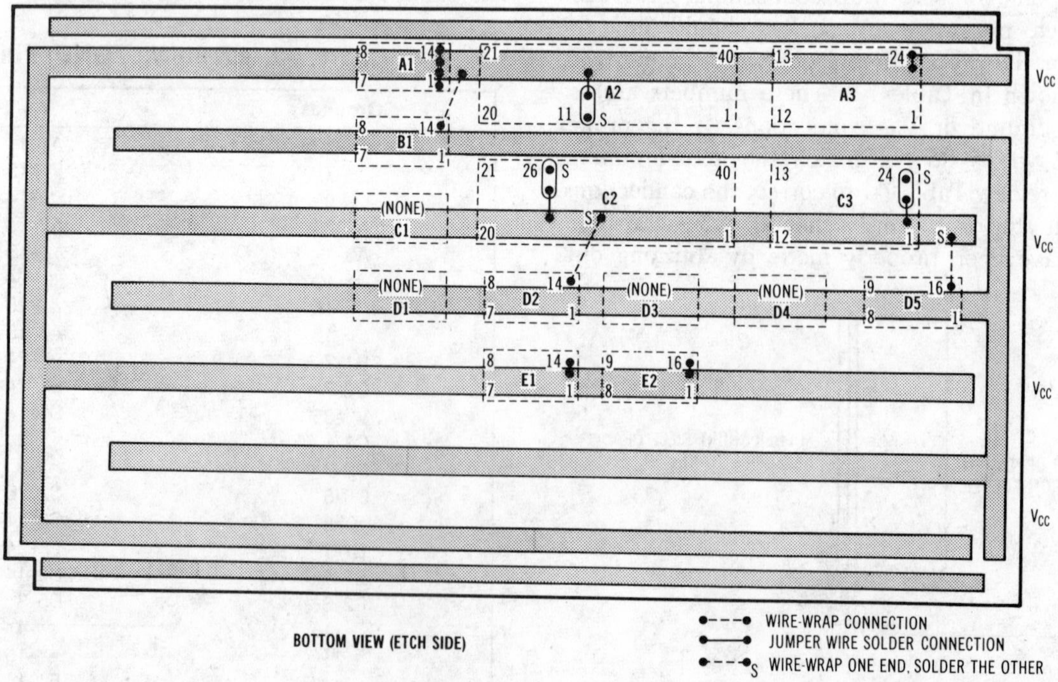

Fig. 7-14. Socket V_{CC} connections.

Table 7-2. Pins vs. Wire-Wrap

Pins	A1	A2	A3	B1	C1	C2	C3	D1	D2	D3	D4	D5	E1	E2
1	1	2	1	1	2	1	1	1	2	1	1	1	0	2
2	0	1	1	1	2	1	1	1	1	1	1	1	1	1
3	0	1	1	1	1	1	1	1	1	1	1	2	0	0
4	0	1	1	1	0	1	1	1	2	1	1	1	1	1
5	0	1	1	1	0	1	1	2	1	0	1	1	0	0
6	1	1	1	1	0	1	1	2	1	1	1	1	1	1
7	0	3	1	0	0	1	1	2	0	0	1	1	0	0
8	1	3	1	1	0	1	1	0	1	0	1	1	1	1
9	0	3	1	1	0	1	1	0	2	1	1	1	0	0
10	0	3	1	1	0	1	1	0	1	1	1	1	1	1
11	0	1	1	1	0	1	1	0	1	1	1	1	0	0
12	0	3	2	0	1	1	0	0	2	1	1	1	0	1
13	1	3	1	0	1	1	1	0	1	1	1	1	0	0
14	0	3	2	1	1	1	1	0	0	1	1	1	0	1
15		3	1			1	1					1		1
16		1	1			1	1					1		0
17		1	1			1	1							
18		0	1			1	1							
19		2	1			1	1							
20		1	1			1	1							
21		1	1			1	1							
22		2	1			1	1							
23		0	1			1	1							
24		2	1			0	1							
25		2				0								
26		0				0								
27		0				1								
28		0				1								
29		0				1								
30		3				1								
31		3				1								
32		2				1								
33		2				1								
34		2				1								
35		2				1								
36		2				1								
37		1				1								
38		1				1								
39		1				1								
40		1				1								

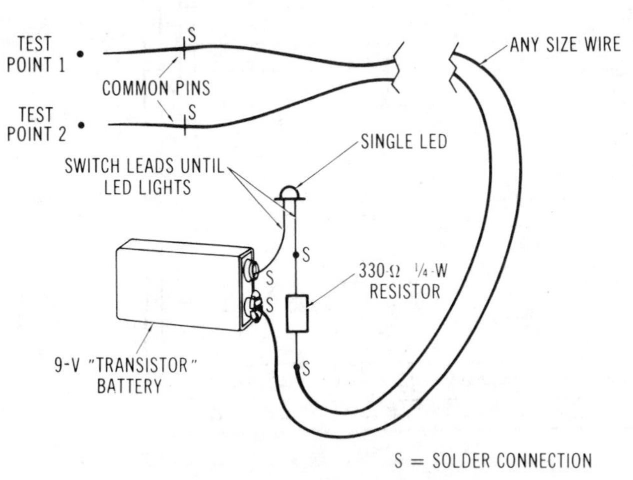

Fig. 7-15. Continuity tester.

tinuity from the top side of the board. Clip leads and common pins will be a help in getting into the IC socket pins.

Use the same technique in checking the pins for V_{CC} and ground connections. Put one lead of the continuity tester on the ground or V_{CC} bus and use the other to probe the IC socket. Refer to Chart 7-2 for appropriate pins.

WIRE-WRAP: FINAL CONNECTIONS

The microcomputer board is now wired except for several small components. These components should be soldered to the pins of the IC sockets after positioning between the pins, as shown in Fig. 7-16. Make certain that the *polarities* on the capacitors are as indicated. The polarity is represented by a "+" sign or "−" sign on the body of the capacitor.

Complete the wiring to potentiometers R1 and R2 as shown in Fig. 7-17.

Connect disk bypass capacitors (0.01 μF each) from the V_{CC} bus to the ground bus at the points shown in Fig. 7-18.

The microcomputer board is now wired. The next step is to construct the simple power supply for the EZ-80. Continue at the "Power Supply Construction" section.

WIRING THE MICROCOMPUTER PC BOARD

The printed-circuit board layout of the EZ-80 is shown in Appendix F of this book. If you have purchased a kit, complete instructions are given to make the solder connections on the board. If you are etching your own board, then presumably you know as much (or more) than the author about construction techniques for pc board construction. The one obvious piece of advice that can be given is to use a socket for the 2758 or 2716, if you wish to use several applications programs or write your own applications programs.

POWER-SUPPLY CONSTRUCTION

The following section assumes that the reader is using a chassis similar to the one shown in Fig. 7-2. If another is being used, mounting of the components may be somewhat different to leave room for the microcomputer board.

The power supply schematic is shown in Fig. 7-19. It is a simple full-wave bridge power supply with all components from the bridge on mounted on the microcomputer board. The remaining components are the line cord, on/off switch, fuse and fuse holder, and

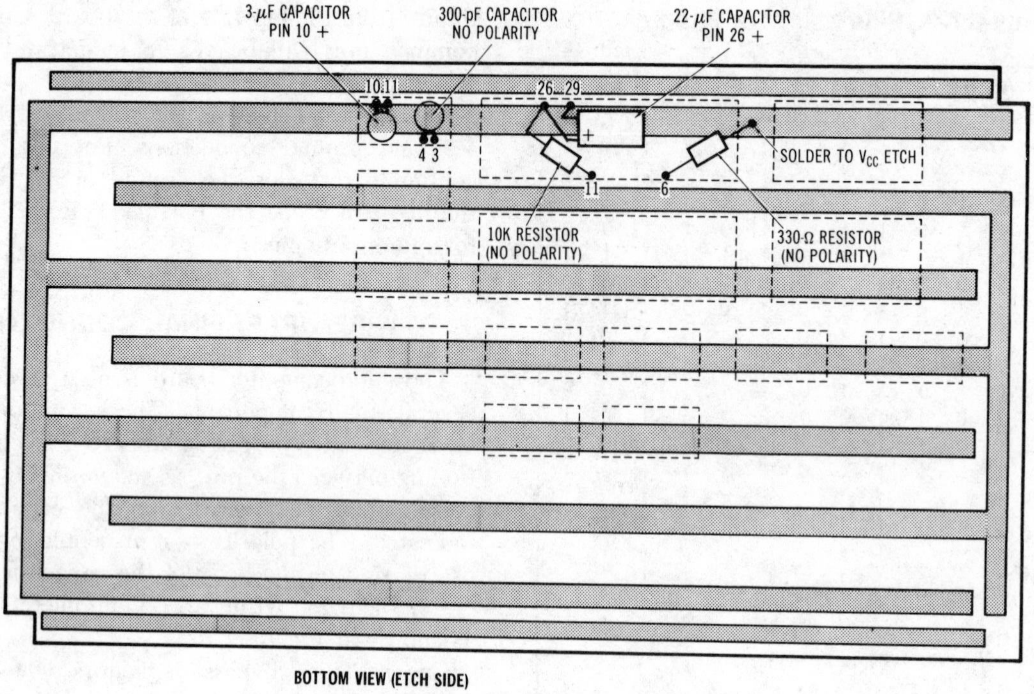

Fig. 7-16. Final component soldering.

transformer. Use the following steps to mount these components.

1. Drill five holes in the chassis, as shown in Fig. 7-20.
2. Mount the fuse holder, on/off switch, and grommet for the power cord as shown in Fig. 7-20.
3. Mount the transformer to the chassis as shown in Fig. 7-20.
4. Solder the power line cord and primary (black) transformer leads to the fuse holder and on/off

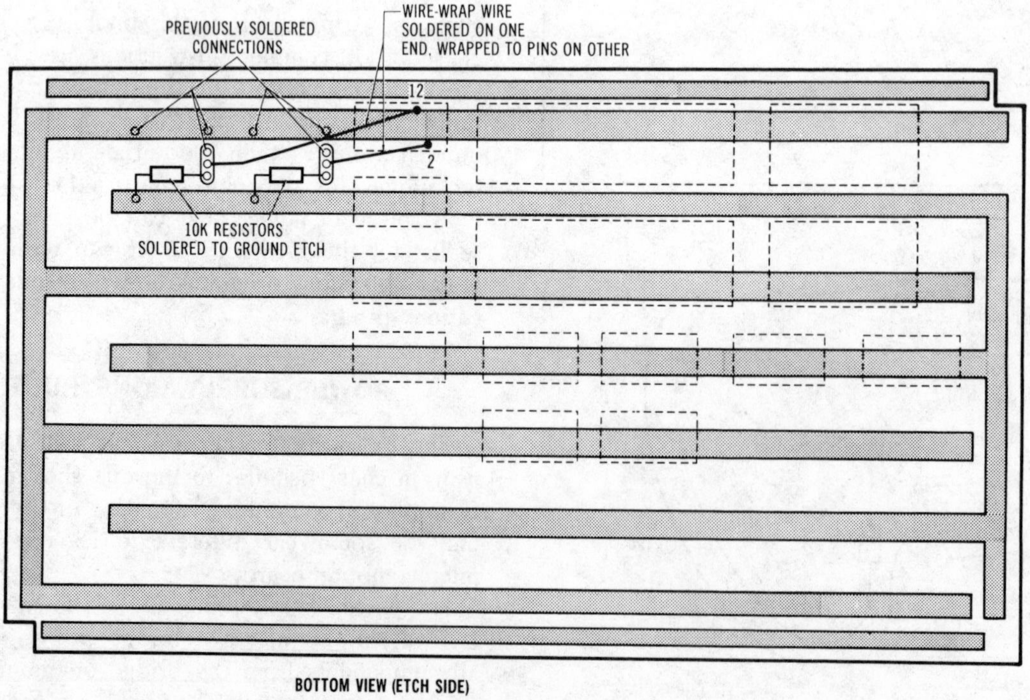

Fig. 7-17. Final potentiometer wiring.

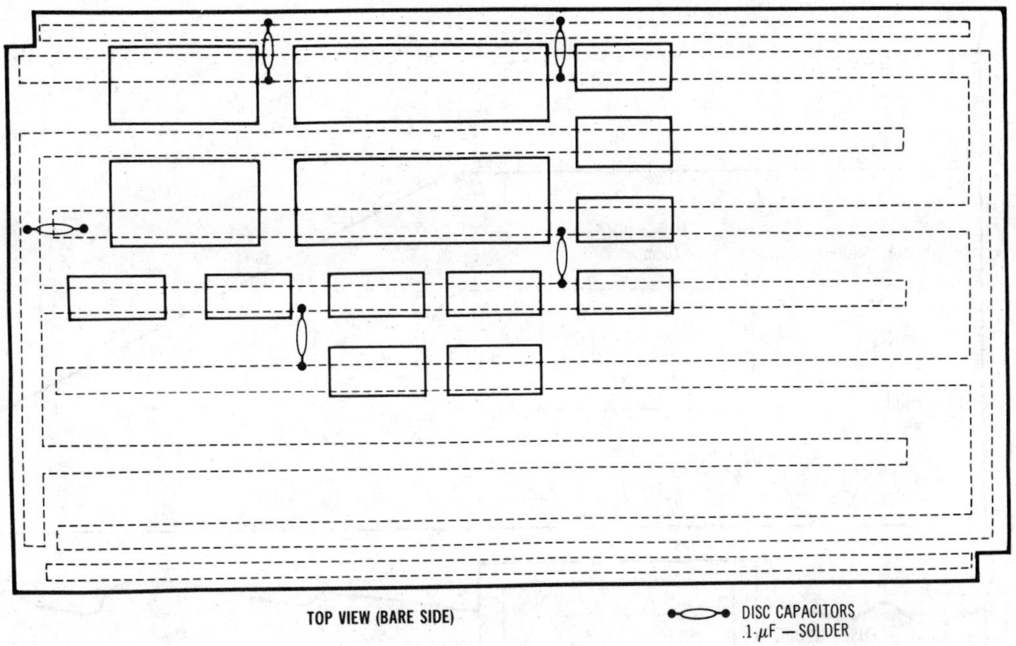

Fig. 7-18. Bypass capacitors.

switch as shown. Use short pieces of spaghetti or heat-shrinkable tubing to cover exposed metallic contacts on the switches and fuse holders (see Fig. 7-21).

WARNING!

110 VOLTS AC CAN KILL! *MAKE CERTAIN* THAT THERE ARE NO UNINSULATED METAL PARTS AND THAT NO POWER-LINE CONNECTIONS CONTACT THE CHASSIS.

The power supply is now wired. To check the operation of this portion of the power supply, use a 12.6-volt light bulb (or vom), as shown in Fig 7-22. Attach the bulb to the secondary leads of the transformer by clip leads or soldering. Plug in the line cord and turn on the on/off switch. The bulb should light. If the bulb does not light, unplug the line cord and recheck the connections (is the fuse in the fuse-holder?).

POWER SUPPLY/MICROCOMPUTER BOARD TESTING

The power supply can now be integrated with the microcomputer board. Mount the microcomputer board to the chassis with two screws, as shown in Fig. 7-23. After verifying the mounting, remove the board and solder the two secondary transformer wires to the board and remount the board.

With the microcomputer board mounted on the chassis, perform the following steps to verify that power connections have been properly made.

1. Plug in the line cord.
2. Turn on the power switch and then quickly turn off.

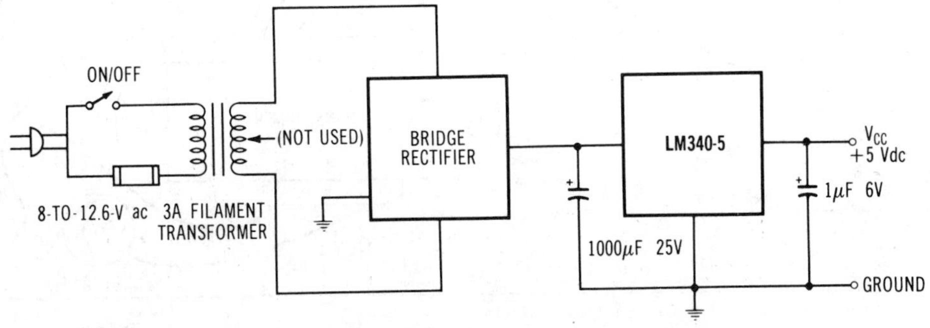

Fig. 7-19. EZ-80 power supply schematic diagram.

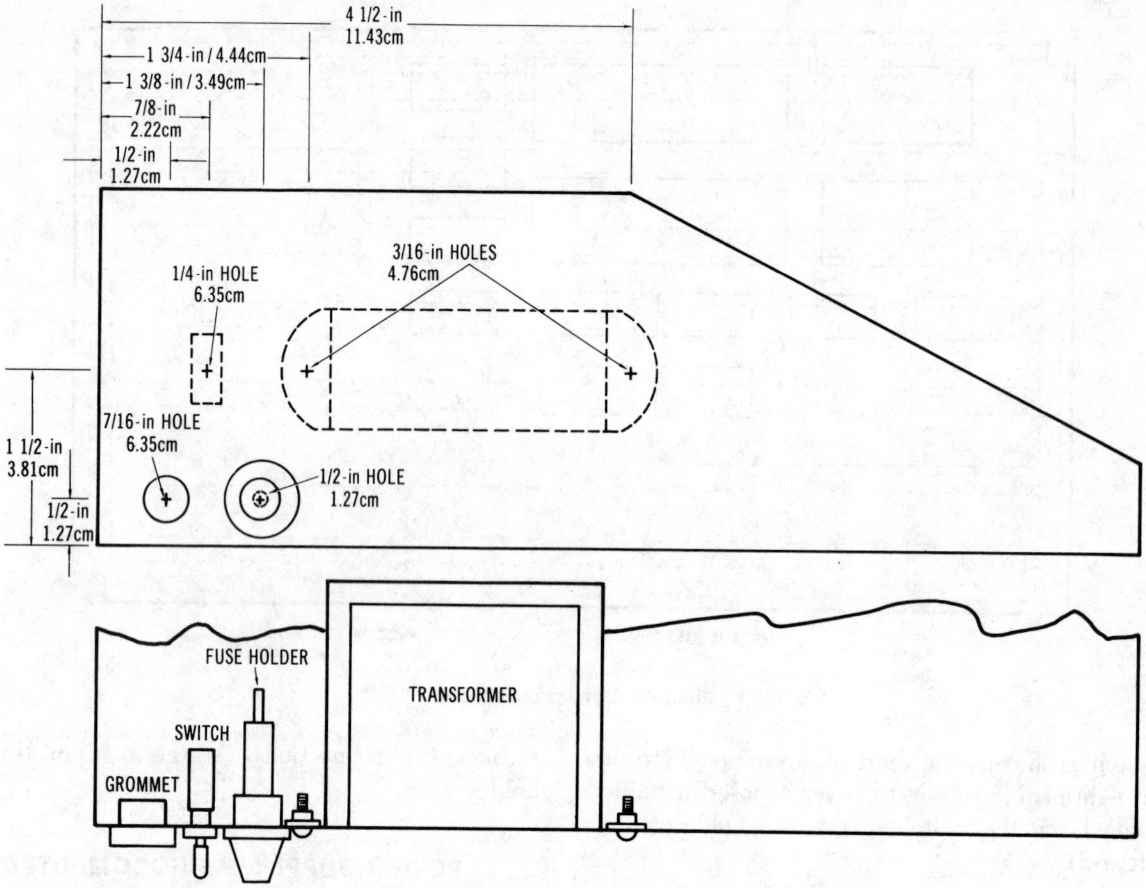

Fig. 7-20. Power supply parts mounting.

3. Remove the fuse. It should be intact. If not, review the power supply and wire-wrap connections for a short circuit.
4. Turn on the power switch. There should be no visible smoke (really!). There should be no "hot" smell when you are sniffing cautiously above the power supply components.
5. Cautiously test the regulator chip and bridge rectifier as you would a hot iron. If a 12-V ac transformer is being used, the regulator may be quite hot; use largest practical heat sink. If a lower voltage transformer is being used, the regulator will run cooler.
6. Leave the power on. With a voltmeter, oscilloscope, logic probe, or the device shown in Fig. 7-24, check every pin on the top of the microcomputer board. A voltage of +5 volts should be present *only* for the V_{CC} pins shown in Table

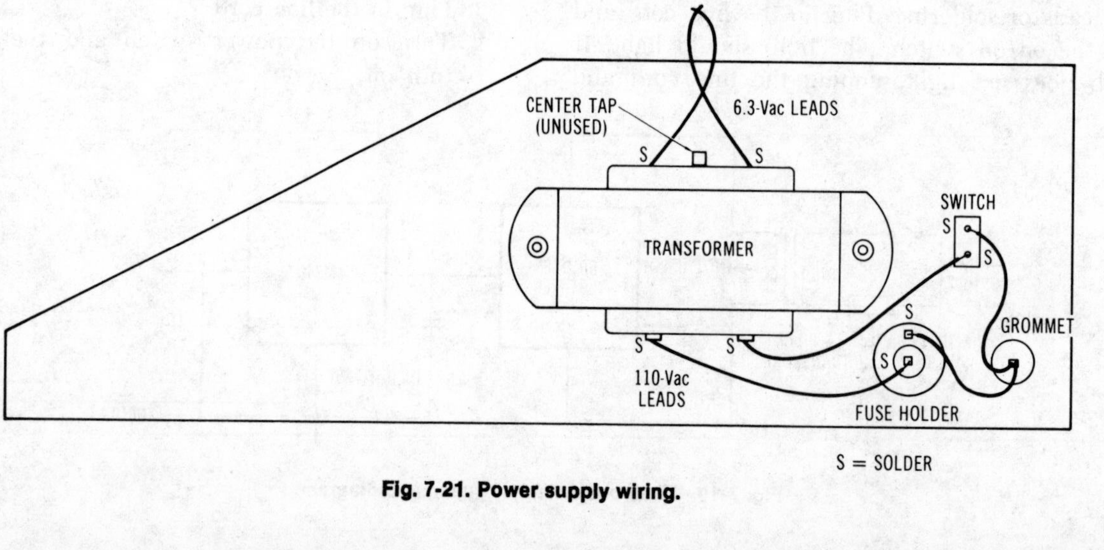

Fig. 7-21. Power supply wiring.

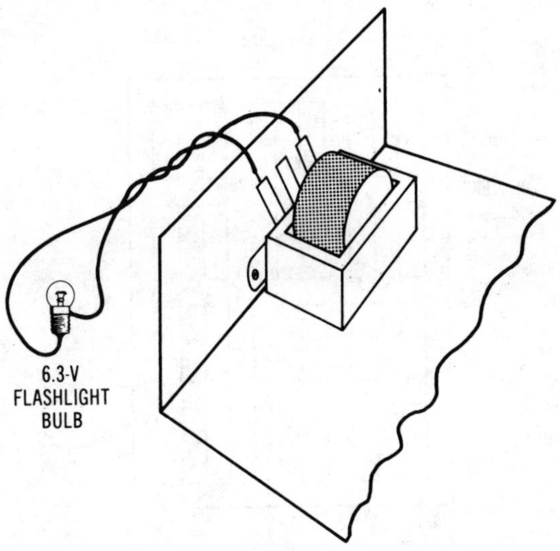

Fig. 7-22. Power supply testing.

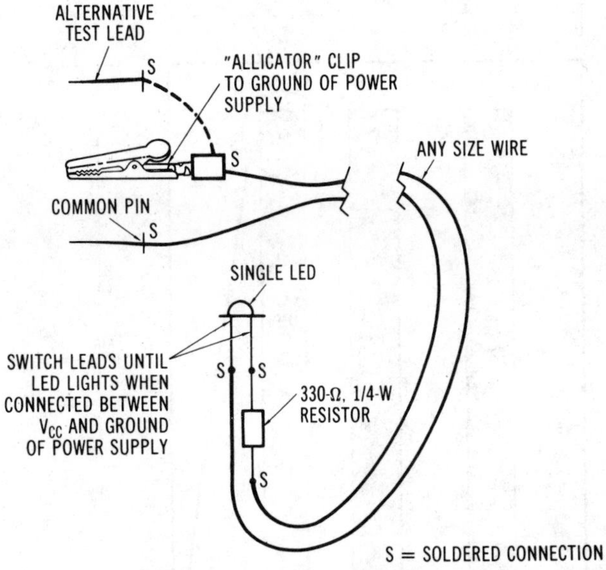

Fig. 7-24. Power pin tester.

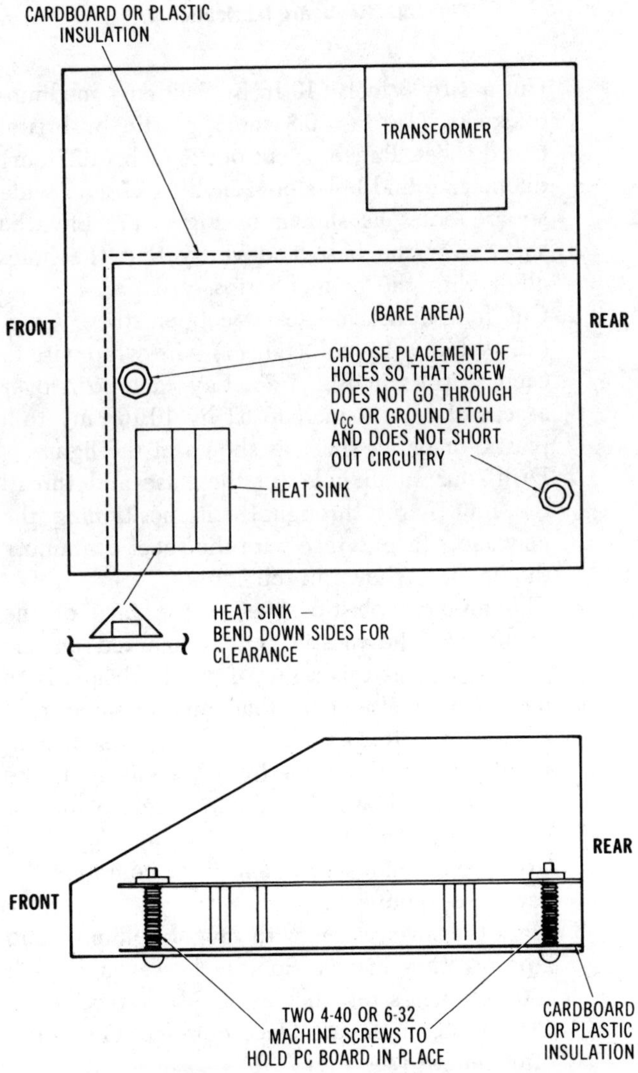

Fig. 7-23. Microcomputer board mounting.

7-4 and pins A2-6, A2-26, and B1-2. From 2.5 to +5 volts will be present on pins A1-2 and A1-12. If +5 V is present for other pins, recheck the power supply and (especially) the wire-wrap connections.

7. Plug in the semiconductor ICs (except for the 2758 or 2716) as shown in Fig. 7-8. Note that pin 1 of the IC is always oriented to the left of the socket. Pin 1 on the chip is "keyed" by a notch on the pin 1 side of the chip or by a "dot"

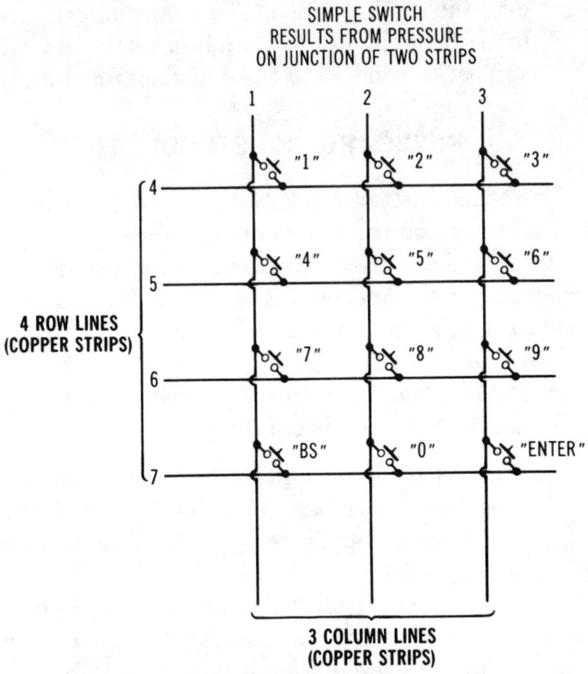

Fig. 7-25. Keyboard schematic diagram.

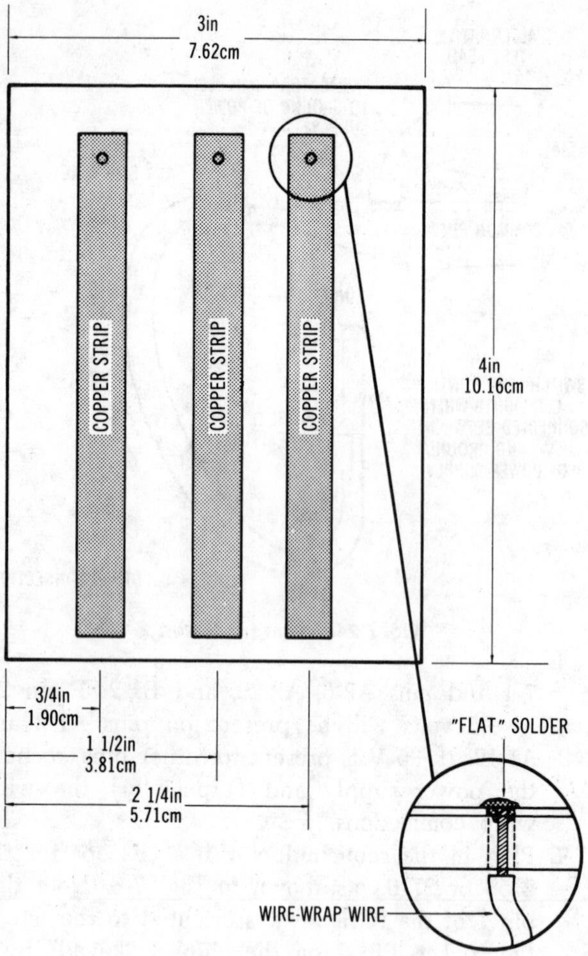

Fig. 7-26. Keyboard fabrication 1.

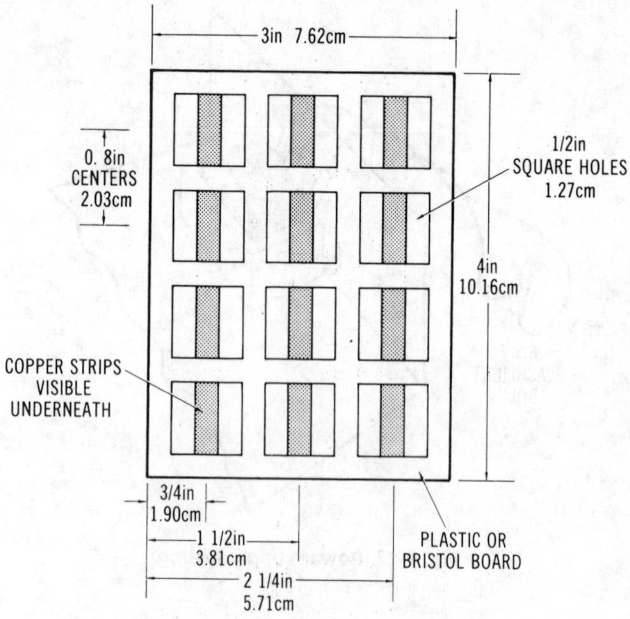

Fig. 7-27. Keyboard fabrication 2.

over the pin 1 position. The chip pins may have to be bent slightly to fit the socket (use a table surface to bend all of them at the same time).

KEYBOARD CONSTRUCTION

To reduce costs of the EZ-80 a simple but effective keyboard is constructed from thin sheets of copper (available from most electronic parts stores). The schematic of the keyboard is shown in Fig. 7-25. The keyboard functions by connecting a row line with a column line, as shown in the figure. When key 5 is pressed, for example, lines 5 and 2 will be connected.

To fabricate the keyboard, follow these steps:

1. Cut a 4 by 3 inch (10.16 by 7.62 cm) composition board as a base. Lay three strips of adhesive-backed copper strips on the base, as shown in Fig. 7-26.
2. Drill three small holes as shown. Push the "stripped" end of a 12-inch (30.48 cm) wire-wrap wire through each hole. Carefully solder the three wires to the copper strips as shown.
3. Cut a 4 by 3 inch (10.16 by 7.62 cm) medium-thickness (1/32 in = 0.8 mm) plastic or bristol board sheet. Punch or cut out ½ inch (1.27 cm) diameter round holes or ½ inch (1.27 cm) wide square holes as shown in Fig. 7-27. Lay the sheet over the base and verify that the holes align with the copper strips.
4. Cut four adhesive-backed copper strips. Carefully solder a 12-inch (30-cm) wire-wrap wire to each strip as in Fig. 7-28. Lay each strip over a second 3 by 4 inch (7.62 by 10.16 cm) thin plastic or paper sheet as shown in the figure.
5. Drill four small holes in the base and thread the four wires through them, positioning the new sheet face to face with the sheet containing the holes, as shown in the figure.
6. The topmost plastic sheet is the face of the keyboard. The plastic can be marked on the reverse side at this point, if the keyboard is to be mounted elsewhere than on the slope-front chassis. A pattern for the marking is shown in Fig. 7-29. If the slope-front chassis is to be used, the keyboard face plate is left blank.
7. Drill four small holes as shown in Fig. 7-30. Using four small screws and nuts, compress the keyboard sandwich.
8. Mark the seven wires with row or column using tape or other means. Bundle the seven 12-inch (30-cm) wires together using "cable-ties," electrical tape, or thread. Once bundled, cut to the same length (see Fig. 7-31).
9. Solder the seven wires to a small 14-pin "dip-

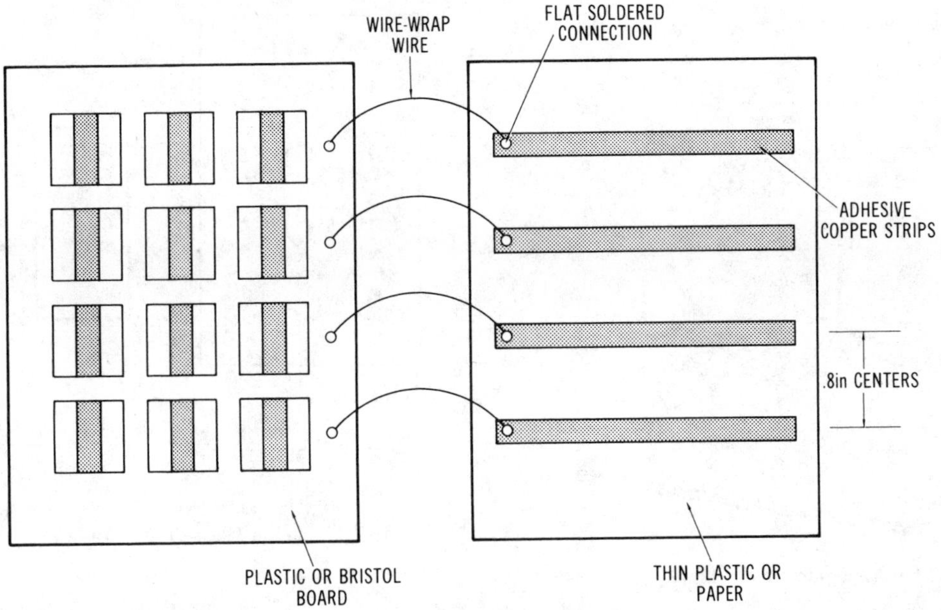

Fig. 7-28. Keyboard fabrication 3.

plug," as shown in Fig. 7-32. Remove the wire labels.

10. The keyboard can now be tested by using a continuity tester connected to the appropriate row and column and checking the key depression, as shown in Fig. 7-33.

LED DISPLAY

The microcomputer board as built will operate with a four-digit LED display. The one we are using in the EZ-80 is the HP5082-7404 display, which is a 12-pin LED display that fits the 14-pin socket of D3. The display chip may be plugged directly into D3 if the physical layout of the EZ-80 is the "bare bones" version. The second alternative is to fabricate a single-chip display assembly that is mounted on the front panel of the EZ-80. The third alternative is a larger LED display. The larger LED display uses four common-cathode LED displays mounted in four wire-wrap sockets. This four-chip assembly is shown in Fig. 7-34.

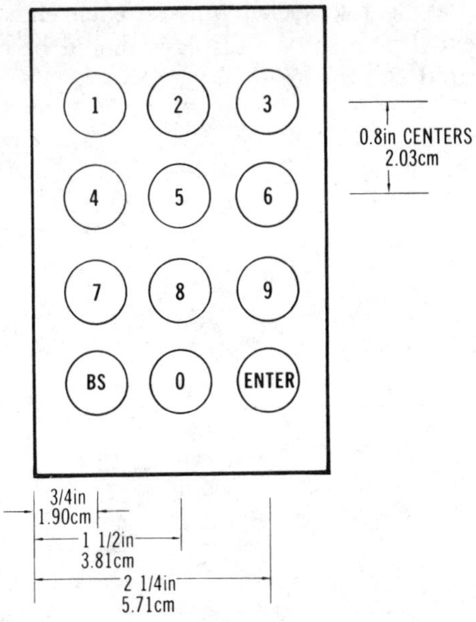

Fig. 7-29. Keyboard markings.

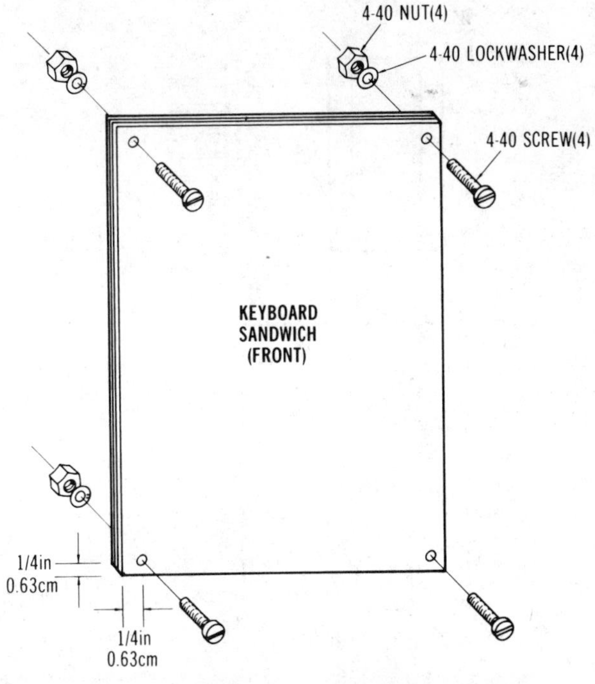

Fig. 7-30. Keyboard fabrication 4.

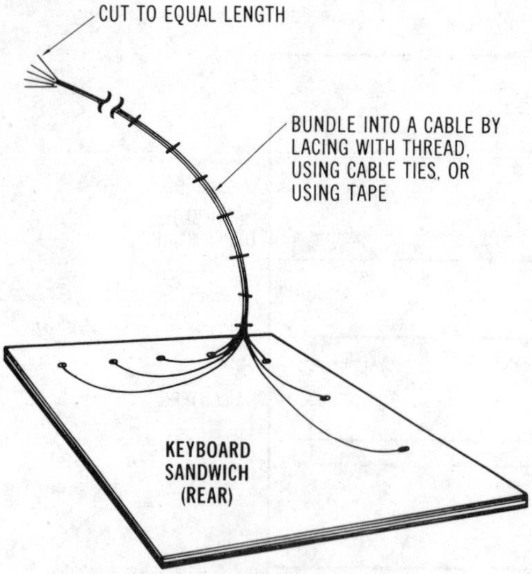

Fig. 7-31. Keyboard fabrication 5.

The single-chip display is bright, but small. The four-chip display is much larger, but sacrifices some brightness. The choice is up to the reader.

To make the single-chip (7404) display, assemble a 14-pin dip plug and cable from wire-wrap wire, as shown in Fig. 7-35. The pins of the display chip may be soldered directly to the wire-wrap wires (solder quickly to avoid excessive heat!). Bundle the cable by cable ties, tape, or thread, and set it aside.

To make the four-chip display, break a small piece of perfboard to the dimensions shown in Fig. 7-36.

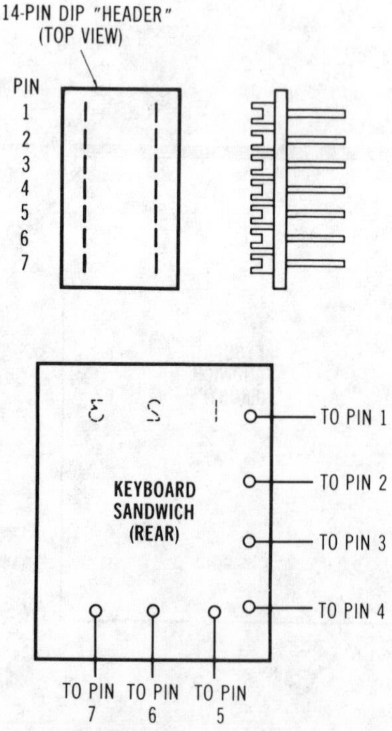

Fig. 7-32. Keyboard fabrication 6.

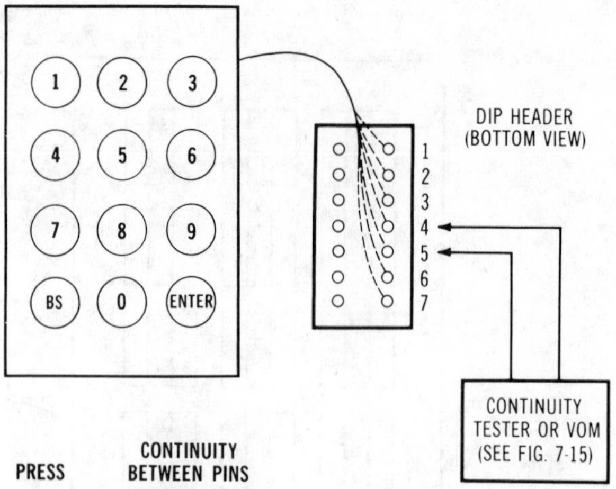

PRESS	CONTINUITY BETWEEN PINS
1	1-5
2	1-6
3	1-7
4	2-5
5	2-6
6	2-7
7	3-5
8	3-6
9	3-7
BS	4-5
0	4-6
ENTER	4-7

Fig. 7-33. Keyboard testing.

The board breaks easily if it is aligned over the edge of a desk and pressure is put on the unsupported section. Use four 14-pin wire-wrap sockets. Attach the sockets to the board by wire-wrapping the pins shown in Fig. 7-36. Mark the wires and solder to the dip plug. Remove the labels and bundle the wires by cable ties, tape, or thread. Mount the LED chips so that the 10 pins of the chip are in the *inside* 10 of the socket, leaving two socket pins on each end unused. The decimal point of the displays should be oriented as indicated. Set the assembly aside.

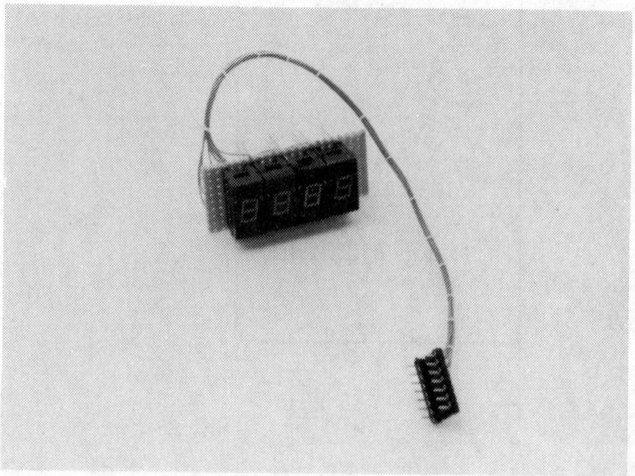

Fig. 7-34. Four-chip display.

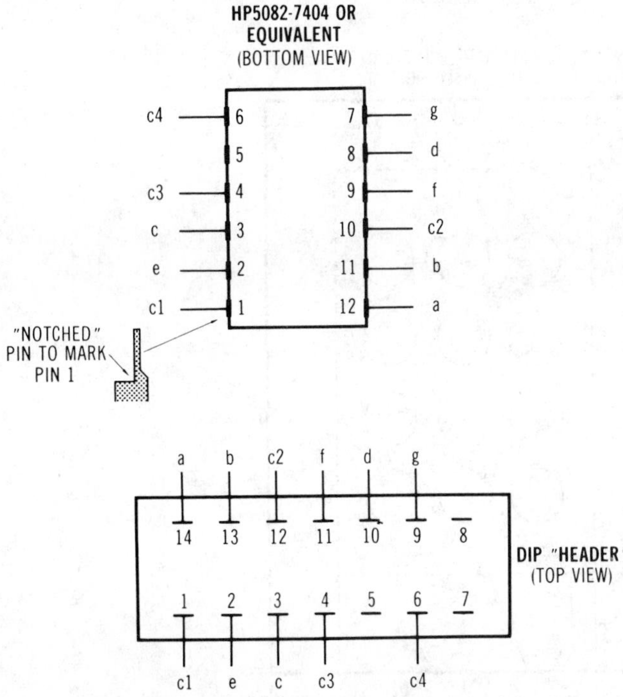

Fig. 7-35. Single-chip display fabrication.

EZ-80 PANEL

The suggested layout for the slope-front chassis is shown in Fig. 7-37. Twelve ½-inch (1.27-cm) holes are drilled in the front panel for key depressions. The keyboard sandwich will be attached to the rear of the panel as shown in the figure. A rectangular hole to fit either the single-chip LED display or the four-chip LED display is cut into the panel, as shown in Fig. 7-37. The four-chip display is mounted by two screws as shown in Fig. 7-38. The one-chip LED display can be mounted by securing a thin plastic strip with sticky tape as shown in the figure. In both the one-chip and four-chip versions of the display, a piece of red plastic faceplate material should be used between the display and panel to act as a filter. This can be glued to the rear of the panel or attached with screws as shown.

The panel overlays are shown in Fig. 7-39. The overlays can be photographically produced or can be drawn onto a paper stock with the help of transfer sheets and mounted behind protective plastic sheets. Circles of pressboard or other material should be glued to the back of the keyboard overlay to contact the keyboard through the panel. This prevents excessive travel to make contact with a key on the keyboard sandwich.

ALTERNATIVES TO FLASHY PANELS!

Bear in mind that the preceding description is only one way to lay out the EZ-80 panel. The keypad is of

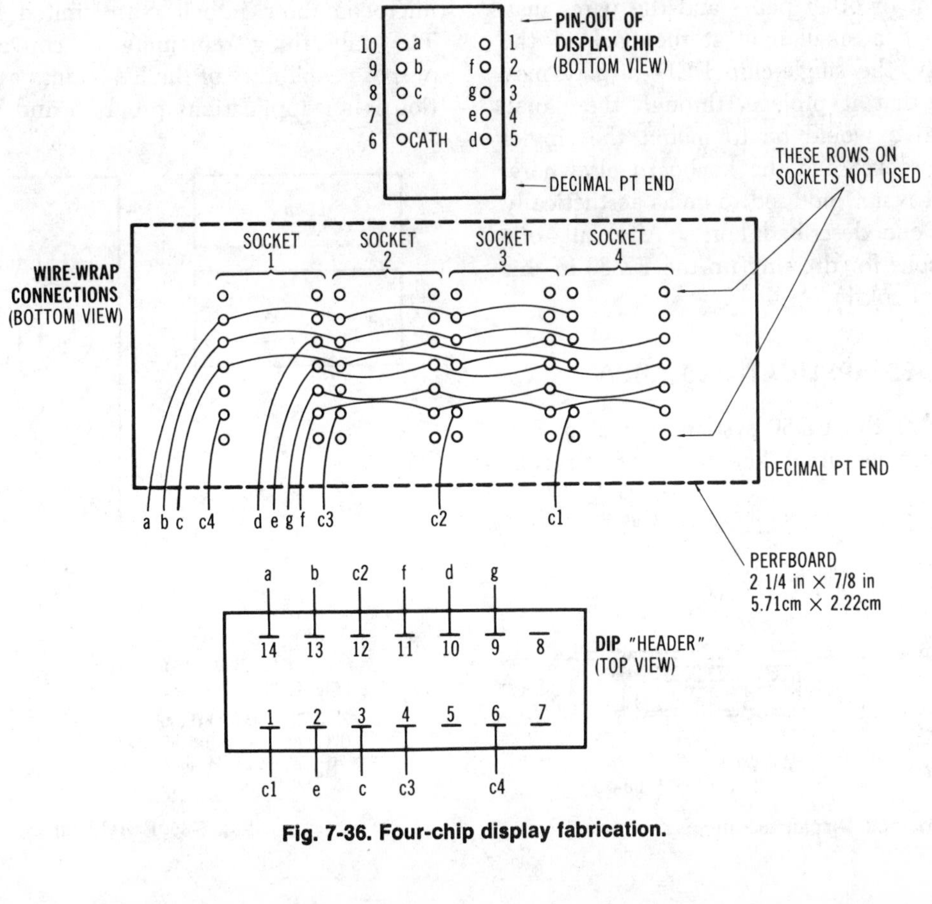

Fig. 7-36. Four-chip display fabrication.

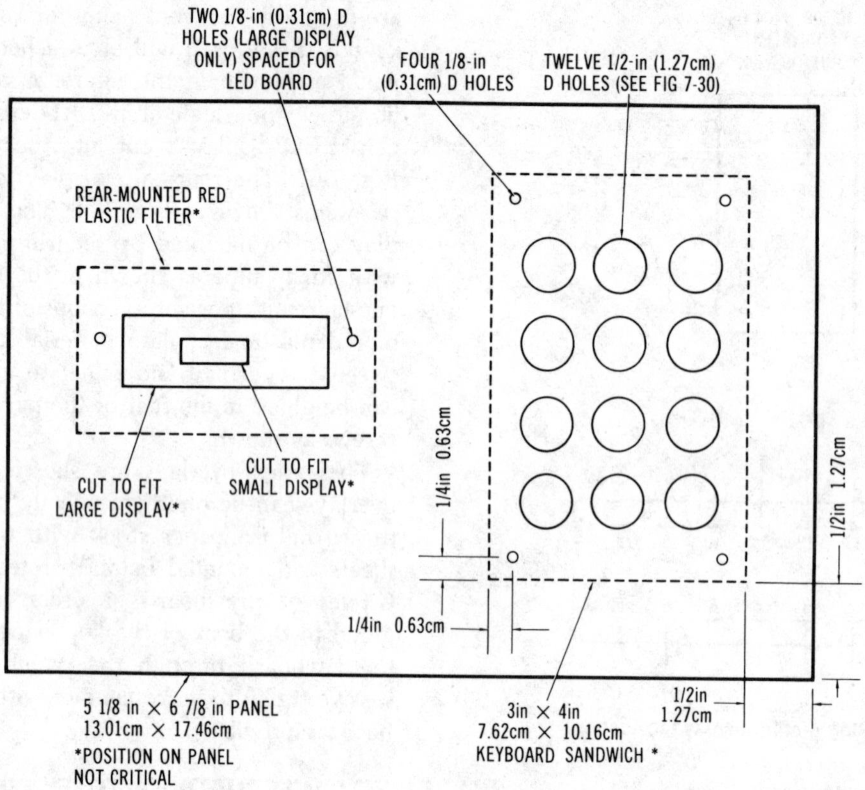

Fig. 7-37. Panel layout.

such a construction that it can be mounted directly on the slope-front or other panel and the wires may be routed through a small hole at the back of the keypad. Similarly, the single-chip LED display may be mounted so that it projects through the panel. Another alternative would be to mount the single-digit in the D3 socket and the keyboard elsewhere, for a system that is not required to be as aesthetically pleasing as the one described here. (After all, one of the chief reasons for dressing up the EZ-80 in this case was to sell books!)

THE EZ-80 APPLICATIONS AREA

The fifth part of the EZ-80 system shown in Fig. 7-1 is the applications area. The result of the construction thus far has been a complete general-purpose microcomputer (albeit with limited RAM memory). The only thing remaining to convert the general-purpose capability of the EZ-80 into a specific application is an applications program and some additional

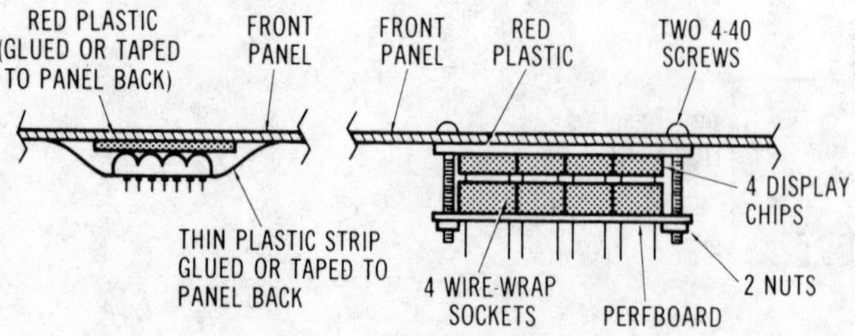

Fig. 7-38. Display mounting.

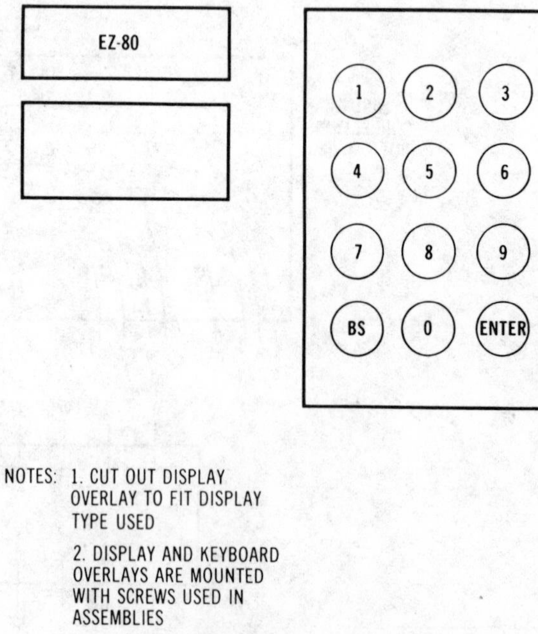

Fig. 7-39. Panel overlay.

"hardware." Both the applications programs and hardware are covered in Section 3 of this book. The additional hardware required varies with the application. In all cases it is minimal. An application such as a telephone dialer involves only an additional small relay. The music synthesizer requires a resistor network, an audio amplifier chip, and a small speaker. The layouts of the wire-wrap and printed-circuit boards are designed so that most of the additional circuitry can be added on the microcomputer board. All of the additions to the basic microcomputer board will be discussed in Section 3, "EZ-80 Projects."

CHAPTER 8

Programming the EPROMs

The EZ-80 uses a 2758 or 2716 erasable programmable read-only memory (EPROM). The 2758 holds 1024 bytes of instructions or data, while the 2716 holds twice that amount—2048 bytes. In the EZ-80 the EPROM holds either the applications program(s) or diagnostic program. Complete listings of the applications programs are provided in Section 3 of this book. The diagnostic program is described in the following chapter of this section; the diagnostic is used to test the functioning of the EZ-80.

There are several approaches that may be used to program the 2758 or 2716. The EPROM(s) may be programmed by the manufacturer's distributor, by a computer store with EPROM programming capability, by a friend who has an S-100 EPROM programmer or a "programmer" on another type of computer system, or by the use of an easy-to-build EPROM programmer described in this chapter. We'll discuss all approaches, and you can decide which is best for you. Erasing the EPROM is done by exposing the EPROM to strong ultraviolet light. We'll also discuss the methods of erasure in this chapter.

THE 2758 VERSUS THE 2716

Which EPROM should be used in the EZ-80, the 2758, or the 2716? The 2758 EPROM is an upgrade of the 2708 EPROM, a device that required *three* power supply voltages for operation and a sophisticated programming method. The 2716 is another member of the same *family* and may prove to be more popular than the 2758. The price of the 2716 is about 60 percent more than the 2758 for double the memory size. If you intend to use the EZ-80 as a single dedicated microcomputer for one or two applications, then the 2758 may be your best bet. If your goal is experimentation or running several applications, then the 2716 will provide more EPROM memory for the applications programs. Review Section 3 to determine how much memory you will require for your applications software.

The diagnostic program described in the next chapter is a good place to start for EPROM programming. Once you have obtained a "burned-in" version of the EZ-80 Diagnostic, you may wish to retain the EPROM so that the Diagnostic can be run at a later time to verify that the EZ-80 is still operative. For this reason it might be wise to burn-in the Diagnostic on a 2758.

A complete set of applications programs can be programmed on a few EPROMs. Different applications can be swapped at will in the EZ-80 by plugging in the required EPROM. You may wish to keep several EPROMs for permanent copies of the applications programs described here and for experimentation.

If you want to plug in different EPROMs, a "zero- insertion-force" EPROM socket can be used in the EZ-80.

The only difference in operation between the 2758 and 2716 is that the A10 address line is always a logic zero when the 2758 is used; locations 1024–2047 (400H–7FFH) are never addressed.

DISTRIBUTOR PROGRAMMING OF EPROMS

The first approach to programming the EPROMs used in the EZ-80 is that of having the manufacturer's distributor perform the programming. Distributors for Intel (the primary source for the 2758 and 2716) are located in all major U.S. and international cities. Information about the nearest distributor may be obtained by contacting Intel Corporation, 3055 Bowers Avenue, Santa Clara, CA 95051. The distributor is naturally anxious to sell you parts but in many cases will program EPROMs at a very reasonable cost (less than five dollars), even if the EPROMs are not purchased from him or her. The distributor will probably program them free if they are purchased from his or her supply.

The distributors normally have a computer system in-house on which they can easily and quickly program the EPROMs. The only thing required from you is a listing of the program to be burned in, a "paper tape" version of the program, or a *punched-*

card version of the program. Burning-in the program from a listing will be more expensive than supplying the distributor a paper tape or punched-card version of the program. The paper tape copy of the program may be produced by typing the program on a Teletype such as one used in some home computer systems, or for Telex. The punched-card version is punched on standard 80-column computer punch cards. Possible sources for access to either a Teletype or card punch are computer clubs (Teletypes), business (Teletypes or card punches), high schools or universities (Teletypes or card punches for computer installations), computer stores (Teletypes), or keypunch services (punched-card service).

The formats used for the paper tape or punched cards vary with the installation at the distributor. It is best to contact the distributor to find out his or her exact requirements. The format will either represent the program as a series of binary values (P for 0, N for 1) or as a series of hexadecimal digits. Either form can be generated from the applications or diagnostic program supplied in this book.

The disadvantages of programming the EPROMs by this method, of course, are the inconvenience of preparing and delivering the listings, tapes, or punched cards, the waiting time before the EPROM is prepared, and the expense of having the work done by the distributor. Another decided disadvantage is the fact that there is no way to verify that the data burned into the EPROM is truly correct once the EPROM has been delivered.

COMPUTER STORE PROGRAMMING OF EPROMS

The second approach to programming EPROMs is to enlist the aid of a computer store. As the reader probably knows, there are hundreds of computer stores throughout the U.S. and internationally. Many sell EPROMs and some will program the EPROMs free or at a reasonable price. Here, again, it is necessary to check with the computer store to determine the exact format of the source document required. It will probably be in hexadecimal format, as are the listings in this book.

PROGRAMMING THE EPROMS ON A PERSONAL COMPUTER SYSTEM

The third approach to programming the EPROMs for the EZ-80 system is to use an EPROM programmer on a personal computer system. There are many types available and most will program both 2758s and 2716s. Fig. 8-1 shows such a programmer designed for the "S-100" series of personal computers. Programmers such as this are available for S-100 systems, the popular KIM-1 microcomputer, the Radio Shack TRS-80™ computer system, and others. In addition, numerous articles have appeared in the personal computer magazines, such as *Byte* and *Kilobaud Microcomputing*, for inexpensive EPROM programmer designs that may be constructed and used on most personal computer systems. Good sources for access

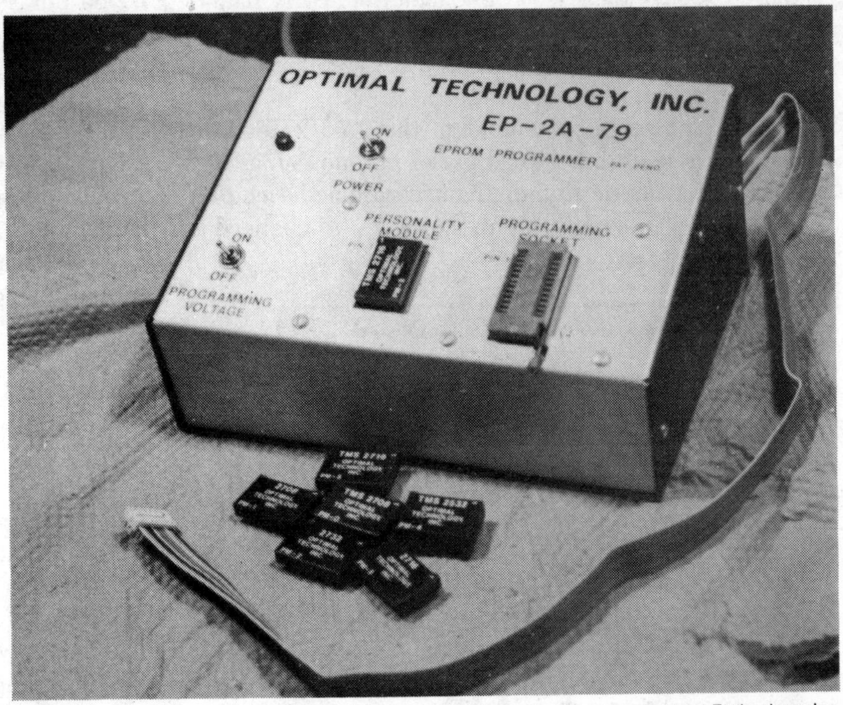

Fig. 8-1. EPROM programmer for personal computer.

Courtesy Optimal Technology, Inc.

to such a programmer are computer clubs in your area.

A SIMPLE EPROM PROGRAMMER

If the reader does not care to program the EPROMs for the EZ-80 by any of the above methods, or if the reader does not have his or her own personal computer with a programmer, then he or she may choose to build the simple and inexpensive EPROM programmer described here. It may be used to program either 2758 or 2716 EPROMs.

An illustration of the EZ-80 Programmer is shown in Fig. 8-2. Before we discuss the operation of the Programmer, let's discuss the operation of the 2758/2716 once more. Fig. 8-3 shows the *pinout* of the 2758/2716. Lines A9–A0 are the address lines of the chip. We know that 10 address lines can address 1024 unique locations from 00 0000 0000 through 11 1111 1111. In the 2716 an eleventh address line, A10, replaces the AR input of the 2758. The 2716 can therefore address 2048 locations from 000 0000 0000 through 111 1111 1111.

The address lines are used during operation of the 2758/2716 in the EZ-80 to determine the location from which data will be read. In the Programmer they are used for exactly the same purpose when *verifying* data contained in the chip. In addition, they are used to select the location to be programmed (written to) during the burn-in process.

There are eight data lines in the 2758/2716, designated O7–O0. In the EZ-80 these data lines carry data read from the location addressed by A9 (A10)–A0. In the Programmer these lines also carry data to be written into the EPROM.

The V_{CC} power supply input to the 2758/2716 remains the same during normal use or programming. It supplies +5 volts dc to the circuitry within the chip. The V_{PP} power supply input, however, is changed

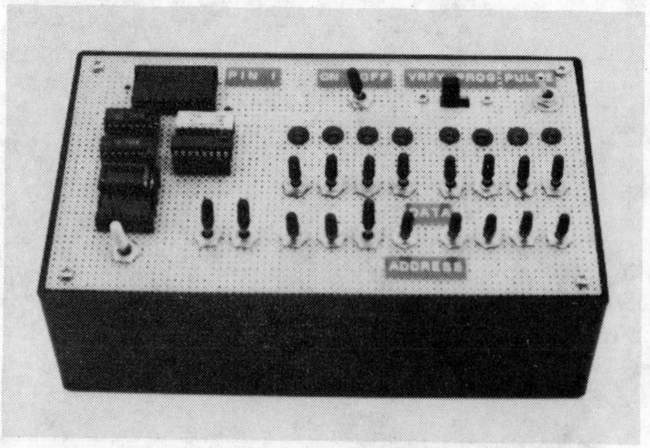

Fig. 8-2. EZ-80 programmer.

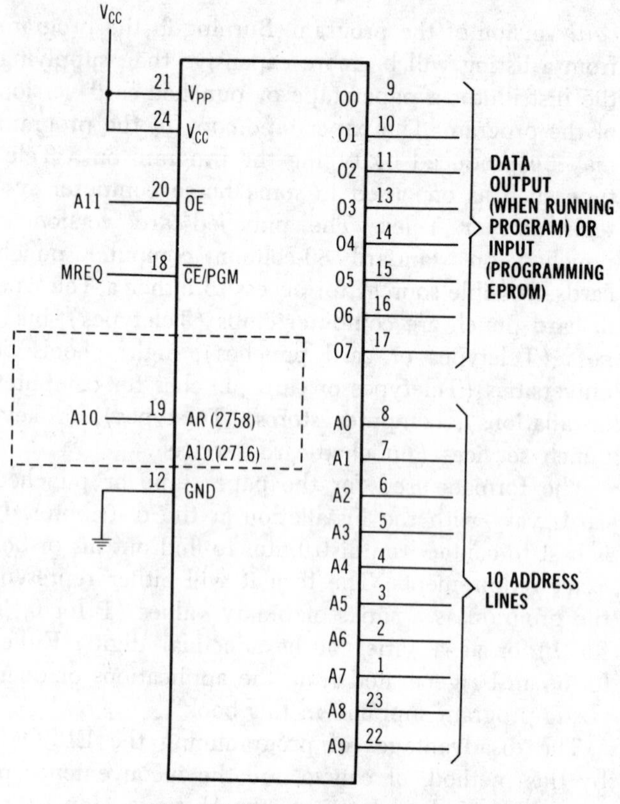

Fig. 8-3. Pin out of 2758/2716.

from +5 volts dc to *+25 volts dc* during programming. This higher voltage is used to electrically program the selected location in the EPROM.

The chip enable ($\overline{CE}$) input is also changed during programming. During normal operation in the EZ-80 this signal is used to *select* or *enable* the chip for a memory read. The memory request signal ($\overline{MREQ}$) is used for this function. During programming, this input is used to perform the programming of the data on O7–O0 into the location addressed by A9 (A10)–A0. Instead of a *low* input as during the memory request, this input is brought *from* a low to a high and back, or pulsed.

The last input, output enable ($\overline{OE}$), is low (ground or logic 0) during normal operation. It is a signal that is used to select the EPROM (along with $\overline{MREQ}$) by address output A11 of the Z-80. $\overline{OE}$ is high (logic 1) during programming.

The steps of programming a single location of the 2758 or 2716 are as follows:

1. Put the address of the location to be programmed onto address lines A9 (A10) through A0.
2. Put the 8 bits to be written on data lines O7 through O0.
3. Put +5 volts on $\overline{OE}$ and +24 volts on V_{PP}.
4. Bring input $\overline{CE}$ from low to high and back again for 50 milliseconds (1/20 of a second).

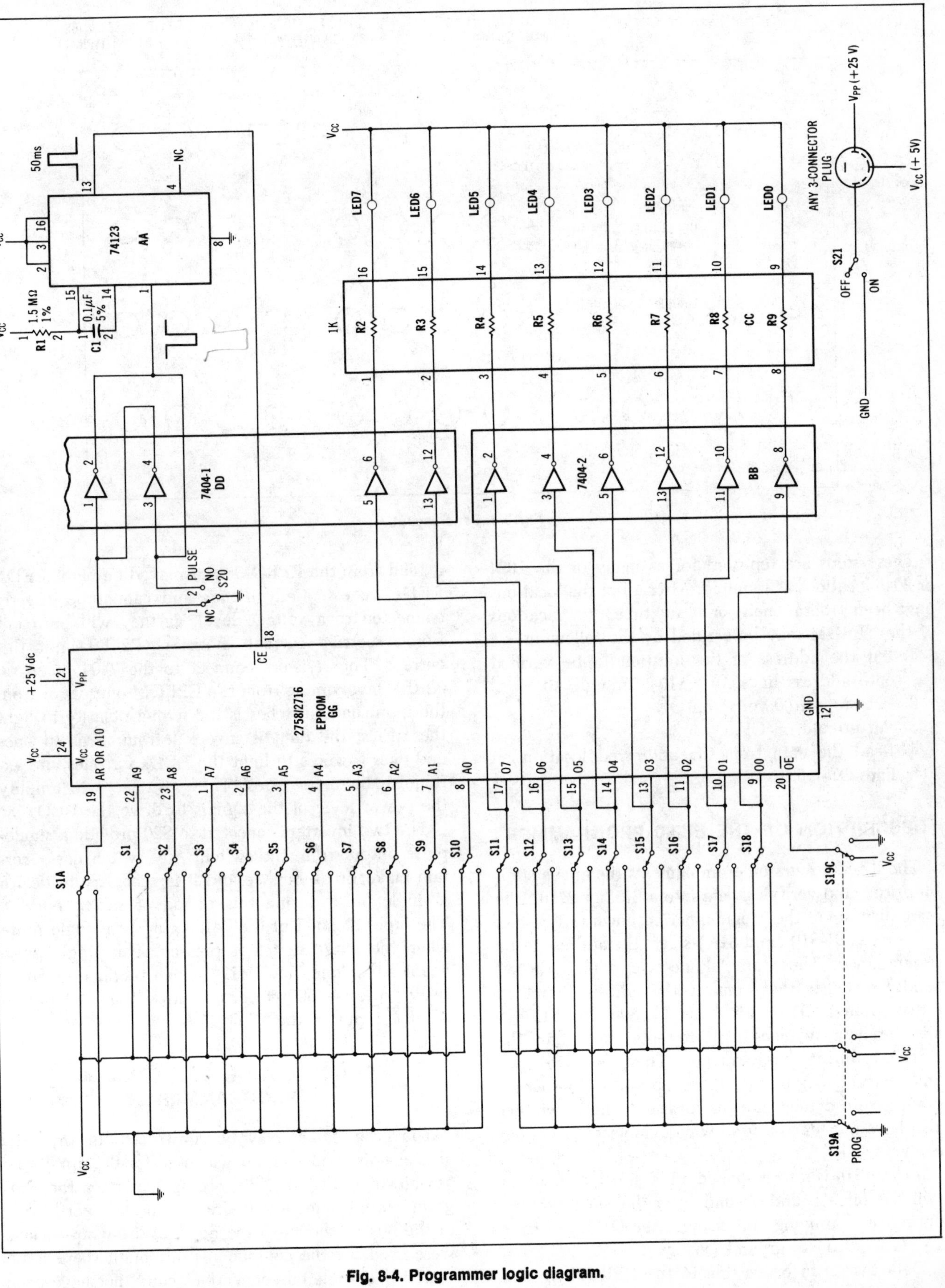

Fig. 8-4. Programmer logic diagram.

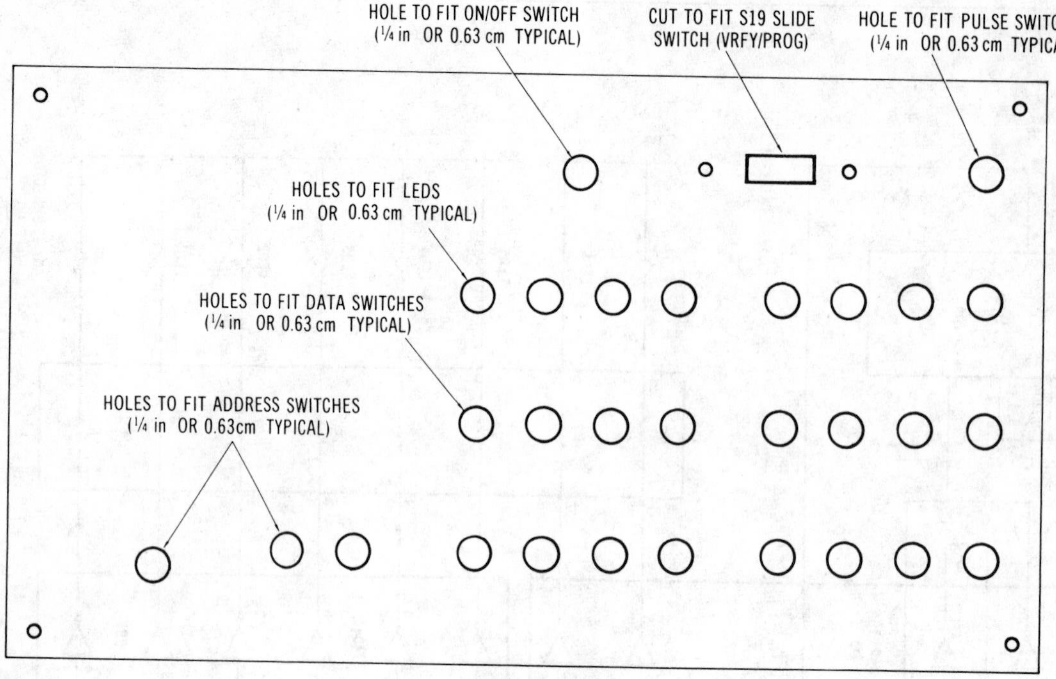

Fig. 8-5. Panel layout.

These steps are repeated for as many of the 1024 or 2048 locations as required. After all of the locations have been programmed (or at any time), the locations of the EPROM may be verified by the following:

1. Put the address of the location to be verified onto address lines A9 (A10) through A0.
2. Put ground (0 volts) on $\overline{OE}$.
3. Put ground on $\overline{CE}$.
4. Read the data from the addressed location on lines O7–O0.

DESCRIPTION OF THE EZ-80 PROGRAMMER

The EZ-80 Programmer implements the above steps of writing and verifying data into a 2758 or 2716. The logic diagram of the programmer is shown in Fig. 8-4.

Switches S1-S10 (and S1A) select the address to be programmed. These are "single-pole double throw" (spdt) switches that connect the address input to either ground (0) or +5 volts (1). Switches S11-S18 are the data switches used to enter data into the EPROM during programming. They are also spdt and connect to ground (0) or +5 volts (1) to program a zero or one into the location. These switches also have a *center position* which connects to neither contact.

Switch S19 is a three-pole double-throw switch that switches off V_{CC} and ground from the data switches during programming and changes the $\overline{OE}$ input from V_{CC} (PROGRAM) to ground (VERIFY).

Data that is to be written to the EPROM or that is read from the EPROM is displayed on eight LEDs. LEDs are essentially *diodes* and cannot be directly connected to a voltage level, as they will burn out from excessive current. Resistors R2–R9 limit this current. The resistors connect to the 7404 *inverters.* As the data coming from the EPROM outputs or from the input data switches is the wrong polarity to light the LEDs, the data is inverted from zeros to ones and ones to zeros to light the LEDs for ones and extinguish them for zeros. They also serve to amplify the power level of the signals to drive the LEDs.

The two inverters conected to S20 provide a single-pulse output from the switch. Any switch has a certain make/break bounce and it is necessary to derive a single pulse during this period of *switch bounce.* The input at pin 1 of the 74123 chip is a single pulse when the PULSE switch is pressed. This single pulse enables the "one-shot" 74123 which produces a (relatively) precise 50-millisecond pulse that is input to the $\overline{CE}$ input of the 2758/2716.

CONSTRUCTION OF THE EZ-80 PROGRAMMER

The Programmer may be constructed in any suitable chassis. A plastic box was used for the prototype, as shown in Fig. 8-2. The components for the Programmer were mounted directly on the "perfboard" of the box as shown in the figure. Wire-wrap sockets were used for the components, although there is no reason that soldered connections could not have been used as well. The description of the Programmer construction assumes that the wire-wrap approach will be used.

Using a small drill, drill holes for the eleven ADDRESS switches, eight DATA switches, ON/OFF switch, VERIFY/PROGRAM switch, and PULSE switch, as shown in Fig. 8-5. Mount the switches as shown in Fig. 8-6. Mount the LED indicator lights as shown in Fig. 8-7.

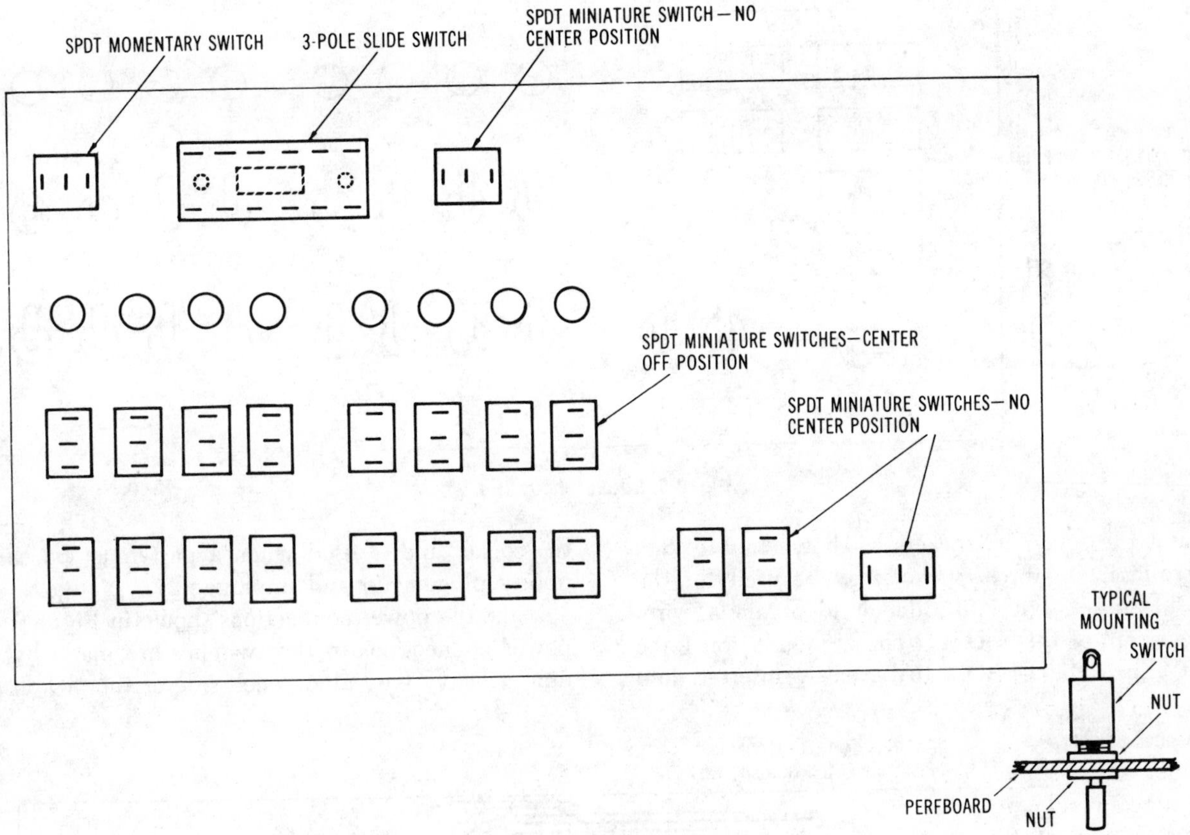

Fig. 8-6. Switch mounting.

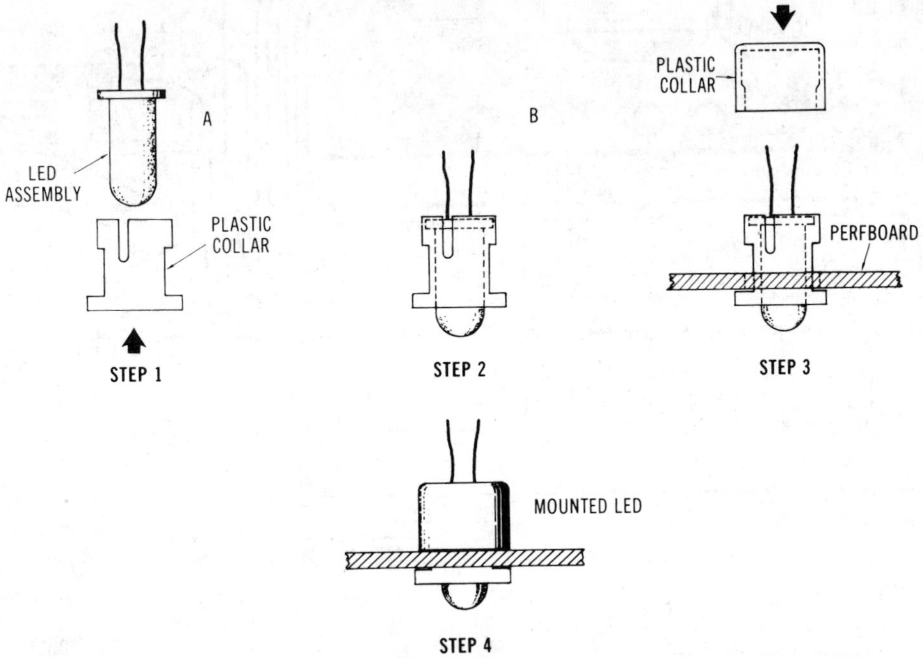

Fig. 8-7. LED mounting.

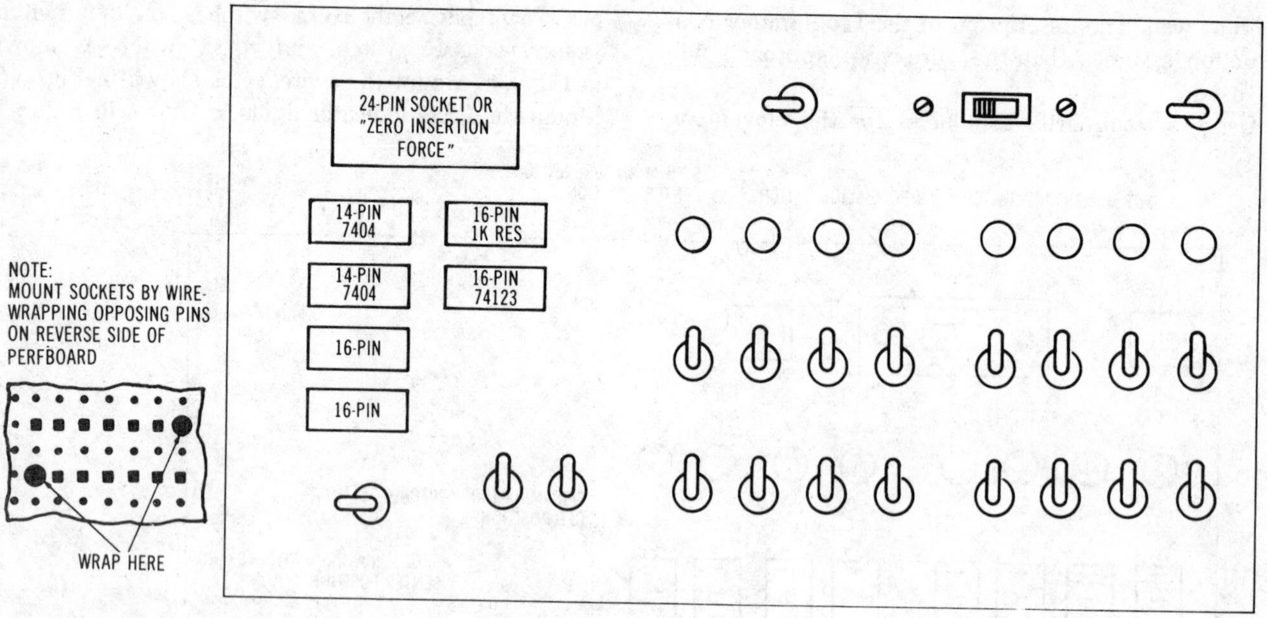

Fig. 8-8. Socket mounting.

Mount the seven IC sockets as shown in Fig. 8-8. A "zero-insertion force" socket may be used for the EPROM socket, but it is difficult to obtain a wire-wrap version of this socket. (The zero-insertion force socket allows the EPROM to be easily inserted into the socket and is used when a part must be continuously plugged in and unplugged.)

Make the power connections shown in Fig. 8-9. The power connections to the switches are made by running a heavy wire along each side of the switch con-

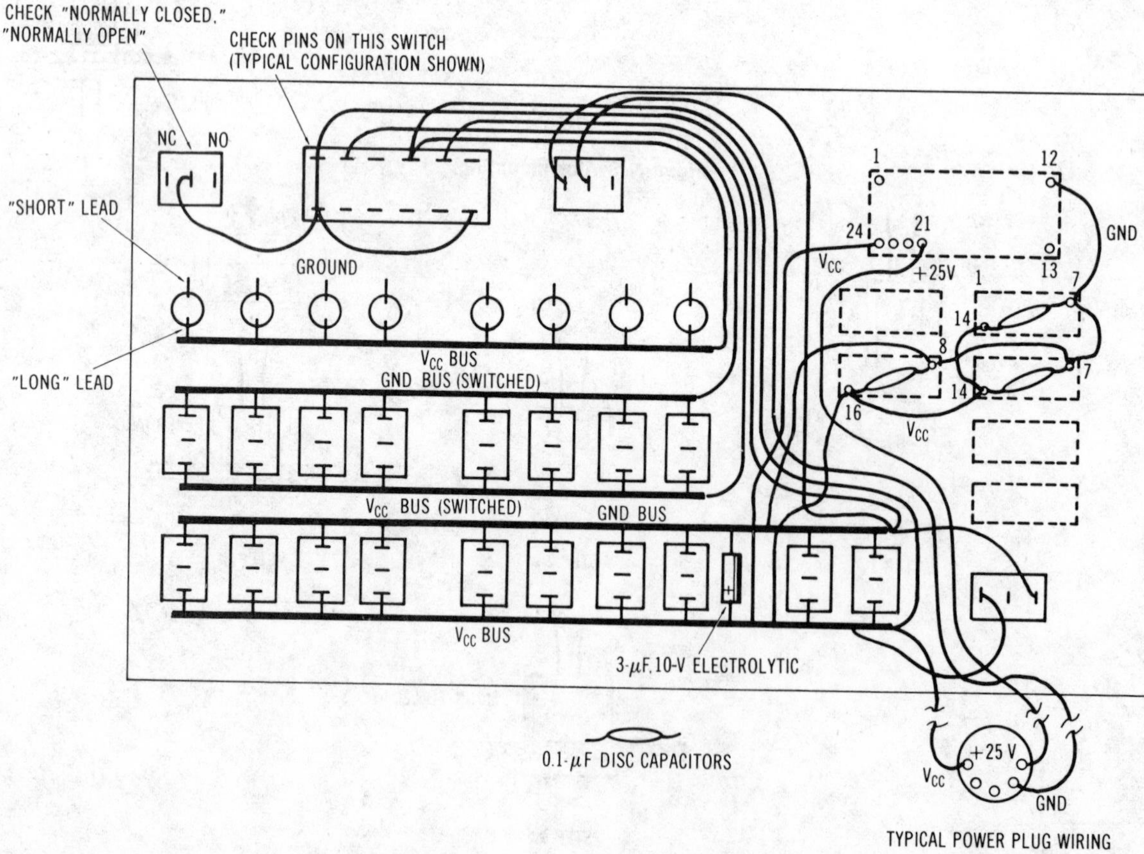

Fig. 8-9. Programmer power connections.

Chart 8-1. Programmer Wire-Wrap List

Signal	Wrap Pins
SA10(AR) to post	S1A-C to FF-3
SA9 to post	S1-C to FF-2
SA8 to post	S2-C to FF-1
SA7 to post	S3-C to FF-9
SA6 to post	S4-C to FF-10
SA5 to post	S5-C to FF-11
SA4 to post	S6-C to FF-12
SA3 to post	S7-C to FF-13
SA2 to post	S8-C to FF-14
SA1 to post	S9-C to FF-15
SA0 to post	S10-C to FF-16
S00 to post	S18-C to EE-8
S01 to post	S17-C to EE-9
S02 to post	S16-C to EE-7
S03 to post	S15-C to EE-10
S04 to post	S14-C to EE-6
S05 to post	S13-C to EE-11
S06 to post	S12-C to EE-5
S07 to post	S11-C to EE-12
00 LED	LED0-C to CC-9
01 LED	LED1-C to CC-10
02 LED	LED2-C to CC-11
03 LED	LED3-C to CC-12
04 LED	LED4-C to CC-13
05 LED	LED5-C to CC-14
06 LED	LED6-C to CC-15
07 LED	LED7-C to CC-16
O7	GG-17 to DD-5
O6	GG-16 to DD-13
O5	GG-15 to BB-1
O4	GG-14 to BB-3
O3	GG-13 to BB-5
O2	GG-11 to BB-13
O1	GG-10 to BB-11
O0	GG-9 to BB-9
A10 to post	GG-19 to FF-3
A9 to post	GG-22 to FF-2
A8 to post	GG-23 to FF-1

Signal	Wrap Pins
A7 to post	GG-1 to FF-9
A6 to post	GG-2 to FF-10
A5 to post	GG-3 to FF-11
A4 to post	GG-4 to FF-12
A3 to post	GG-5 to FF-13
A2 to post	GG-6 to FF-14
A1 to post	GG-7 to FF-15
A0 to post	GG-8 to FF-16
$\overline{CE}$ to one-shot	GG-18 to AA-13
$\overline{OE}$ to PROG/VERIFY switch	GG-20 to S19C-C
Inverter input to O0	BB-9 to EE-8
Inverter input to O1	BB-11 to EE-9
Inverter input to O2	BB-13 to EE-7
Inverter input to O3	BB-5 to EE-10
Inverter input to O4	BB-3 to EE-6
Inverter input to O5	BB-1 to EE-11
Inverter input to O6	DD-13 to EE-5
Inverter input to O7	DD-5 to EE-12
Inverter output to R9	BB-8 to CC-8
Inverter output to R8	BB-10 to CC-7
Inverter output to R7	BB-12 to CC-6
Inverter output to R6	BB-6 to CC-5
Inverter output to R5	BB-4 to CC-4
Inverter output to R4	BB-2 to CC-3
Inverter output to R3	DD-12 to CC-2
Inverter output to R2	DD-6 to CC-1
Inverter input to PULSE NC	DD-1 to S20-1
Inverter input to PULSE NO	DD-3 to S20-2
Inverter output to input	DD-4 to DD-1
Inverter output to input	DD-2 to DD-3
Inverter output to one-shot trigger	DD-2 to AA-1
V_{CC}	AA-2 to AA-16
V_{CC}	AA-2 to AA-3
One-shot R/C to DIP socket	AA-15 to EE-16
One-shot C to DIP socket	AA-14 to EE-1
Common C1, R1-2	EE-16 to EE-2
R1-1 to V_{CC}	EE-15 to DD-14

tacts. The power connections to the semiconductor chips may be made by connections to the V_{CC} or ground "bus." Also install three 0.1-μF disc capacitors and one 3-μF, 10-V electrolytic capacitor as shown.

Wire-wrap the logic connections by following the wire-wrap table of Chart 8-1. Some of the wire-wrap connections are soldered on one end. The wires running to the switches may be tied together in a cable using cable ties, tape, or thread.

The power required for the Programmer is +5 volts dc and +25 volts dc. A good source for this is a set of four 6-volt lantern batteries. They last for many programmings and supply very close to +25 volts. Another alternative is a +25-volt supply if the reader has access to one, or is able to build one. We'll discuss the battery approach. A simple regulator circuit that supplies both +25 volts and +5 volts is shown in Fig. 8-10. The board holding the parts can be taped to the batteries, or the entire assembly may be contained within the programmer box.

PROGRAMMER CHECKOUT

Verify that the power supply circuit is working by connecting the power supply leads to the Programmer without the semiconductor chips in their sockets. Turn the power switch on and *cautiously* test the temperature of the regulator IC. It should be warm, but not hot. Put the PROGRAM/VERIFY switch in the PROGRAM position and all data switches in the up position. All LEDs should light. Now, put all DATA switches in the center (no connection) position. The LEDs should still be on. Now, put all DATA switches in the off (down) position. All LEDs should go off. Put the PROGRAM/VERIFY switch in the VERIFY position. All LEDs should light. If these actions do not occur, check the power and wire-wrap connections for the switches and 7404 chips.

Now, all semiconductor chips except for the 2758 or 2716 can be inserted in their sockets. Turn off the power and insert the chips, as shown in Fig. 8-11. The chip holding the two components is constructed by soldering the resistor and capacitor to a small DIP "header."

Turn on the power and cautiously test the temperature of the chips. None of them should be hot. Insert an LED/resistor combination into pins 18 and 12 (ground) of the 2758/2716 socket (see Fig. 7-24 in Chapter 7). Set the VERIFY/PROGRAM switch to PROGRAM. Momentarily switch the PULSE switch. The LED

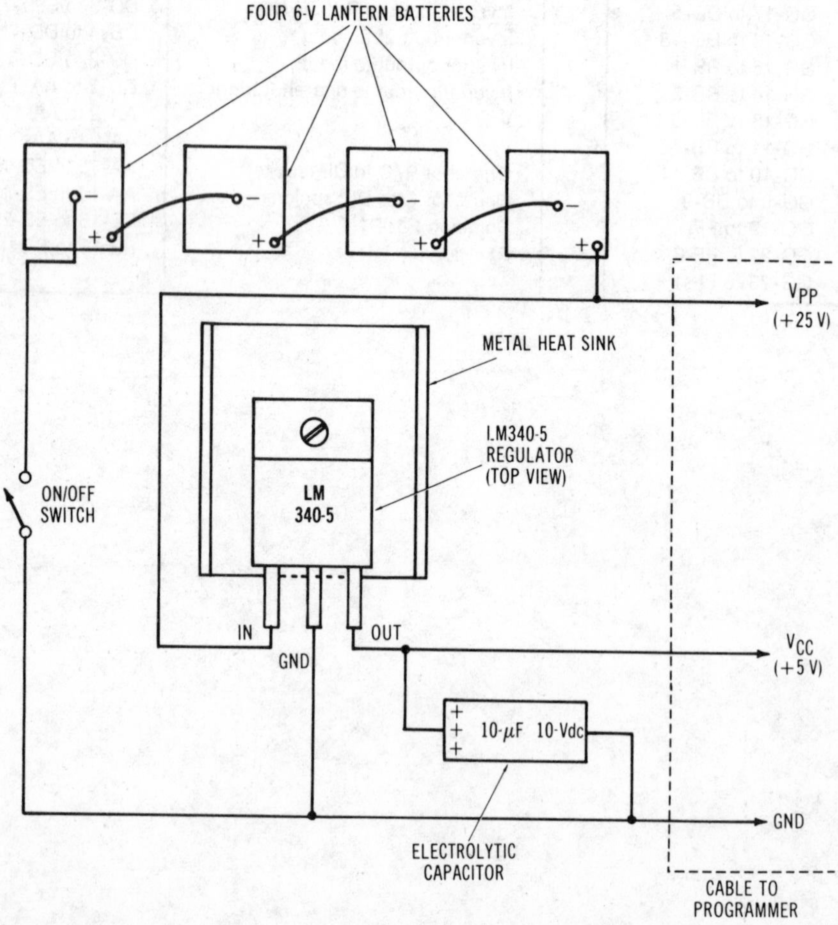

Fig. 8-10. Regulator circuit.

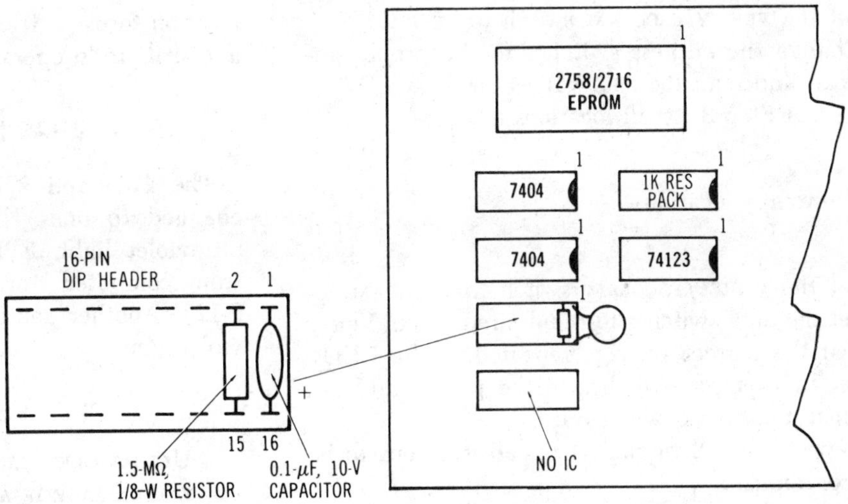

Fig. 8-11. Semiconductor chip placement.

should briefly flash. If this does not occur, check the 74123 wiring.

Using the LED/resistor combination (or a vom or oscilloscope), check between the pins of the 2758, as shown in Table 8-1. If incorrect results occur, check the 2758/2716 wiring.

Put the VERIFY/PROGRAM switch to VERIFY. Set all DATA switches to the center position. Plug in a 2758 or 2716 EPROM. Make certain that pin 1 is oriented toward the proper end. Turn on the power. Set the ADDRESS switches to various settings. All settings should produce all ones (all LEDs lighted) on the LEDs.

The next step is to check the programming operation of the unit. For this step it is obviously necessary to actually program an EPROM. Probably the wisest approach is to plan on using one EPROM as a test device before attempting a large-scale programming operation. To verify that the programming operation is functioning, perform the following steps.

1. Turn power on.
2. Set VERIFY/PROGRAM to PROGRAM.

Table 8-1. Programmer Power Connections

2758/2716 Pin	Switch Settings	Result
12	Don't care	Ground
21	Don't care	+25 Vdc
24	Don't care	+5 Vdc
1, 2, 3, 4, 5, 6, 7, 8, 19, 22, 23	All address switches up	+5 Vdc
1, 2, 3, 4, 5, 6, 7, 8, 19, 22, 23	All address switches down	Ground
9, 10, 11, 13, 14, 15, 16, 17	All data switches up and PROG/VRFY set to PROG	+5 Vdc
9, 10, 11, 13, 14, 15, 16, 17	All data switches down and PROG/VRFY set to PROG	Ground

3. Set the ADDRESS switches to the values given in Table 8-2 and the DATA switches to the values in the same table. After every new set of values, *pulse* the switch one time.
4. Set all DATA switches to the center position.
5. Set VERIFY/PROGRAM to VERIFY.
6. Set the address switches to the values given in Table 8-2. Read the data output on the LEDs. It should correspond to the values previously programmed.

If the above operations have been performed correctly, the EZ-80 Programmer is assumed to be operating in both the programming and verify modes. If the programming did not take place properly, check the component values of C1 and R1 and the wire-wrap connections. It may also help to enlist the aid of a friend with an oscilloscope to check the duration of the CE pulse. It should be 50 milliseconds ±5 milliseconds.

OPERATING THE PROGRAMMER

Operation of the Programmer is identical with the VERIFY/PROGRAM operation described above. To read any location:

1. *Set all DATA switches to the center position.*

Table 8-2. Test Program Values

Address	Data
00000000000	00000000
00000000001	11111111
00000000010	10101010
00000000011	01010101
01000000000	00110011
01111111111	01110111
(2716 only)	
10000000000	00110011
11111111111	01110111

2. Set the VERIFY/PROGRAM switch to VERIFY.
3. Change the address switches to the proper address and read the data values on the LEDs.
4. Repeat Step 3 for all locations to be read.

To write to any location:

1. Set the VERIFY/PROGRAM switch to PROGRAM.
2. Set the data switches to the desired value. Verify that the correct value is repeated in the LEDs.
3. Set the ADDRESS switches to the proper address.
4. *Pulse* the PULSE switch once.
5. Repeat Steps 2 through 4 for all locations to be programmed.

One important word of advice—if the wrong value is programmed into the 2758 or 2716, it is generally not recoverable. The EPROMS come with all ones programmed into every location. If a zero has been written into a bit of a location that should have been a one, then the only way to redo that location is to erase the EPROM and start all over. If a one has been erroneously programmed, then it *is* possible to redo the operation by repeating the programming with a zero, for the "one" programming was a "no action" operation.

The implications of this are somewhat staggering. Don't program the EPROMs late at night! You're bound to put a zero bit into a location where a one should have gone. This always occurs about three quarters of the way through a programming operation.

The time required to program 500 locations is about two hours. Although this seems a bit much, it is very comparable to the time spent in traveling to another location to use a friend's equipment or in waiting for a distributor's operation.

ERASING THE EPROMS

The 2758 and 2716 can be erased (all locations changed to ones) by exposing the chip to strong ultraviolet light. EPROM erasers can be purchased from computer stores at reasonable cost (see Fig. 8-12). Another source is a medicinal type of ultraviolet lamp.

WARNING!

ULTRAVIOLET LIGHT CAN CAUSE PERMANENT EYE DAMAGE IF A USER LOOKS INTO THE LIGHT FOR EXTENDED PERIODS! BE CAREFUL.

The preceding warning is cautionary only. One should never look directly into a strong ultraviolet light source, as it may cause an optical "sunburn." Just handle the light prudently.

Erasure times vary with the light output of the ultraviolet eraser and distance of the chip type, but a period of several hours is typical. Verify several locations before reprogramming to make certain that all data values read are ones. When erasing, place the chip(s) as close to the light source as possible with the translucent window uncovered.

The window does not have to be covered after programming, as even strong sunlight will take several weeks to erase the EPROM. Covering the window with masking tape or a label is probably not a bad idea, however, if the EPROM has been permanently programmed with an applications program.

In the next chapter, we'll discuss the EZ-80 Diagnostic Program, which is an excellent choice for your first programming project.

Fig. 8-12. EPROM eraser.

CHAPTER 9

A Diagnostic Program for the EZ-80

This chapter describes a diagnostic program for the EZ-80. The Diagnostic can be programmed into the EPROM and used to help exercise and diagnose problems with the EZ-80. The Diagnostic is not a prerequisite for operation of EZ-80 applications programs, but the reader is prodded (if not urged) to test the EZ-80 with the EZ-80 Diagnostic before implementing the applications programs. The EZ-80 Diagnostic is also useful if failures occur after the EZ-80 has been "brought up" and is successfully operating. Although the chances are good that a failure in the latter case will be a bad semiconductor chip that can be verified by replacement, the EZ-80 Diagnostic serves as a good confidence check for the "hardware" and may help in defining hardware problems.

Probably the most useful application of the EZ-80 Diagnostic is to verify that the hardware is indeed operative when a new applications program has been programmed into the EPROM. Most errors that occur in working computer systems are human errors, and the EZ-80 is no exception to this rule. If the EZ-80 Diagnostic runs successfully, then the probability is very good that the problem is in the erroneous programming of the EPROM, in the case of the applications programs that are "precanned" in this book, or in the erroneous design or programming of other programs that the reader has constructed.

EZ-80 DIAGNOSTIC PROGRAMMING

Fig. 9-1 shows the complete listing of the EZ-80 Diagnostic. Program a 2758 or 2716 EPROM by using the EPROM Programmer described in Chapter 8, or by any of the other methods described. The EZ-80 Diagnostic occupies EPROM memory locations 0000 through 16DH, as shown in the listing. Let's review the listing format so that the reader is certain of the data values to be used. The first column on the listing contains the memory locations in hexadecimal. The next column contains the *contents* of the memory locations in hexadecimal. The second column contains two, four, eight, or sixteen hexadecimal digits representing one, two, three, or four *bytes* in EPROM memory. The first column contains the *starting* memory address of the one, two, three, or four bytes represented.

Location 25H, for example, holds a DAH. Locations 26 and 27 contain 24H and 00H respectively. The next location is location 28H, as shown in column 1. Occasionally, there will be "gaps" in the locations in the EZ-80 Diagnostic and other programs described in this book. An example of this is at locations 63H and 64H, which hold 18H and 04H, respectively. The next location in column one is location 66H. Where did location 65H go? This location is a "don't care" and does not have to be programmed. The effect of this is that it will contain all ones, the initial state of the EPROM.

The next column is the "line number" reference, and is meaningless as far as EPROM programming and program execution. The next four columns represent the *source line* assembly-language code— label (optional), op-code mnemonic (mandatory), operands (variable), and comments (optional). The contents of the memory locations in the second column represent the *machine-language* instructions for the associated source line.

For convenience in programming the EPROM, the contents of every location and the memory location itself are listed in Fig. 9-2. The contents are given in both hexadecimal and binary, as is the memory location value.

To program the EPROM using the EPROM Programer described in Chapter 8, follow the step-by-step operating instructions of the chapter. Be certain that all locations are correctly programmed by verifying the contents of the locations *twice*. (It may help to have someone else read off the contents as you check the list of data in the table. Once the EPROM has been correctly programmed and verified,

```
                00110 ;*                                           *
                00120 ;*         Z-80 MDP DIAGNOSTIC               *
                00125 ;*             00-00                          *
                00126 ;*            3/29/78                         *
                00130 ;*                                           *
                00140 ;*********************************************
0000            00150         ORG     0
                00160 ;
                00170 ; INITIALIZE STACK AND PPI
                00180 ;
0000 318008     00190 START   LD      SP,880H        ;TOP OF RAM+1
0003 3E89       00200         LD      A,89H          ;MODE CONTROL WD
0005 D303       00210         OUT     (3),A          ;SET MODE 0,SUBMODE 3
0007 AF         00220         XOR     A              ;CLEAR A
0008 D300       00230         OUT     (0),A          ;RESET LEDS
000A D301       00240         OUT     (1),A          ;RESET OUTPUT LINES
                00250 ;
                00260 ;LOOP HERE 10 SECONDS FOR SCOPING
                00270 ;
000C 0607       00280 SCOPE   LD      B,7            ;OUTER LOOP COUNT
000E 11FFFF     00290         LD      DE,-1          ;DECREMENT =-1
0011 21FFFF     00300 SCP10   LD      HL,-1          ;INNER LOOP COUNT
0014 19         00310 SCP20   ADD     HL,DE           ;DECREMENT HL
0015 DA1400     00320         JP      C,SCP20         ;LOOP IF NOT DONE
0018 10F7       00330         DJNZ    SCP10          ;OUTER LOOP
                00340 ;
                00350 ;SEQUENCE LED DIGITS RIGHT TO LEFT
                00360 ;
001A 3E10       00370 LEDDGT  LD      A,10H          ;0 TO RIGHTMOST DIGIT
001C D300       00380 LED05   OUT     (0),A          ;OUTPUT CURRENT VALUE
001E 21FFFF     00390         LD      HL,-1          ;FOR DELAY COUNT
0021 01FFFF     00400         LD      BC,-1          ;FOR DELAY DECMNT
0024 09         00410 LED10   ADD     HL,BC           ;DECRE COUNT
0025 DA2400     00420         JP      C,LED10         ;LOOP IF NOT 64K
0028 C601       00430         ADD     A,1            ;BUMP DIGIT VALUE
002A 47         00440         LD      B,A            ;SAVE
002B E60F       00450         AND     0FH            ;GET DIGIT VALUE
002D FE0A       00460         CP      0AH            ;OUTPUT 0-9?
002F 78         00470         LD      A,B            ;RESTORE
0030 C21C00     00480         JP      NZ,LED05       ;GO IF MORE
0033 E6F0       00490         AND     0F0H           ;GET POSITION FIELD
0035 CB27       00500         SLA     A              ;MOVE TO NEXT POSITION
0037 FE00       00510         CP      0              ;AT LEFTMOST?
0039 C21C00     00520         JP      NZ,LED05       ;GO IF NO
                00530 ;
                00540 ;TEST 1:TEST RAM ADDRESSES AND DATA
                00550 ;
003C 3E11       00560 RAMTST  LD      A,11H          ;FOR TEST 1
003E D300       00570         OUT     (0),A          ;OUTPUT TO LEDS
0040 AF         00580         XOR     A              ;0 TO A
0041 320208     00590         LD      (802H),A       ;STORE 0 IN FIRST RAM
0044 3A0208     00600         LD      A,(802H)       ;GET CONTENTS
0047 FE00       00610         CP      0              ;ZERO?
```

Fig. 9-1. EZ-80

```
0049 C24900  RAM10   JP      NZ,RAM10        ;LOOP HERE ON ERROR
004C 2F              CPL                     ;-1 TO A
004D 320208          LD      (802H),A        ;STORE -1
0050 3A0208          LD      A,(802H)        ;GET CONTENTS
0053 3C              INC     A               ;TEST FOR ALL ONES
0054 C25400  RAM20   JP      NZ,RAM20        ;LOOP HERE ON ERROR
0057 21FFFF          LD      HL,-1           ;FOR DELAY CNT
005A 01FFFF          LD      BC,-1           ;FOR DELAY DECREMENT
005D 09      RAM30   ADD     HL,BC              ;DECREMENT COUNT
005E DA5D00          JP      C,RAM30            ;LOOP IF NOT 64K
             ;
             ;TEST 2:SHORT RAM MEMORY TEST
             ;
0061 3E12    MEMTST  LD      A,12H           ;FOR TEST 2
0063 1804            JR      69H             ;BYPASS NMI VECTOR
             ;
             ;NM INTERRUPT VECTOR
             ;
0066                 ORG     66H
0066 C36101          JP      NMIHAN          ;GO TO PROCESS NMI
0069                 ORG     69H
0069 D300            OUT     (0),A           ;OUTPUT TO LEDS
006B 210208          LD      HL,802H         ;START OF RAM
006E 067C            LD      B,124           ;SIZE OF RAM -WORKING
0070 AF              XOR     A                  ;0 TO A
0071 77      MEM10   LD      (HL),A             ;STORE ALL ZEROES
0072 7E              LD      A,(HL)             ;GET STORED VALUE
0073 FE00            CP      0                  ;IS IT ZERO?
0075 C27500  MEM20   JP      NZ,MEM20           ;LOOP HERE ON ERROR
0078 2F              CPL                        ;-1 TO A
0079 77              LD      (HL),A             ;STORE ALL ONES
007A 7E              LD      A,(HL)             ;GET STORED VALUE
007B 3C              INC     A                  ;IS IT -1
007C C27C00  MEM30   JP      NZ,MEM30           ;LOOP HERE ON ERROR
007F 23              INC     HL                 ;BUMP POINTER
0080 10EF            DJNZ    MEM10              ;CONTINUE HERE FOR 128
0082 21FFFF          LD      HL,-1           ;FOR DELAY CNT
0085 01FFFF          LD      BC,-1           ;FOR DELAY INC
0088 09      MEM40   ADD     HL,BC              ;DECREMENT COUNT
0089 DA8800          JP      C,MEM40            ;LOOP HERE IF NOT 64K
             ;
             ;TEST3:NMI/CLK FREQUENCY TEST
             ;
008C 3E13    NMICLK  LD      A,13H           ;FOR TEST 3
008E D300            OUT     (0),A           ;OUTPUT TO LEDS
0090 213075          LD      HL,30000        ;30 SEC DELAY AT 1 MHZ
0093 CD5301          CALL    DELAY
0096 AF              XOR     A               ;0 TO A
0097 D300            OUT     (0),A           ;CLEAR LEDS
0099 211027          LD      HL,10000        ;10 SEC DELAY
009C CD5301          CALL    DELAY
009F 2138FC          LD      HL,0FC38H       ;FINAGLE FACTOR FOR 10
00A2 220008          LD      (TIME),HL       ;INITIALIZE RTC CNT
00A5 3E13            LD      A,13H           ;SECOND PART OF TEST 3
```

Diagnostic program.

```
00A7 D300      01150            OUT     (0),A        ;OUTPUT TO LEDS
00A9 2A0008    01160  NMI10     LD      HL,(TIME)     ;GET CURRENT RTC COUNT
00AC 7D        01170            LD      A,L           ;LOW ORDER BYTE
00AD B4        01180            OR      H             ;MERGE HIGH-ORDER BYTE
00AE C2A900    01190            JP      NZ,NMI10      ;GO IF NOT TO ZERO
00B1 AF        01200            XOR     A            ;0 TO A
00B2 D300      01210            OUT     (0),A        ;CLEAR LEDS
00B4 211027    01220            LD      HL,10000     ;10 SEC DELAY
00B7 CD5301    01230            CALL    DELAY
               01240  ;
               01250  ;TEST 4:OUTPUT LINES TEST
               01260  ;
00BA 061E      01270  OUTLN     LD      B,30          ;30 SECS FOR TEST
00BC 3E14      01280            LD      A,14H         ;FOR TEST 4
00BE D300      01290            OUT     (0),A         ;OUTPUT TO LEDS
00C0 3EFF      01300  OUT10     LD      A,0FFH        ;ALL ON
00C2 D301      01310            OUT     (1),A         ;OUTPUT TO LINES
00C4 21F401    01320            LD      HL,500        ;1/2 SEC DELAY
00C7 C5        01325            PUSH    BC            ;SAVE BC
00C8 CD5301    01330            CALL    DELAY
00CB AF        01340            XOR     A             ;0 TO A
00CC D301      01350            OUT     (1),A         ;ALL OFF
00CE 21F401    01355            LD      HL,500        ;1/2 SEC DELAY
00D1 CD5301    01356            CALL    DELAY
00D4 C1        01357            POP     BC            ;RESTORE BC
00D5 10E9      01360            DJNZ    OUT10         ;GO IF NOT 30 SECS
               01370  ;
               01380  ;TEST 5:INPUT LINES TEST
               01390  ;
00D7 3E15      01400  INLINE    LD      A,15H         ;FOR TEST 5
00D9 D300      01410            OUT     (0),A         ;OUTPUT TO LEDS
00DB 211027    01420            LD      HL,10000      ;FOR 10 SEC DELAY
00DE CD5301    01430            CALL    DELAY
00E1 2148F4    01440            LD      HL,0F448H     ;FINAGLE FACTOR FOR 30 S
00E4 220008    01450            LD      (TIME),HL     ;INITIALIZE RTC COUNT
00E7 0608      01460  INL02     LD      B,08H         ;IN5 MASK
00E9 0E05      01470            LD      C,5           ;IN DIGIT #
00EB DB02      01480  INL05     IN      A,(02H)       ;INPUT LINES
00ED A0        01490            AND     B             ;GET LINE0
00EE CAF400    01500            JP      Z,INL10       ;GO IF 0
00F1 3E10      01510            LD      A,10H         ;FOR RIGHTMOST LED
00F3 81        01520            ADD     A,C           ;MERGE LINE #
00F4 D300      01530  INL10     OUT     (0),A         ;OUTPUT 0 OR #
00F6 21C800    01540            LD      HL,200        ;1/5 SEC DELAY
00F9 C5        01545            PUSH    BC            ;SAVE BC
00FA CD5301    01550            CALL    DELAY
00FD C1        01555            POP     BC            ;RESTORE BC
00FE 0D        01560            DEC     C             ;DECREMENT DIGIT #
00FF CB20      01570            SLA     B             ;ALIGN MASK
0101 C2EB00    01580            JP      NZ,INL05      ;GO IF NOT LAST
0104 3A0108    01590            LD      A,(TIME+1)    ;RTC SIGN
0107 B7        01600            OR      A             ;TEST SIGN
0108 FAE700    01610            JP      M,INL02       ;GO FOR ANOTHER PASS
               01620  ;
```

Fig. 9-1 cont'd. EZ-80

```
                 01630 ;TEST 6:KEYBOARD SCAN TEST
                 01640 ;
010B 3E16        01650 KBSCAN  LD      A,16H           ;FOR TEST 6
010D D300        01660         OUT     (0),A           ;OUTPUT TO LEDS
010F 211027      01670         LD      HL,10000              ;FOR 10 SEC DELAY
0112 CD5301      01680         CALL    DELAY
0115 2148F4      01690         LD      HL,0F448H       ;FINAGLE FACTOR FOR 30 S
0118 220008      01700         LD      (TIME),HL       ;INITIALIZE RTC COUNT
011B 0610        01710 KBS05   LD      B,10H              ;ROW # MASK
011D 0E04        01720         LD      C,4                ;ROW # COUNT
011F 78          01730 KBS10   LD      A,B                    ;ROW # MASK
0120 DB02        01740         IN      A,(2)                  ;READ INPUT LINES
0122 E607        01750         AND     7                      ;PROCESS ONLY KB
0124 EE07        01755         XOR     7                      ;ACTIVE LOW LINES
0126 CA4001      01760         JP      Z,KBS20                ;GO IF NO DEPRESS
0129 C610        01770         ADD     A,10H                  ;FOR RIGHT LED
012B D300        01780         OUT     (0),A                  ;OUTPUT TO LEDS
012D 21C800      01790         LD      HL,200                 ;1/5 SEC DELAY
0130 C5          01795         PUSH    BC                     ;SAVE BC
0131 CD5301      01800         CALL    DELAY
0134 79          01810         LD      A,C                    ;GET ROW #
0135 C610        01820         ADD     A,10H                  ;FOR RIGHT LED
0137 D300        01830         OUT     (0),A                  ;OUTPUT TO LEDS
0139 21C800      01840         LD      HL,200                 ;1/5 SEC DELAY
013C CD5301      01850         CALL    DELAY
013F C1          01855         POP     BC                     ;RESTORE BC
0140 AF          01860 KBS20   XOR     A                      ;0 TO A
0141 D300        01870         OUT     (0),A                  ;CLEAR LEDS
0143 0D          01880         DEC     C                      ;DECREMENT ROW CNT
0144 CB20        01890         SLA     B                      ;GET NEXT ROW #
0146 C21F01      01900         JP      NZ,KBS10               ;GO IF NOT LAST ROW
0149 3A0108      01910         LD      A,(TIME+1)          ;GET SIGN OF RTC CNT
014C B7          01920         OR      A                   ;TEST SIGN
014D FA1B01      01930         JP      M,KBS05             ;GO IF NOT PAST 0
                 01940 ;
                 01950 ;RETURN TO BEGINNING OF PROGRAM
                 01960 ;
0150 C30000      01970         JP      START
                 01980 ;
                 01990 ;DELAY SUBROUTINE.DELAYS 1 MS * COUNT IN HL
                 02000 ;
0153 11FFFF      02010 DELAY   LD      DE,-1           ;DECREMENT VALUE
0156 064A        02020 DEL05   LD      B,04AH          ;FINAGLE FACTOR
0158 19          02030         ADD     HL,DE           ;DECREMENT HL COUNT
0159 D0          02040         RET     NC              ;RETURN IF DONE
015A 10FE        02050 DEL10   DJNZ    DEL10               ;INNER DELAY
015C FD2B        02060         DEC     IY                  ;WASTE TIME
015E C35601      02070         JP      DEL05               ;RETURN TO OUTER LOOP
                 02080 ;
                 02090 ;NMI INTERRUPT HANDLER
                 02100 ;
0161 08          02110 NMIHAN  EX      AF,AF'          ;SAVE FLAGS,A
0162 D9          02120         EXX                     ;SAVE OTHER REGS
0163 2A0008      02130         LD      HL,(TIME)       ;GET TIME CNT
```

Diagnostic program.

```
0166 23          02140          INC      HL              ;BUMP BY ONE
0167 220008      02150          LD       (TIME),HL       ;STORE
016A D9          02160          EXX                      ;RESTORE REGS
016B 08          02170          EX       AF,AF'          ;RESTORE FLAGS,A
016C ED45        02180          RETN                     ;RETURN FROM NMI INTR
                 02190
0800             02200          ORG      800H            ;FIRST RAM LOCATION
0800 0000        02210 TIME     DEFW     0               ;RTC COUNT
0000             02220          END
00000 TOTAL ERRORS

DEL05   0156 02020   02070
DEL10   015A 02050   02050
DELAY   0153 02010   01070 01110 01230 01330 01356 01430 01550
                     01680 01800 01850
INL02   00E7 01460   01610
INL05   00EB 01480   01580
INL10   00F4 01530   01500
INLINE  00D7 01400
KBS05   011B 01710   01930
KBS10   011F 01730   01900
KBS20   0140 01860   01760
KBSCAN  010B 01650
LED05   001C 00380   00480 00520
LED10   0024 00410   00420
LEDDGT  001A 00370
MEM10   0071 00870   00960
MEM20   0075 00900   00900
MEM30   007C 00950   00950
MEM40   0088 00990   01000
MEMTST  0061 00750
NMI10   00A9 01160   01190
NMICLK  008C 01040
NMIHAN  0161 02110   00820
OUT10   00C0 01300   01360
OUTLN   00BA 01270
RAM10   0049 00620   00620
RAM20   0054 00670   00670
RAM30   005D 00700   00710
RAMTST  003C 00560
SCOPE   000C 00280
SCP10   0011 00300   00330
SCP20   0014 00310   00320
START   0000 00190   01970
TIME    0800 02210   01130 01160 01450 01590 01700 01910 02130
                     02150
```

Fig. 9-1 cont'd. EZ-80 Diagnostic program.

	LOCATION	CONTENTS	
000	000 0000 0000	31	0011 0001
001	000 0000 0001	80	1000 0000
002	000 0000 0010	08	0000 1000
003	000 0000 0011	3E	0011 1110
004	000 0000 0100	89	1000 1001
005	000 0000 0101	D3	1101 0011
006	000 0000 0110	03	0000 0011
007	000 0000 0111	AF	1010 1111
008	000 0000 1000	D3	1101 0011
009	000 0000 1001	00	0000 0000
00A	000 0000 1010	D3	1101 0011
00B	000 0000 1011	01	0000 0001
00C	000 0000 1100	06	0000 0110
00D	000 0000 1101	07	0000 0111
00E	000 0000 1110	11	0001 0001
00F	000 0000 1111	FF	1111 1111
010	000 0001 0000	FF	1111 1111
011	000 0001 0001	21	0010 0001
012	000 0001 0010	FF	1111 1111
013	000 0001 0011	FF	1111 1111
014	000 0001 0100	19	0001 1001
015	000 0001 0101	DA	1101 1010
016	000 0001 0110	14	0001 0100
017	000 0001 0111	00	0000 0000
018	000 0001 1000	10	0001 0000
019	000 0001 1001	F7	1111 0111
01A	000 0001 1010	3E	0011 1110
01B	000 0001 1011	10	0001 0000
01C	000 0001 1100	D3	1101 0011
01D	000 0001 1101	00	0000 0000
01E	000 0001 1110	21	0010 0001
01F	000 0001 1111	FF	1111 1111
020	000 0010 0000	FF	1111 1111
021	000 0010 0001	01	0000 0001
022	000 0010 0010	FF	1111 1111
023	000 0010 0011	FF	1111 1111
024	000 0010 0100	09	0000 1001
025	000 0010 0101	DA	1101 1010
026	000 0010 0110	24	0010 0100
027	000 0010 0111	00	0000 0000
028	000 0010 1000	C6	1100 0110
029	000 0010 1001	01	0000 0001
02A	000 0010 1010	47	0100 0111
02B	000 0010 1011	E6	1110 0110
02C	000 0010 1100	0F	0000 1111
02D	000 0010 1101	FE	1111 1110
02E	000 0010 1110	0A	0000 1010
02F	000 0010 1111	78	0111 1000
030	000 0011 0000	C2	1100 0010
031	000 0011 0001	1C	0001 1100
032	000 0011 0010	00	0000 0000
033	000 0011 0011	E6	1110 0110
034	000 0011 0100	F0	1111 0000
035	000 0011 0101	CB	1100 1011
036	000 0011 0110	27	0010 0111
037	000 0011 0111	FE	1111 1110
038	000 0011 1000	00	0000 0000
039	000 0011 1001	C2	1100 0010
03A	000 0011 1010	1C	0001 1100
03B	000 0011 1011	00	0000 0000
03C	000 0011 1100	3E	0011 1110
03D	000 0011 1101	11	0001 0001
03E	000 0011 1110	D3	1101 0011
03F	000 0011 1111	00	0000 0000
040	000 0100 0000	AF	1010 1111
041	000 0100 0001	32	0011 0010
042	000 0100 0010	02	0000 0010
043	000 0100 0011	08	0000 1000
044	000 0100 0100	3A	0011 1010
045	000 0100 0101	02	0000 0010
046	000 0100 0110	08	0000 1000
047	000 0100 0111	FE	1111 1110
048	000 0100 1000	00	0000 0000
049	000 0100 1001	C2	1100 0010
04A	000 0100 1010	49	0100 1001
04B	000 0100 1011	00	0000 0000
04C	000 0100 1100	2F	0010 1111
04D	000 0100 1101	32	0011 0010
04E	000 0100 1110	02	0000 0010
04F	000 0100 1111	08	0000 1000
050	000 0101 0000	3A	0011 1010
051	000 0101 0001	02	0000 0010
052	000 0101 0010	08	0000 1000
053	000 0101 0011	3C	0011 1100
054	000 0101 0100	C2	1100 0010
055	000 0101 0101	54	0101 0100
056	000 0101 0110	00	0000 0000
057	000 0101 0111	21	0010 0001
058	000 0101 1000	FF	1111 1111
059	000 0101 1001	FF	1111 1111
05A	000 0101 1010	01	0000 0001
05B	000 0101 1011	FF	1111 1111
05C	000 0101 1100	FF	1111 1111
05D	000 0101 1101	09	0000 1001
05E	000 0101 1110	DA	1101 1010
05F	000 0101 1111	5D	0101 1101
060	000 0110 0000	00	0000 0000
061	000 0110 0001	3E	0011 1110
062	000 0110 0010	12	0001 0010
063	000 0110 0011	18	0001 1000
064	000 0110 0100	04	0000 0100
065	000 0110 0101	FF	1111 1111
066	000 0110 0110	C3	1100 0011
067	000 0110 0111	61	0110 0001
068	000 0110 1000	01	0000 0001

Fig. 9-2. EZ-80 Diagnostic contents.

	LOCATION	CONTENTS	
069	000 0110 1001	D3	1101 0011
06A	000 0110 1010	00	0000 0000
06B	000 0110 1011	21	0010 0001
06C	000 0110 1100	02	0000 0010
06D	000 0110 1101	08	0000 1000
06E	000 0110 1110	06	0000 0110
06F	000 0110 1111	7C	0111 1100
070	000 0111 0000	AF	1010 1111
071	000 0111 0001	77	0111 0111
072	000 0111 0010	7E	0111 1110
073	000 0111 0011	FE	1111 1110
074	000 0111 0100	00	0000 0000
075	000 0111 0101	C2	1100 0010
076	000 0111 0110	75	0111 0101
077	000 0111 0111	00	0000 0000
078	000 0111 1000	2F	0010 1111
079	000 0111 1001	77	0111 0111
07A	000 0111 1010	7E	0111 1110
07B	000 0111 1011	3C	0011 1100
07C	000 0111 1100	C2	1100 0010
07D	000 0111 1101	7C	0111 1100
07E	000 0111 1110	00	0000 0000
07F	000 0111 1111	23	0010 0011
080	000 1000 0000	10	0001 0000
081	000 1000 0001	EF	1110 1111
082	000 1000 0010	21	0010 0001
083	000 1000 0011	FF	1111 1111
084	000 1000 0100	FF	1111 1111
085	000 1000 0101	01	0000 0001
086	000 1000 0110	FF	1111 1111
087	000 1000 0111	FF	1111 1111
088	000 1000 1000	09	0000 1001
089	000 1000 1001	DA	1101 1010
08A	000 1000 1010	88	1000 1000
08B	000 1000 1011	00	0000 0000
08C	000 1000 1100	3E	0011 1110
08D	000 1000 1101	13	0001 0011
08E	000 1000 1110	D3	1101 0011
08F	000 1000 1111	00	0000 0000
090	000 1001 0000	21	0010 0001
091	000 1001 0001	30	0011 0000
092	000 1001 0010	75	0111 0101
093	000 1001 0011	CD	1100 1101
094	000 1001 0100	53	0101 0011
095	000 1001 0101	01	0000 0001
096	000 1001 0110	AF	1010 1111
097	000 1001 0111	D3	1101 0011
098	000 1001 1000	00	0000 0000
099	000 1001 1001	21	0010 0001
09A	000 1001 1010	10	0001 0000
09B	000 1001 1011	27	0010 0111
09C	000 1001 1100	CD	1100 1101

	LOCATION	CONTENTS	
09D	000 1001 1101	53	0101 0011
09E	000 1001 1110	01	0000 0001
09F	000 1001 1111	21	0010 0001
0A0	000 1010 0000	38	0011 1000
0A1	000 1010 0001	FC	1111 1100
0A2	000 1010 0010	22	0010 0010
0A3	000 1010 0011	00	0000 0000
0A4	000 1010 0100	08	0000 1000
0A5	000 1010 0101	3E	0011 1110
0A6	000 1010 0110	13	0001 0011
0A7	000 1010 0111	D3	1101 0011
0A8	000 1010 1000	00	0000 0000
0A9	000 1010 1001	2A	0010 1010
0AA	000 1010 1010	00	0000 0000
0AB	000 1010 1011	08	0000 1000
0AC	000 1010 1100	7D	0111 1101
0AD	000 1010 1101	B4	1011 0100
0AE	000 1010 1110	C2	1100 0010
0AF	000 1010 1111	A9	1010 1001
0B0	000 1011 0000	00	0000 0000
0B1	000 1011 0001	AF	1010 1111
0B2	000 1011 0010	D3	1101 0011
0B3	000 1011 0011	00	0000 0000
0B4	000 1011 0100	21	0010 0001
0B5	000 1011 0101	10	0001 0000
0B6	000 1011 0110	27	0010 0111
0B7	000 1011 0111	CD	1100 1101
0B8	000 1011 1000	53	0101 0011
0B9	000 1011 1001	01	0000 0001
0BA	000 1011 1010	06	0000 0110
0BB	000 1011 1011	1E	0001 1110
0BC	000 1011 1100	3E	0011 1110
0BD	000 1011 1101	14	0001 0100
0BE	000 1011 1110	D3	1101 0011
0BF	000 1011 1111	00	0000 0000
0C0	000 1100 0000	3E	0011 1110
0C1	000 1100 0001	FF	1111 1111
0C2	000 1100 0010	D3	1101 0011
0C3	000 1100 0011	01	0000 0001
0C4	000 1100 0100	21	0010 0001
0C5	000 1100 0101	F4	1111 0100
0C6	000 1100 0110	01	0000 0001
0C7	000 1100 0111	C5	1100 0101
0C8	000 1100 1000	CD	1100 1101
0C9	000 1100 1001	53	0101 0011
0CA	000 1100 1010	01	0000 0001
0CB	000 1100 1011	AF	1010 1111
0CC	000 1100 1100	D3	1101 0011
0CD	000 1100 1101	01	0000 0001
0CE	000 1100 1110	21	0010 0001
0CF	000 1100 1111	F4	1111 0100
0D0	000 1101 0000	01	0000 0001

Fig. 9-2. cont'd. EZ-80

LOCATION		CONTENTS	
0D1	000 1101 0001	CD	1100 1101
0D2	000 1101 0010	53	0101 0011
0D3	000 1101 0011	01	0000 0001
0D4	000 1101 0100	C1	1100 0001
0D5	000 1101 0101	10	0001 0000
0D6	000 1101 0110	E9	1110 1001
0D7	000 1101 0111	3E	0011 1110
0D8	000 1101 1000	15	0001 0101
0D9	000 1101 1001	D3	1101 0011
0DA	000 1101 1010	00	0000 0000
0DB	000 1101 1011	21	0010 0001
0DC	000 1101 1100	10	0001 0000
0DD	000 1101 1101	27	0010 0111
0DE	000 1101 1110	CD	1100 1101
0DF	000 1101 1111	53	0101 0011
0E0	000 1110 0000	01	0000 0001
0E1	000 1110 0001	21	0010 0001
0E2	000 1110 0010	48	0100 1000
0E3	000 1110 0011	F4	1111 0100
0E4	000 1110 0100	22	0010 0010
0E5	000 1110 0101	00	0000 0000
0E6	000 1110 0110	08	0000 1000
0E7	000 1110 0111	06	0000 0110
0E8	000 1110 1000	08	0000 1000
0E9	000 1110 1001	0E	0000 1110
0EA	000 1110 1010	05	0000 0101
0EB	000 1110 1011	DB	1101 1011
0EC	000 1110 1100	02	0000 0010
0ED	000 1110 1101	A0	1010 0000
0EE	000 1110 1110	CA	1100 1010
0EF	000 1110 1111	F4	1111 0100
0F0	000 1111 0000	00	0000 0000
0F1	000 1111 0001	3E	0011 1110
0F2	000 1111 0010	10	0001 0000
0F3	000 1111 0011	81	1000 0001
0F4	000 1111 0100	D3	1101 0011
0F5	000 1111 0101	00	0000 0000
0F6	000 1111 0110	21	0010 0001
0F7	000 1111 0111	C8	1100 1000
0F8	000 1111 1000	00	0000 0000
0F9	000 1111 1001	C5	1100 0101
0FA	000 1111 1010	CD	1100 1101
0FB	000 1111 1011	53	0101 0011
0FC	000 1111 1100	01	0000 0001
0FD	000 1111 1101	C1	1100 0001
0FE	000 1111 1110	0D	0000 1101
0FF	000 1111 1111	CB	1100 1011
100	001 0000 0000	20	0010 0000
101	001 0000 0001	C2	1100 0010
102	001 0000 0010	EB	1110 1011
103	001 0000 0011	00	0000 0000
104	001 0000 0100	3A	0011 1010

LOCATION		CONTENTS	
105	001 0000 0101	01	0000 0001
106	001 0000 0110	08	0000 1000
107	001 0000 0111	B7	1011 0111
108	001 0000 1000	FA	1111 1010
109	001 0000 1001	E7	1110 0111
10A	001 0000 1010	00	0000 0000
10B	001 0000 1011	3E	0011 1110
10C	001 0000 1100	16	0001 0110
10D	001 0000 1101	D3	1101 0011
10E	001 0000 1110	00	0000 0000
10F	001 0000 1111	21	0010 0001
110	001 0001 0000	10	0001 0000
111	001 0001 0001	27	0010 0111
112	001 0001 0010	CD	1100 1101
113	001 0001 0011	53	0101 0011
114	001 0001 0100	01	0000 0001
115	001 0001 0101	21	0010 0001
116	001 0001 0110	48	0100 1000
117	001 0001 0111	F4	1111 0100
118	001 0001 1000	22	0010 0010
119	001 0001 1001	00	0000 0000
11A	001 0001 1010	08	0000 1000
11B	001 0001 1011	06	0000 0110
11C	001 0001 1100	10	0001 0000
11D	001 0001 1101	0E	0000 1110
11E	001 0001 1110	04	0000 0100
11F	001 0001 1111	78	0111 1000
120	001 0010 0000	DB	1101 1011
121	001 0010 0001	02	0000 0010
122	001 0010 0010	E6	1110 0110
123	001 0010 0011	07	0000 0111
124	001 0010 0100	EE	1110 1110
125	001 0010 0101	07	0000 0111
126	001 0010 0110	CA	1100 1010
127	001 0010 0111	40	0100 0000
128	001 0010 1000	01	0000 0001
129	001 0010 1001	C6	1100 0110
12A	001 0010 1010	10	0001 0000
12B	001 0010 1011	D3	1101 0011
12C	001 0010 1100	00	0000 0000
12D	001 0010 1101	21	0010 0001
12E	001 0010 1110	C8	1100 1000
12F	001 0010 1111	00	0000 0000
130	001 0011 0000	C5	1100 0101
131	001 0011 0001	CD	1100 1101
132	001 0011 0010	53	0101 0011
133	001 0011 0011	01	0000 0001
134	001 0011 0100	79	0111 1001
135	001 0011 0101	C6	1100 0110
136	001 0011 0110	10	0001 0000
137	001 0011 0111	D3	1101 0011
138	001 0011 1000	00	0000 0000

Diagnostic contents.

LOCATION				CONTENTS	
139	001 0011 1001		21	0010 0001	
13A	001 0011 1010		C8	1100 1000	
13B	001 0011 1011		00	0000 0000	
13C	001 0011 1100		CD	1100 1101	
13D	001 0011 1101		53	0101 0011	
13E	001 0011 1110		01	0000 0001	
13F	001 0011 1111		C1	1100 0001	
140	001 0100 0000		AF	1010 1111	
141	001 0100 0001		D3	1101 0011	
142	001 0100 0010		00	0000 0000	
143	001 0100 0011		0D	0000 1101	
144	001 0100 0100		CB	1100 1011	
145	001 0100 0101		20	0010 0000	
146	001 0100 0110		C2	1100 0010	
147	001 0100 0111		1F	0001 1111	
148	001 0100 1000		01	0000 0001	
149	001 0100 1001		3A	0011 1010	
14A	001 0100 1010		01	0000 0001	
14B	001 0100 1011		08	0000 1000	
14C	001 0100 1100		B7	1011 0111	
14D	001 0100 1101		FA	1111 1010	
14E	001 0100 1110		1B	0001 1011	
14F	001 0100 1111		01	0000 0001	
150	001 0101 0000		C3	1100 0011	
151	001 0101 0001		00	0000 0000	
152	001 0101 0010		00	0000 0000	
153	001 0101 0011		11	0001 0001	
154	001 0101 0100		FF	1111 1111	
155	001 0101 0101		FF	1111 1111	
156	001 0101 0110		06	0000 0110	
157	001 0101 0111		4A	0100 1010	
158	001 0101 1000		19	0001 1001	
159	001 0101 1001		D0	1101 0000	
15A	001 0101 1010		10	0001 0000	
15B	001 0101 1011		FE	1111 1110	
15C	001 0101 1100		FD	1111 1101	
15D	001 0101 1101		2B	0010 1011	
15E	001 0101 1110		C3	1100 0011	
15F	001 0101 1111		56	0101 0110	
160	001 0110 0000		01	0000 0001	
161	001 0110 0001		08	0000 1000	
162	001 0110 0010		D9	1101 1001	
163	001 0110 0011		2A	0010 1010	
164	001 0110 0100		00	0000 0000	
165	001 0110 0101		08	0000 1000	
166	001 0110 0110		23	0010 0011	
167	001 0110 0111		22	0010 0010	
168	001 0110 1000		00	0000 0000	
169	001 0110 1001		08	0000 1000	
16A	001 0110 1010		D9	1101 1001	
16B	001 0110 1011		08	0000 1000	
16C	001 0110 1100		ED	1110 1101	
16D	001 0110 1101		45	0100 0101	

Fig. 9-2 cont'd. EZ-80 Diagnostic contents.

plug it into the 24-pin socket on the wire-wrap or printed-circuit board. Be certain that pin 1 is oriented in the same direction as the other chips on the board. Now you are ready to verify the operation of the EZ-80 by running the Diagnostic Program.

"BRINGING UP" THE EZ-80: PRELIMINARY CHECKS

At this point the reader should have made the checks of the EZ-80 described in Chapter 7. The following list of steps are suggested as a reasonable way to cautiously "bring up" the system. (Alas, the author has been known to throw caution to the winds and just plug the damn thing in to see if it worked. Temper this detailed list with your own experience!)

1. Remove any cabinetry so that the EZ-80 wire-wrap or pc board is accessible. Keep the LED display and keyboard connected.
2. Make certain the 2758 (or 2716) EPROM is in the proper position (check pin 1 as described in Chapter 7).
3. Turn on the power switch and then quickly off.
4. Check the fuse. It should be intact. If not, repeat the preliminary steps given in Chapter 7. Bear in mind that you may have burned out some chips.
5. Turn on the power switch. There should be no smoke visible (seriously!). Sniff a few cursory sniffs above the board. There should be no "hot" smell.
6. *Cautiously* test each semiconductor chip by wetting your finger and testing them as you would a hot iron. Some should be warm, but *not hot*. You should be able to keep your finger on all but the *regulator chip*. The regulator chip will probably be too warm to keep your finger on.
7. If all is well at this point, you may have seen a display on the LED display. If so, things are proceeding nicely. If a display of 0, 1, 2, 3, etc., is not forthcoming in about 20 seconds from power on, there may be problems with the EZ-80.

"BRINGING UP" THE EZ-80: DIAGNOSTIC OPERATION

The sequence of operation of the EZ-80 Diagnostic from power on is as follows:

1. Power switch turned on.
2. LED display clears. No visible display.
3. Pause 1 to 20 seconds.
4. LED display counts from right to left. Each digit position counts from 0 to 9.
5. A display of 1 is displayed for a second or so.
6. A display of 2 is displayed for a second or so.
7. A display of 3 is displayed. After approximately 30 seconds, the display is cleared and there is a 10-second pause. A display of 3 is again displayed for about 10 seconds. The display is cleared for about 10 seconds.
8. A display of 4 is displayed for about 30 seconds.
9. A display of 5 is displayed for about 10 seconds. The display is cleared. A pause of about 30 seconds follows.
10. A display of 6 is displayed for about 10 seconds, followed by a clear of the LED display and a pause of about 30 seconds.
11. Steps 2 through 10 repeat continuously.

If the EZ-80 goes through this sequence several times, almost all of the system is operative. If no display occurs, go to the section labeled "Catastrophe!" for remedial action. If the display continuously displays 1, go to the section labeled "Test 1: RAM Memory" for corrective action. If the display continuously displays 2, go to the section labeled "Test 2: RAM Memory." If the display continuously displays 3, go to the section labeled "Test 3: Clock Frequency/NMI" for remedial action. If the 3 is displayed for a time grossly different than 30 seconds, go to the section labeled "Test 3: Clock Frequency/NMI." "Grossly different" means a display time greater than 1 minute or less than 16 seconds (use a stopwatch).

If the sequence above *has* been successfully repeated several times, continue with the following description of each test. Some of the tests require no action, while others require adjustments or other manual operations.

CATASTROPHE!

If the EZ-80 does not at least sequence through the digit display, read this section for corrective action. Otherwise, this section may be skipped. Have you performed the checks given in Chapter 7? If you have not, now is a good time to perform the simple checks given there. Bear in mind that it may be necessary to replace one or more burned-out chips. If you have performed the checks in Chapter 7, then the chips are probably operative and further checks may be made.

The Z-80 used in the EZ-80 is made for operation at a maximum clock frequency of 2 megahertz (2 million cycles per second). Potentiometer R1 controls this frequency. If the frequency is above 2 megahertz,

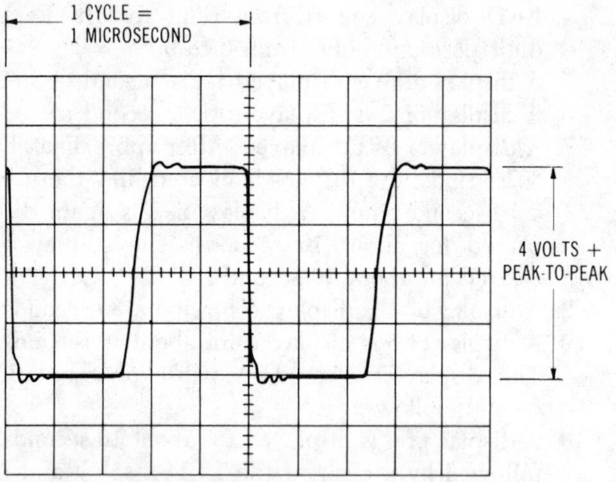

Fig. 9-3. EZ-80 clock waveform.

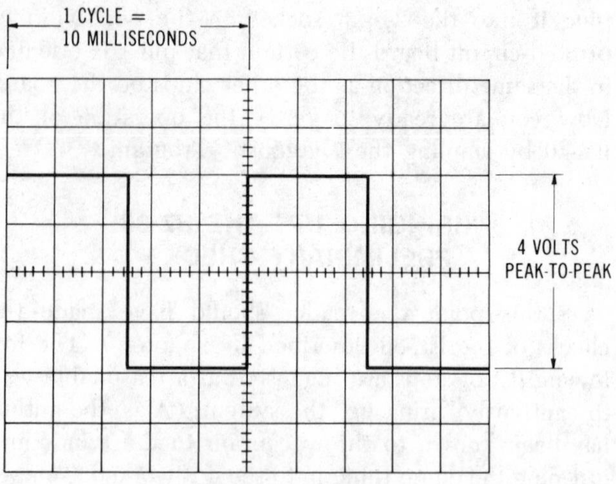

Fig. 9-4. NMI waveform.

it may simply be too high for operation of the Z-80 microprocessor. Adjust R1 from one "stop" to the other in several steps. For each adjustment, turn the power off, then on after a delay of at least 3 seconds and wait for a display of sequencing digits. If sequencing occurs, go back to the previous section for further checks. For those readers with oscilloscopes, check the clock at pin 6 of the Z-80 and adjust R1 for 1 megahertz. The (typical) clock waveform is shown in Fig. 9-3.

If adjustment of R1 does not help, *set the potentiometer midrange* and adjust R2 in similar fashion. R2 controls the rate of real-time-clock interrupts. The real-time-clock (NMI) interrupts should occur at 100 per second. If the potentiometer is at an extreme, this could conceivably affect proper operation of the EZ-80. For those readers with oscilloscopes, check the NMI interrupt at pin 17 of the Z-80 and adjust for 100 hertz. The (typical) NMI waveform is shown in Fig. 9-4.

If neither of the above actions results in digit sequencing, the following suggestions may be followed.

1. Recheck all wiring with chips removed.
2. Perform the checks given in Chapter 7 with all chips inserted except for the 2758 (or 2716).
3. Verify the programming of the 2758 once more.
4. Replace the Z-80, 6810, and 8255 and repeat the Diagnostic operation.

Remember, there is a logical reason for failure of the EZ-80 and it must fall into one (or more) of the following categories: wiring problems, erroneous EPROM programming, misadjustment of the clock or NMI, or bad chips (roughly in that order of probability)!

INITIALIZATION

When power is turned on, execution of the EZ-80 Diagnostic starts at location 0. The stack pointer SP is loaded with 880H to initialize the stack to the top of RAM memory. Next, the PPI is initialized by outputting a value of 89H. The LED display is then cleared by zeroing PA0–PA7 of the 8255. With PA4–PA7 equal to zero, no current will flow in any of the LED segments.

Next (SCOPE), the EZ-80 Diagnostic *loops* from location 14 to 15 for 7*65,536 counts, or approximately 10 seconds for a clock frequency of 1 megahertz. This time may be used to check the data and address outputs of the Z-80 with an oscilloscope. There should be activity in the form of pulses of less than a microsecond on many of address lines A0–A8, and data lines D7–D0. The pulses observed will not be very regular and sample waveforms cannot be shown.

LED DIGIT SEQUENCING

The next section of the EZ-80 Diagnostic sequences the LED digits from right to left, counting each from 0 to 9. Each digit is displayed for about 1 second by the loop at LED10. An outer loop at LED05 increments the character displayed from 0 through 9. Another outer loop at LED05 enables first the rightmost digit (10H address), and then the other three digit positions (20H, 40H, and 80H).

TEST 1: RAM MEMORY

Test 1 of the EZ-80 Diagnostic performs a very cursory check on 6810 RAM memory operation. First, zeros are stored in RAM memory location 802H and then read back. If other than zero is read back, the EZ-80 Diagnostic loops at location 49H. Next, all ones are stored in RAM memory location 802H and then read back. If other than ones are read back, the program loops at location 54H. In either case, the effect of the loop is to cause 1 to be displayed continuously on the LED display indicating that one or more data lines connecting the Z-80 to 6810 are bad, or that the 6810 chip is bad. Corrective action would be to recheck 6810/Z-80 wiring and to replace the 6810.

TEST 2: RAM MEMORY

Test 2 performs a check on all locations in 6810 RAM memory from 802H through 87FH. Zeros and ones are alternately stored in each location. The test is repeated 65,536 times. If other than zeros or ones are read back, the program loops at 75H or 7CH, resulting in a continuous display of 2. Corrective action would be to replace the 6810 RAM.

NMI INTERRUPT PROCESSING

From the instant that the EZ-80 is "powered up," NMI interrupts occur at a rate of (ideally) 100 times per second. Each interrupt causes an automatic branch to location 66H. The contents of 66H is a jump to location NMIHAN (161H). This *NMI Interrupt Processing Routine* increments (adds one) to the contents of locations 800/801H, treated as a 16-bit value. These locations serve as a real-time-clock count that counts from 0000H through FFFFH (0 through 65,535 in decimal notation) every 65,535/100 = 655.35 seconds.

The real-time-clock count is used for Test 3 of the EZ-80 Diagnostic on, as a means to determine delays. Resetting the locations to 0 and then checking for a count of 100, for example, would indicate that 1 second has elapsed.

It is important to note that the NMI interrupts occur independently (and invisibly) of the operation of the rest of the EZ-80 Diagnostic. The action of the NMI exercises the top locations of 6810 RAM (for storage of the return address) and the first two bottom locations of RAM. In fact, then, memory test 1 is probably redundant if the NMI interrupt is active. One operation that could be performed in case of a catastrophic failure in the EZ-80 would be to place 0 volts on pin 17 of the Z-80 (Fig. 9-5) to see if the Diagnostic sequences through to Test 3 (where it will remain). If this fix allows proper operation up

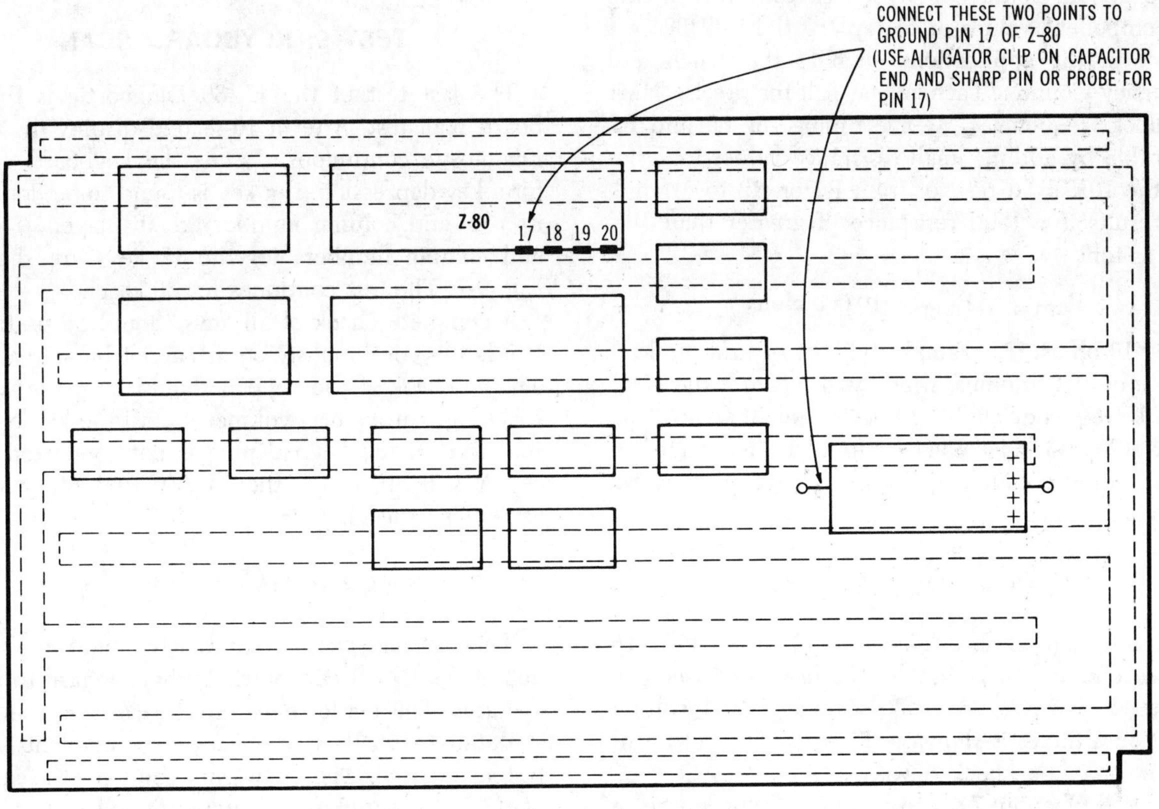

Fig. 9-5. NMI disable.

to Test 3, further checks should be made on the NMI real-time-clock interrupt.

TEST 3: CLOCK FREQUENCY/NMI

This test in the EZ-80 Diagnostic is used to calibrate the clock frequency of the EZ-80 and the NMI frequency. The time between the first display of 3 and the blanking of the 3 should be exactly 30 seconds. Use a stopwatch to adjust R1 until the period is as close to 30 seconds as possible. If the period is not adjustable to 30 seconds ± ½ second, check component values or use a new MC4024.

The second part of this test tests the NMI frequency. The time between the second disappearance of the 3 and the appearance of 4 should be exactly 10 seconds. Use a stopwatch to adjust R2 until this period is as close to 10 seconds as possible. If the period is not adjustable to 10 seconds ± ½ second, check component values or replace the MC4024. Fine tuning of the NMI frequency can be performed during the applications programs that require a real-time-clock (not all of them do).

If the EZ-80 Diagnostic "hangs" during this test, and continually displays the second occurrence of the digit 3, the NMI interrupt is not operative. Corrective action would be to recheck the NMI wiring and component values or to replace the MC4024.

Some of the applications, such as the Timer and Frequency Counter/Tachometer, call for precise NMI and clock frequencies. A "fine tuning" of R1 and R2 is possible by adding small resistance values in series with the 10K fixed resistor from R1 or R2 to ground. This results in a total resistance of greater than 10K ohms as follows:

$$R_{TOTAL} = R_{NEW} + 10{,}000 \text{ ohms}$$

adding 10 ohms, for example, will result in a total resistance of 10,010 ohms, which will *increase* the NMI or clock frequency slightly. Either a small *series* fixed or variable resistance may be used to "fine tune" in this fashion to obtain frequencies very close to 100 Hz or 1 MHz.

TEST 4: OUTPUT LINES

This test enables output lines OUT1 through OUT6 for ½ second and then disables the lines for ½ second. This action is repeated for 30 seconds. The resulting output on all lines is shown in Fig. 9-6. The output of any line may be checked with a simple LED logic probe (see Chapter 7), a commercial logic probe, a voltmeter, or an oscilloscope. Cycling from 0 to 1 and back should occur at a 1-second rate for 30 seconds. If any of the six lines do not show the cycling, recheck the wiring to the 74368 or replace the chip.

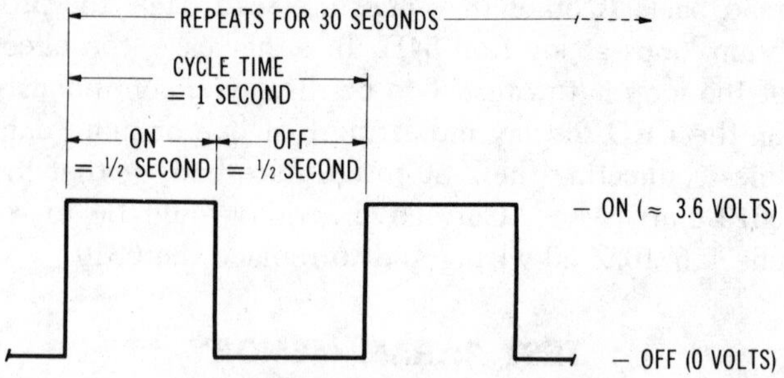

Fig. 9-6. Test 4 OUT line waveforms.

TEST 5: INPUT LINES

This EZ-80 Diagnostic test checks the state of input lines IN1 through IN5. All five lines are scanned for 30 seconds. If any line is low (ground), its number is displayed. One or more lines may be made low by clipping a lead from ground to the line (ground is shown in Fig. 9-5). All lines should be tested in this fashion and the wiring around the 74LS04 rechecked or the chip replaced if any line fails to be detected.

TEST 6: KEYBOARD SCAN

The last test of the EZ-80 Diagnostic is the keyboard scan test. After a 10-second display of "6," the Diagnostic continuously *scans* the keyboard, looking for a key depression. If a key is found to be depressed, its row and column number are displayed. The row and column numbers for the 12 keys are shown in Fig. 9-7. The test continues for 30 seconds.

A complete check of all keys should be performed. If a key is continuously on or cannot be activated, an off line check of the keypad should be made with an LED logic probe or a voltmeter until the key operates smoothly. If the keypad plug is not connected and a key is still on, check the 74LS05 and other wiring, or replace the chip.

THE EZ-80 DIAGNOSTIC

We've been speaking primarily about the operation of the EZ-80 Diagnostic without regard to *how* it operates. The reader may care to examine the listing in detail to see how the various components of the system operate. The comments column (the last column) is indented to show *nesting* of loops, which may help the reader in following the flow. The program proceeds from start to end in straightforward

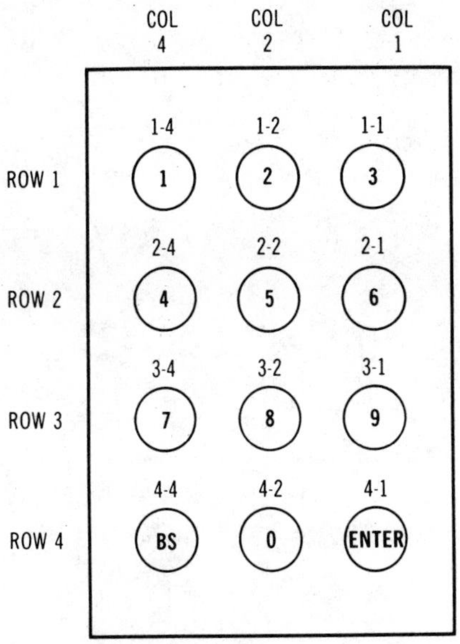

Fig. 9-7. Keyboard scan testing.

fashion, with the exception of NMI processing. An NMI may occur at any time in any part of the program. Where it does, a transfer to location 66H is made with the return address saved in the stack. Location 66H contains a jump to NMIHAN at 161H. This routine first swaps the general registers (EX and EXX) and then bumps the real-time-clock count in 800/801H by one. The general registers are then swapped again and a RETN (*RET*urn from *N*onmaskable Interrupt) is made to return control to the interrupted instruction.

Only one other subroutine is used in the EZ-80 Diagnostic, the DELAY subroutine at 153H. This subroutine can be called at any time and simply delays 1 millisecond (1/1000 second) for every count in the HL register pair, assuming a clock frequency of 1 megahertz.

SECTION 3

EZ-80 Projects

CHAPTER 10

EZ-80 Applications Programs

This section describes the EZ-80 *software*. Previous chapters have described the theory and construction of the EZ-80 hardware with some general software theory. Section 3 will in large part consist of descriptions of applications programs for the EZ-80, i.e.:

- A Microcomputer Educator for running short tutorial programs
- A Combination Lock to create a coded electronic lock
- A Burglar Alarm that detects up to five inputs
- A Morse Code Generator that sends random code for code practice
- A Telephone Dialer that records and automatically calls up to 100 telephone numbers
- A Morse Code Sender that sends Morse code messages for amateur radio or other applications
- A Frequency Counter/Tachometer that counts frequency pulses up to 50,000 pulses per minute
- A Timer that can be programmed for 2 minutes to 100-day cycles
- A Music Synthesizer that plays electronic music

In addition, a chapter is presented on "blue-sky" projects for the EZ-80. With proper user programming the EZ-80 can be used for a variety of user projects including intelligent controllers for computer systems and distributed processing.

The remainder of this chapter describes the Common Area program used in all applications programs of this section and "standard" hardware devices that can be attached to the EZ-80 for control, output, and input for the applications.

MEMORY MAPPING

The memory mapping for all applications in this section is shown in Fig. 10-1. The area from location 0 to 1FFH (511) is taken up by a program called the *Common Area.* The Common Area is a collection of subroutines that are useful in applications programs, in addition to a routine that processes the NMI (real-time-clock) interrupt and updates the display.

The second half of EPROM from about 200H (512) to 3FFH (1023) is available for the applications programs in this book. In many cases the applications program will require almost all of this area. In a few cases the applications programs are shorter and more than one can be put into EPROM at the same time. A special case occurs when a 2716 EPROM is used. The 2716 adds another 1024 bytes of EPROM, making it possible to use more than one program in EPROM. However, the programs presented here must be *relocated* by some special techniques in this case. These techniques are described later in the chapter.

The RAM area is located at locations 800H (2048) to 87FH (2175). The first 24H locations of RAM (800H–823H) are used for *variable storage* for variables used by the Common Area. The last 20 or so locations are used by the memory stack for CALLs and storage of temporary data. The area used by the stack probably does not exceed 20 bytes although at any given time it is variable and is dependent upon the number of *nested* levels of CALLs and PUSHes in effect. Two bytes of stack are used for every level of CALL or for every PUSH. The remaining RAM area is available for applications program variable or table storage. Assuming 20 locations for stack use and 36 for Common Area use, this leaves 128 − 56 or about 72 locations from 824H through 86C.

COMMON AREA PROGRAM

The Common Area program is shown in Fig. 10-2. This data must be programmed into EPROM for all applications programs in this book. The only locations that will change are locations 1 and 2. These two locations define the address of the applications program. In many cases the starting address of the applications program will be 220H, and a 20H can be programmed into location 1 and a 02H can be

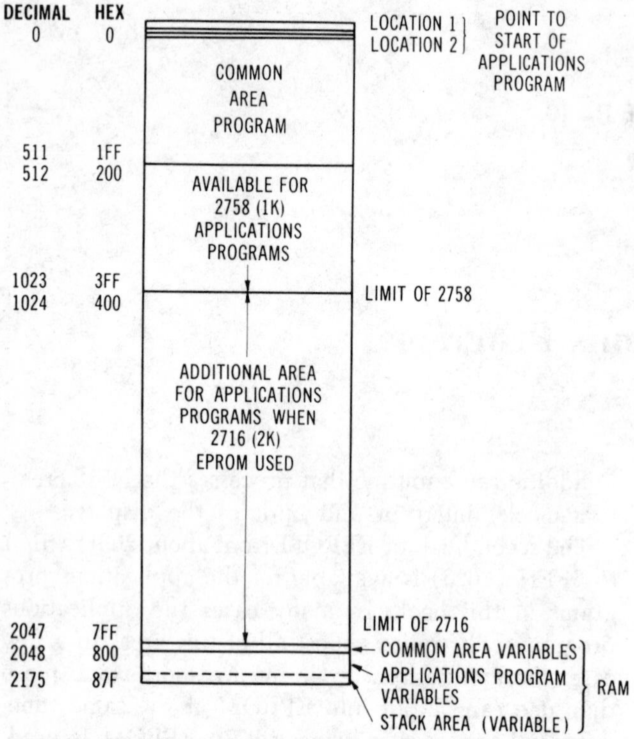

Fig. 10-1. EZ-80 memory mapping for applications programs.

programmed into location 2. Another caution: Note that locations 36H and 37H are left unprogrammed as are 5DH–65H. This is noted so that the user does not erroneously go on to the next byte if he or she is programming while looking at the listing.

SUBROUTINE VECTORS

The first instruction executed after powering up the EZ-80 is the "JP PROGRAM" at locations 0–3. With the address of the applications program in locations 2 and 3, this will result in a jump to the start of the applications program (typically 220H).

The applications program uses 10 subroutines in the Common Area. The *vectors* for these subroutines are at locations 3–20H. These vectors are simply jumps to the subroutines. When an applications program wants to read a character from the keyboard, for example, it executes a "CALL GETCHR," which calls the instruction at location 9. This instruction jumps to subroutine GETCHS at 109H, where the character is read and a return is made back to the applications program. The only reason that a CALL is not made directly to the subroutine is to conveniently group the locations of all subroutines.

INITIALIZATION SUBROUTINE

The primary subroutine in the Common Area is the initialization subroutine INIT (all subroutines will be called by their vector designations). When INIT is called at the start of the applications program, it initializes the 8255 PPI by outputting an 89H. This sets up the 8255 as 8 sets of outputs (PA7–PA0), 8 sets of outputs (PB7–PB0), and 8 sets of inputs (PC7–PC0). The second thing that INIT does is to move certain variables from the applications area to the applications RAM area starting at PROGR or 824H. The variables that will be moved range from none to seventy or so, depending upon the applications area. In moving the variables, they are initialized to initial conditions which are necessary in many cases. For example, the Combination Lock applications program uses a default sequence of code digits. Every time INIT is called, this default sequence is loaded into RAM. The sequence may be redefined in the program, but the default values allow initialization of a known code.

COMMON VARIABLES

The RAM area below 824H is dedicated to the Common Area variables used by the Common Area program and, in some cases, the applications program. The first 5 bytes represent the real-time-clock variables of days, hours, minutes, seconds, and hundredths of seconds. The next 7 bytes are the LED display buffer; the first three bytes are never displayed but are used to hold garbage stored during binary to bcd conversion (BINBCD). The real-time-clock may be disabled by storing a nonzero value in DISABL. Two variables associated with automatic (NMI) update of the display are next: LEDNO and LEDPOS. BLINV may be set to automatically blink the display. The next 16 bytes are dedicated to the input buffer INBUF. Input digits are stored in this area as they are read in from the keyboard. The last variable is NOCHR, which holds the number of characters input during entry of keyboard commands.

NMI INTERRUPT HANDLER

The NMI Interrupt Handler is always active. Every 1/100 second this routine is automatically entered at location 66H (NMIHAN). The NMI routine serves two functions: It updates the real-time-clock and it outputs the next digit to the LED display.

When NMIHAN is entered, the cpu registers are switched; this action keeps any flags and registers used by the applications program and Common Area routines intact. If the DISABL flag is not set, the routine then updates the real-time-clock.

The real-time-clock is updated by adding 1 to the HUNDS (hundredths) variable. If this is equal to

```
              00100 ;*****************************************************
              00101 ;                  Z80MDP COMMON AREA                *
              00102 ;                        00-04                       *
              00103 ;*****************************************************
              00140 ;
0000          00150           ORG     0                ;EPROM LOCATION 0
              00160 ;
              00170 ; JUMP TO PROGRAM
              00180 ;
0000 C3       00190           DEFB    0C3H             ;"JP  PROGRAM"
0001 FFFF     00191           DEFW    -1               ;PUT ADDRESS HERE
              00200 ;
              00210 ;
              00220 ; SUBROUTINE VECTORS
              00230 ;
0003 C32100   00240 INIT      JP      INITS            ;INITIALIZATION SR
0006 C3CF00   00250 INPUT     JP      INPUTS           ;INPUT SR
0009 C30901   00260 GETCHR    JP      GETCHS           ;GET ONE KB CHARACTER SR
000C C31C01   00270 KEYSCN    JP      KEYSCS           ;SCAN KEYBOARD SR
000F C35201   00280 ROW       JP      ROWS             ;SCAN ROW SR
0012 C36501   00290 BCDBIN    JP      BCDBIS           ;CONVERT BCD TO BINARY SR
0015 C38001   00300 BINBCD    JP      BINBCS           ;CONVERT BINARY TO BCD SR
0018 C3AD01   00310 DELAY     JP      DELAYS           ;DELAY SR
001B C3BA01   00320 BLINK     JP      BLINKS           ;BLINK LEDS SR
001E C3CA01   00330 BRANCH    JP      BRANCS           ;BRANCH SR
              00340 ;
              00350 ;*****************************************************
              00360 ;* INITIALIZATION PROGRAM. MOVES INITIALIZATION DATA  *
              00370 ;*      FROM EPROM TO RAM.                           *
              00380 ;*            ENTRY:(HL)=START OF PROGRAM DATA       *
              00390 ;*                   (BC)=# OF BYTES OF INIT DATA    *
              00395 ;*                   CALL  INIT                      *
              00400 ;*            EXIT: PROGRAM DATA MOVED               *
              00410 ;*****************************************************
              00420 ;
0021          00430 INITS     EQU     $
0021 3E89     00440           LD      A,89H            ;SET MODE CONTROL WORD
0023 D303     00450           OUT     (3),A            ;SET MODE 0, SUBMODE 3
0025 112408   00460           LD      DE,PROGR         ;START OF PROGRAM RAM
0028 EDB0     00470           LDIR                         ;MOVE PROGRAM DATA
002A 213900   00480           LD      HL,INITD                   ;START OF GEN VARIABLES
002D 110008   00490           LD      DE,800H                    ;EPROM DEFAULTS
0030 012400   00500           LD      BC,INITL         ;EPROM SIZE
0033 EDB0     00510           LDIR                         ;MOVE GEN VARBLS
0035 C9       00520           RET                      ;RETURN TO CALLING PROG
              00522 ;
              00523 ; RESTART 38H LOCATION FOR PATCHES
              00524 ;
0038          00525           ORG     38H
0038 C9       00526           RET                      ;RETURN TO FF INSTRUCTION
              00530 ;
              00540 ; INITIALIZATION DATA COMMON TO ALL PROGRAMS
              00550 ;
0039 00       00560 INITD     DEFB    0                ;RTC DAYS (DAYS)
```

Fig. 10-2. Common Area program listing.

```
003A 00       00570          DEFB    0              ;RTC HOURS (HOURS)
003B 00       00575          DEFB    0              ;RTC MINUTES (MINS)
003C 00       00580          DEFB    0              ;RTC SECONDS (SECS)
003D 00       00590          DEFB    0              ;RTC HUNDREDTHS (HUNDS)
003E 00       00600          DEFB    0              ;PROTECT BYTES FOR LED
003F 00       00610          DEFB    0              ;PROTECT BYTES FOR LED
0040 00       00620          DEFB    0              ;PROTECT BYTES FOR LED
0041 00       00630          DEFB    0              ;LED BUFFER (LEDBUF)
0042 00       00640          DEFB    0              ;LED BUFFER DIGIT 2
0043 00       00650          DEFB    0              ;LED BUFFER DIGIT 3
0044 00       00660          DEFB    0              ;LED BUFFER DIGIT 4
0045 00       00670          DEFB    0              ;DISABLE RTC (DISABLE)
0046 03       00680          DEFB    3              ;LED DIGIT# (LEDNO)
0047 10       00690          DEFB    10H            ;LED ADDRESS (LEDPOS)
0048 00       00700          DEFB    0              ;BLINK (BLINV)
0049 00       00710          DEFB    0              ;PROTECT BYTE FOR INPUT
004A 00       00720          DEFB    0              ;PROTECT BYTE FOR INPUT
004B 00       00730          DEFB    0              ;PROTECT BYTE FOR INPUT
004C 0000     00740          DEFW    0              ;INPUT BUFFER (INBUF)
004E 0000     00750          DEFW    0
0050 0000     00760          DEFW    0
0052 0000     00770          DEFW    0
0054 0000     00780          DEFW    0
0056 0000     00790          DEFW    0
0058 0000     00800          DEFW    0
005A 0000     00810          DEFW    0
005C 00       00820          DEFB    0              ;# OF INPUT CHRS (NOCHR)
0024          00830 INITL    EQU     $-INITD        ;SIZE OF DEFAULTS
              00840 ;
              00850 ; LOCATIONS OF VARIABLES AFTER RELOCATION
              00860 ;
0800          00870 DAYS     EQU     800H
0801          00880 HOURS    EQU     DAYS+1
0802          00885 MINS     EQU     HOURS+1
0803          00890 SECS     EQU     MINS+1
0804          00900 HUNDS    EQU     SECS+1
0808          00910 LEDBUF   EQU     HUNDS+4
080C          00920 DISABL   EQU     LEDBUF+4
080D          00930 LEDNO    EQU     DISABL+1
080E          00935 LEDPOS   EQU     LEDNO+1
080F          00940 BLINV    EQU     LEDPOS+1
0813          00950 INBUF    EQU     BLINV+4
0823          00960 NOCHR    EQU     INBUF+16
0824          00970 PROGR    EQU     NOCHR+1
              00980 ;***********************************************************
              00990 ;* NMI INTERRUPT HANDLER. UPDATES RTC AND DISPLAY          *
              01000 ;* ENTERED ONCE EACH 1/100TH SECOND                        *
              01010 ;***********************************************************
              01020 ;
0066          01025          ORG     66H            ;FIXED NMI LOCATION
0066          01030 NMIHAN   EQU     $
0066 08       01040          EX      AF,AF'         ;SAVE A,F
0067 D9       01050          EXX                    ;SAVE OTHER REGISTERS
0068 3A0C08   01060          LD      A,(DISABL)     ;IS RTC FUNCTION REQ'D?
```

Fig. 10-2 cont'd. Common

```
006B B7         01070              OR      A              ;TEST DISABLE
006C 2028       01080              JR      NZ,LEDOUT      ;GO IF NO RTC REQ''D
                01090 ;
                01100 ; CODE TO UPATE RTC.UPDATES DHMSH IN 5 BYTES
                01110 ;
006E            01120 UPRTC        EQU     $
006E 210408     01130              LD      HL,HUNDS       ;POINT TO 100THS
0071 34         01140              INC     (HL)           ;BUMP 100THS
0072 7E         01150              LD      A,(HL)         ;GET COUNT
0073 FE64       01160              CP      100            ;TEST FOR 1 SECOND
0075 381F       01170              JR      C,LEDOUT       ;GO IF 0-99
0077 AF         01180              XOR     A              ;0
0078 77         01190              LD      (HL),A         ;STORE 0 AND CARRY
0079 2B         01200              DEC     HL             ;POINT TO SECONDS
007A 34         01210              INC     (HL)           ;BUMP SECONDS
007B 7E         01220              LD      A,(HL)         ;GET COUNT
007C FE3C       01230              CP      60             ;TEST FOR 1 MINUTE
007E 3816       01240              JR      C,LEDOUT       ;GO IF 0-59
0080 AF         01250              XOR     A              ;0
0081 77         01260              LD      (HL),A         ;STORE 0 AND CARRY
0082 2B         01270              DEC     HL             ;POINT TO MINUTES
0083 34         01280              INC     (HL)           ;BUMP MINUTES
0084 7E         01290              LD      A,(HL)         ;GET COUNT
0085 FE3C       01300              CP      60             ;TEST FOR 1 HOUR
0087 380D       01310              JR      C,LEDOUT       ;GO IF 0-59
0089 AF         01320              XOR     A              ;0
008A 77         01330              LD      (HL),A         ;STORE 0 AND CARRY
008B 2B         01340              DEC     HL             ;POINT TO HOURS
008C 34         01350              INC     (HL)           ;BUMP TO HOURS
008D 7E         01360              LD      A,(HL)         ;GET COUNT
008E FE18       01370              CP      24             ;TEST FOR 1 DAY
0090 3804       01380              JR      C,LEDOUT       ;GO IF 0-23
0092 AF         01390              XOR     A              ;0
0093 77         01400              LD      (HL),A         ;STORE 0 AND CARRY
0094 2B         01410              DEC     HL             ;POINT TO DAYS
0095 34         01420              INC     (HL)           ;BUMP DAYS
                01430 ;
                01440 ;CODE TO MULTIPLEX LED DISPLAY.  FOUR LED DIGITS
                01450 ;IN LEDBUF.OUTPUT 1 OF 4 TO LEDS.
                01460 ;
0096            01470 LEDOUT       EQU     $
0096 3A0D08     01480              LD      A,(LEDNO)      ;GET DIGIT #
0099 4F         01490              LD      C,A            ;NOW IN C
009A 0600       01500              LD      B,0            ;NOW IN BC
009C 210808     01510              LD      HL,LEDBUF      ;LED BUFFER
009F 09         01520              ADD     HL,BC          ;POINT TO DIGIT
00A0 46         01530              LD      B,(HL)         ;GET CURRENT DIGIT
00A1 3A0E08     01540              LD      A,(LEDPOS)     ;LED POSITION ADDRESS
00A4 B0         01550              OR      B              ;MERGE
00A5 D300       01560              OUT     (0),A          ;OUTPUT
00A7 3A0D08     01565              LD      A,(LEDNO)      ;DIGIT #
00AA 3D         01570              DEC     A              ;BUMP DIGIT #
00AB E603       01580              AND     3              ;MODULO 4
00AD 320D08     01590              LD      (LEDNO),A      ;SAVE DIGIT #
```

Area program listing.

```
00B0 3A0E08    01610          LD     A,(LEDPOS)      ;LED POSITION ADDRESS
00B3 CB27      01620          SLA    A               ;ALIGN
00B5 2002      01630          JR     NZ,LED10        ;GO IF OK
00B7 3E10      01640          LD     A,10H           ;START OVER
00B9 320E08    01650 LED10    LD     (LEDPOS),A      ;SAVE POSITION ADDDRESS
00BC 3A0F08    01660          LD     A,(BLINV)       ;IS BLINK ON?
00BF B7        01670          OR     A               ;TEST
00C0 2809      01690          JR     Z,LED20         ;GO IF NO
00C2 3A0408    01700          LD     A,(HUNDS)       ;GET 100THS
00C5 E640      01710          AND    40H             ;GET 64/100THS BIT
00C7 2002      01720          JR     NZ,LED20        ;GO IF NOT 0
00C9 D300      01730          OUT    (0),A           ;TURN OFF
00CB 08        01740 LED20    EX     AF,AF'          ;SWITCH A,F
00CC D9        01750          EXX                    ;SWITCH OTHER REGS
00CD ED45      01760          RETN                   ;RETURN FROM NMI INT
               01770 ;
               01780 ;*********************************************************
               01790 ;* GET INPUT SUBROUTINE.  GETS AN INPUT STRING OF *
               01800 ;* CHARACTERS.                                    *
               01810 ;*       ENTRY: NO SPECIAL SETUP                  *
               01815 ;*              CALL   INPUT                      *
               01820 ;*       EXIT:  INPUT CHARACTERS IN INBUF         *
               01830 ;*              (HL)=POINTS TO LAST CHARACTER     *
               01840 ;*              (C)=# OF CHARACTERS INPUT         *
               01850 ;*********************************************************
               01860 ;
00CF           01880 INPUTS   EQU    $
00CF 211308    01900          LD     HL,INBUF        ;POINT TO INPUT BUF
00D2 0E00      01910          LD     C,0             ;INITIALIZE # OF CHARS
00D4 E5        01920 INP05    PUSH   HL              ;SAVE POINTER
00D5 C5        01930          PUSH   BC              ;SAVE COUNT
00D6 CD0900    01940          CALL   GETCHR          ;GET CHARACTER
00D9 C1        01950          POP    BC              ;RESTORE COUNT
00DA E1        01960          POP    HL              ;RESTORE POINTER
00DB FEFE      01970          CP     0FEH            ;TEST FOR END
00DD C8        01980          RET    Z               ;RETURN IF DONE
00DE FEFF      01990          CP     0FFH            ;TEST FOR BACKSPACE
00E0 2008      02000          JR     NZ,INP10        ;GO IF NOT BACKSPACE
00E2 79        02010          LD     A,C             ;GET #
00E3 B7        02020          OR     A               ;TEST FOR 0
00E4 28EE      02030          JR     Z,INP05         ;GO IF NONE INPUT
00E6 0D        02040          DEC    C               ;ADJUST COUNT
00E7 2B        02050          DEC    HL              ;ADJUST POINTER TO LST
00E8 18EA      02060          JR     INP05           ;GO FOR NEXT
00EA 77        02070 INP10    LD     (HL),A          ;STORE CHARACTER
00EB 0C        02080          INC    C               ;BUMP COUNT
00EC E5        02090          PUSH   HL              ;SAVE PNTR
00ED C5        02100          PUSH   BC              ;SAVE COUNT
00EE 110B08    02110          LD     DE,LEDBUF+3     ;LED BUFFER DESTINATION
00F1 0600      02120          LD     B,0             ;ZERO HIGH ORDER
00F3 79        02121          LD     A,C             ;GET COUNT 1-X
00F4 FE04      02122          CP     4               ;TEST FOR 1-3
00F6 FAFB00    02123          JP     M,INP11         ;GO IF 1-3
00F9 3E04      02124          LD     A,4             ;4 OR ABOVE
```

Fig. 10-2 cont'd. Common

```
00FB 4F        02125 INP11  LD    C,A              ;COUNT OR 4
00FC ED88      02130        LDDR                   ;TRANSFER FOR DISPLAY
00FE C1        02140        POP   BC               ;RESTORE COUNT
00FF E1        02150        POP   HL               ;RESTORE PNTR
0100 23        02160        INC   HL               ;BUMP POINTER
0101 CB61      02170        BIT   4,C              ;TEST COUNTER FOR 16
0103 28CF      02180        JR    Z,INP05          ;GO IF LT 16
0105 2B        02190        DEC   HL               ;DON'T ALLOW
0106 0D        02200        DEC   C                ;MORE THAN 16
0107 18CB      02210        JR    INP05            ;CONTINUE
               02220 ;
               02230 ;**********************************************************
               02240 ;* GET CHARACTER ROUTINE. GETS ONE KEYBOARD CHARACTER. *
               02250 ;*      ENTRY:NO SPECIAL SETUP                          *
               02255 ;*            CALL  GETCHR                              *
               02260 ;*      EXIT: (A)=BCD DIGIT 0 TO 9, -1 FOR LEFT         *
               02270 ;*            BRACKET, OR -2 FOR RIGHT BRACKET          *
               02280 ;**********************************************************
               02290 ;
0109           02300 GETCHS EQU   $
0109 CD0C00    02310 GET10  CALL  KEYSCN           ;TEST FOR CHAR
010C 28FB      02320        JR    Z,GET10          ;GO IF NONE
010E F5        02330        PUSH  AF               ;SAVE CHARACTER
010F CD0C00    02340 GET20  CALL  KEYSCN           ;TEST FOR CHAR
0112 20FB      02350        JR    NZ,GET20         ;GO IF SAME CHAR
0114 210A00    02360        LD    HL,10            ;10 MILLISEC DELAY
0117 CD1800    02370        CALL  DELAY            ;DELAY SR
011A F1        02380        POP   AF               ;RETRIEVE CHARACTER
011B C9        02390        RET                    ;RETURN
               02400 ;**********************************************************
               02410 ;* KEYBOARD SCAN. TEST FOR KEY PRESS.                  *
               02420 ;*      ENTRY: NO SPECIAL SETUP                         *
               02425 ;*            CALL  KEYSCN                              *
               02430 ;*      EXIT:  Z FLAG SET IF NO KEY ELSE                *
               02440 ;*            (A)=BCD DIGIT 0-9, -1 FOR LEFT BRACKET    *
               02450 ;*            OR -2 FOR RIGHT BRACKET                   *
               02460 ;**********************************************************
               02470 ;
011C           02480 KEYSCS EQU   $
011C 0603      02530        LD    B,3              ;FOR "3" KEY
011E 3E80      02540        LD    A,80H            ;ROW 1
0120 CD0F00    02550        CALL  ROW              ;TEST ROW 1
0123 2025      02560        JR    NZ,KEY10         ;GO IF NON-ZERO
0125 0606      02570        LD    B,6              ;FOR "6" KEY
0127 3E40      02580        LD    A,40H            ;ROW 2
0129 CD0F00    02590        CALL  ROW              ;TEST ROW 2
012C 201C      02600        JR    NZ,KEY10         ;GO IF NON-ZERO
012E 0609      02610        LD    B,9              ;FOR "9" KEY
0130 3E20      02620        LD    A,20H            ;ROW 3
0132 CD0F00    02630        CALL  ROW              ;TEST ROW 3
0135 2013      02640        JR    NZ,KEY10         ;GO IF NON-ZERO
0137 0603      02650        LD    B,3              ;FOR ")" KEY
0139 3E10      02660        LD    A,10H            ;ROW 4
013B CD0F00    02670        CALL  ROW              ;TEST ROW 4
```

Area program listing.

```
013E 2810     02680          JR     Z,KEY20           ;GO IF NO KEY PRESS
0140 D602     02700          SUB    2                 ;NOW -1,0,+1
0142 2806     02710          JR     Z,KEY10           ;GO IF "0" KEY
0144 CB7F     02720          BIT    7,A               ;TEST SIGN
0146 2002     02730          JR     NZ,KEY10          ;GO IF MINUS
0148 3EFE     02740          LD     A,0FEH            ;SET RIGHT BRACKET
014A 06FF     02750 KEY10    LD     B,0FFH            ;DUMMY VALUE
014C CB78     02760          BIT    7,B               ;RESET ZERO FLAG
014E 1801     02770          JR     KEY30             ;RETURN
0150 AF       02780 KEY20    XOR    A                 ;SET ZERO FLAG
0151 C9       02790 KEY30    RET                      ;RETURN
              02800 ;
              02810 ;*****************************************************
              02820 ;* ROW SUBROUTINE. TEST SPECIFIED KEYBOARD ROW       *
              02830 ;*       ENTRY:(B)=RIGHT HAND BCD VALUE             *
              02840 ;*             (A)-ROW ADDRESS                      *
              02845 ;*             CALL  ROW                            *
              02850 ;*       EXIT: (A)=BCD VALUE OF KEY OR ZERO         *
              02860 ;*             (B)=DESTROYED                        *
              02870 ;*             Z FLAG SET IF NO KEY                 *
              02880 ;*****************************************************
              02890 ;
0152          02900 ROWS     EQU    $
0152 DB02     02910          IN     A,(2)             ;GET ROW
0154 E607     02930          AND    7                 ;GET 3 COLUMN BITS
0156 EE07     02935          XOR    7                 ;ACTIVE LOW
0158 0F       02940 ROW10    RRCA                       ;SET CARRY
0159 3807     02950          JR     C,ROW20             ;RETURN IF FOUND
015B 05       02960          DEC    B                   ;ADJUST BCD COUNT
015C B7       02970          OR     A                   ;TEST FOR DONE
015D 20F9     02980          JR     NZ,ROW10            ;TRY AGAIN
015F AF       02990          XOR    A                 ;0 FOR NO KEY
0160 1802     03000          JR     ROW30             ;RETURN
0162 78       03010 ROW20    LD     A,B               ;BCD VALUE
0163 B7       03020          OR     A                 ;SET ZERO VALUE OR NON-0
0164 C9       03030 ROW30    RET                      ;RETURN
              03040 ;***********************************************************
              03050 ;* BCD TO BINARY CONVERSION ROUTINE.  CONVERTS UP TO    *
              03060 ;* 5 DIGITS TO BINARY (0 TO 65535).                     *
              03070 ;*       ENTRY: (IX)=POINTER TO FIRST BCD DIGIT          *
              03080 ;*              (B) =# OF CHARACTERS                     *
              03090 ;*              (DE)=MAXIMUM VALUE                       *
              03095 ;*              CALL  BCDBIN                             *
              03100 ;*       EXIT:  (HL)=BINARY VALUE                        *
              03110 ;*              CARRY SET IF UNDER LIMIT, RESET IF OVER  *
              03112 ;*              OR EQUAL                                 *
              03115 ;***********************************************************
              03120 ;
0165          03130 BCDBIS   EQU    $
0165 D5       03140          PUSH   DE                ;SAVE LIMIT
0166 210000   03150          LD     HL,0              ;INITIALIZE SUBTOTAL
0169 29       03160 BCD10    ADD    HL,HL               ;SUBTOTAL*2
016A E5       03170          PUSH   HL                  ;SAVE ST*2
016B 29       03180          ADD    HL,HL               ;SUBTOTAL*4
```

Fig. 10-2 cont'd. Common

```
016C 29        03190          ADD    HL,HL         ;SUBTOTAL*8
016D D1        03200          POP    DE            ;GET ST*2
016E 19        03210          ADD    HL,DE         ;SUBTOTAL*10
016F 1600      03220          LD     D,0           ;ZERO MS BYTE
0171 DD5E00    03230          LD     E,(IX)        ;GET BCD DIGIT
0174 DD23      03240          INC    IX            ;BUMP POINTER
0176 19        03250          ADD    HL,DE         ;ADD IN LATEST DIGIT
0177 10F0      03260          DJNZ   BCD10         ;CONTINUE IF NOT DONE
0179 D1        03270          POP    DE           ;GET LIMIT
017A E5        03280          PUSH   HL           ;SAVE VALUE
017B B7        03290          OR     A            ;CLEAR CARRY
017C ED52      03300          SBC    HL,DE        ;TEST
017E E1        03310          POP    HL           ;GET VALUE
017F C9        03320          RET                 ;RETURN
               03330 ;
               03340 ;*****************************************************
               03350 ;* BINARY TO BCD CONVERSION SUBROUTINE.  CONVERTS 16- *
               03360 ;* BIT BINARY VALUE TO 5 BCD CHARACTERS.              *
               03370 ;*       ENTRY: (HL)=BINARY VALUE                      *
               03380 ;*              (IX)=POINTER TO BUFFER                 *
               03385 ;*              CALL  BINBCD                           *
               03390 ;*       EXIT:  (FIVE BCD DIGITS UNPACKED IN 5 BYTES OF *
               03400 ;*              BUFFER                                 *
               03410 ;*              (IX) POINTS TO NEXT AVAILABLE          *
               03420 ;*****************************************************
               03430 ;
0180           03440 BINBCS  EQU    $
0180 FD21A101  03450         LD     IY,BTABL      ;TABLE OF CONSTANTS
0184 06FF      03460 BIN05   LD     B,0FFH        ;INITIALIZE BCD DIGIT
0186 FD5E00    03470         LD     E,(IY)          ;GET POWER OF 10
0189 FD5601    03480         LD     D,(IY+1)        ;MS BYTE
018C CB7A      03490         BIT    7,D             ;TEST SIGN BIT
018E C0        03500         RET    NZ              ;RETURN IF DONE
018F 04        03510 BIN10   INC    B                  ;BUMP COUNT(DIGIT)
0190 B7        03520         OR     A                  ;CLEAR CARRY
0191 ED52      03530         SBC    HL,DE              ;SUBTRACT POWER
0193 30FA      03540         JR     NC,BIN10                  ;CONTINUE IF POS
0195 19        03560         ADD    HL,DE           ;RESTORE RESIDUE
0196 DD7000    03570         LD     (IX),B          ;STORE DIGIT
0199 DD23      03580         INC    IX              ;BUMP POINTER
019B FD23      03590         INC    IY              ;BUMP TABLE POINTER
019D FD23      03600         INC    IY              ;PAST 2 BYTES
019F 18E3      03610         JR     BIN05           ;CONTINUE
01A1 1027      03620 BTABL   DEFW   10000         ;TABLE OF POWERS OF 10
01A3 E803      03630         DEFW   1000
01A5 6400      03640         DEFW   100
01A7 0A00      03650         DEFW   10
01A9 0100      03660         DEFW   1
01AB FFFF      03670         DEFW   -1            ;END OF TABLE
               03680 ;*****************************************************
               03690 ;* DELAY SUBROUTINE. DELAYS 1 MS*COUNT IN HL          *
               03700 ;*      ENTRY:(HL)=DELAY IN MILLISECONDS              *
               03705 ;*             CALL  DELAY                            *
               03710 ;*****************************************************
```

Area program listing.

```
                   03715 ;
01AD               03720 DELAYS  EQU     $
01AD 11FFFF        03730         LD      DE,-1           ;DECREMENT VALUE
01B0 064A          03740 DEL05   LD      B,04AH              ;FIANGLE FACTOR
01B2 19            03750         ADD     HL,DE               ;DECREMENT HL COUNT
01B3 D0            03760         RET     NC                  ;RETURN IF DONE
01B4 10FE          03770 DEL10   DJNZ    DEL10                   ;INNER DELAY
01B6 00            03780         NOP                             ;WASTE TIME
01B7 00            03782         NOP                             ;WASTE TIME
01B8 18F6          03790         JR      DEL05               ;RETURN TO OUTER L
                   03800 ;************************************************************
                   03810 ;* SUBROUTINE TO BLINK DISPLAY FOR 5 SECONDS                *
                   03815 ;*              CALL  BLINK                                 *
                   03820 ;************************************************************
                   03830 ;
01BA               03840 BLINKS  EQU     $
01BA 3EFF          03850         LD      A,0FFH          ;ALL ON FOR FLAG
01BC 320F08        03860         LD      (BLINV),A       ;SET BLINK FLAG
01BF 218813        03870         LD      HL,5000         ;5 SECONDS
01C2 CD1800        03880         CALL    DELAY           ;DELAY
01C5 AF            03882         XOR     A               ;0 TO A
01C6 320F08        03884         LD      (BLINV),A       ;RESET BLINK FLAG
01C9 C9            03890         RET                     ;RETURN
                   03900 ;************************************************************
                   03910 ;* SUBROUTINE TO BRANCH OUT TO FUNCTIONS.                   *
                   03920 ;*      ENTRY: (HL)=POINTER TO RELATIVE BRANCH TABLE        *
                   03930 ;*             (DE)=MIN# FOR INPUT,# OF LAST VALID FUNC     *
                   03935 ;*             JP  BRANCH                                   *
                   03950 ;*      EXIT:  BY JUMP TO BRANCH TABLE AFTER VALID          *
                   03960 ;*             INPUT STRING                                 *
                   03970 ;************************************************************
                   03980 ;
01CA               03990 BRANCS  EQU     $
01CA E5            04000         PUSH    HL              ;SAVE POINTER
01CB 1C            04005         INC     E               ;BUMP # OF LAST FUNC
01CC D5            04010         PUSH    DE              ;SAVE PARAMETERS
01CD 210000        04020 BR05    LD      HL,0            ;ZEROES
01D0 220808        04030         LD      (LEDBUF),HL     ;ZERO LED DISPLAY
01D3 220A08        04040         LD      (LEDBUF+2),HL   ;FOUR BYTES TOTAL
01D6 CD0600        04050 BR10    CALL    INPUT             ;INPUT STRING
01D9 79            04060         LD      A,C               ;GET # INPUT
01DA 322308        04070         LD      (NOCHR),A         ;STORE # OF CHARS
01DD D1            04092         POP     DE              ;GET MIN, LAST
01DE 92            04094         SUB     D               ;TEST FOR MINIMUM
01DF CB7F          04096         BIT     7,A             ;TEST IF LT MINIMUM
01E1 2011          04098         JR      NZ,BR15         ;GO IF LT MINIMUM
01E3 3A1308        04100         LD      A,(INBUF)       ;GET FIRST CHAR
01E6 93            04120         SUB     E               ;ACTUAL-LARGEST
01E7 CB7F          04130         BIT     7,A             ;TEST FOR MINUS
01E9 2809          04140         JR      Z,BR15          ;GO IF NOT IN RANGE
01EB D1            04150         POP     DE              ;RESTORE BR TABLE PNTR
01EC 2A1308        04160         LD      HL,(INBUF)      ;GET # TO L
01EF 2600          04162         LD      H,0             ;# NOW IN HL
01F1 29            04180         ADD     HL,HL           ;# TIMES 2
```

Fig. 10-2 cont'd. Common

```
01F2 19       04190          ADD   HL,DE   ;TABLE ADD+#*2
01F3 E9       04200          JP    (HL)    ;JUMP OUT
01F4 D5       04205 BR15     PUSH  DE      ;SAVE LIMITS
01F5 CD1B00   04210          CALL  BLINK   ;BLINK LEDS
01F8 18D3     04220          JR    BR05    ;TRY AGAIN
0000          04250          END
00000 TOTAL ERRORS


BCD10  0169 03160  03260
BCDBIN 0012 00290
BCDBIS 0165 03130  00290
BIN05  0184 03460  03610
BIN10  018F 03510  03540
BINBCD 0015 00300
BINBCS 0180 03440  00300
BLINK  001B 00320  04210
BLINKS 01BA 03840  00320
BLINV  080F 00940  00950 01660 03860 03884
BR05   01CD 04020  04220
BR10   01D6 04050
BR15   01F4 04205  04098 04140
BRANCH 001E 00330
BRANCS 01CA 03990  00330
BTABL  01A1 03620  03450
DAYS   0800 00870  00880
DEL05  01B0 03740  03790
DEL10  01B4 03770  03770
DELAY  0018 00310  02370 03880
DELAYS 01AD 03720  00310
DISABL 080C 00920  00930 01060
GET10  0109 02310  02320
GET20  010F 02340  02350
GETCHR 0009 00260  01940
GETCHS 0109 02300  00260
HOURS  0801 00880  00885
HUNDS  0804 00900  00910 01130 01700
INBUF  0813 00950  00960 01900 04100 04160
INIT   0003 00240
INITD  0039 00560  00480 00830
INITL  0024 00830  00500
INITS  0021 00430  00240
INP05  00D4 01920  02030 02060 02180 02210
INP10  00EA 02070  02000
INP11  00FB 02125  02123
INPUT  0006 00250  04050
INPUTS 00CF 01880  00250
KEY10  014A 02750  02560 02600 02640 02710 02730
KEY20  0150 02780  02680
KEY30  0151 02790  02770
KEYSCN 000C 00270  02310 02340
KEYSCS 011C 02480  00270
LED10  00B9 01650  01630
LED20  00CB 01740  01690 01720
LEDBUF 0808 00910  00920 01510 02110 04030 04040
LEDNO  080D 00930  00935 01480 01565 01590
```

Area program listing.

```
LEDOUT 0096 01470    01080 01170 01240 01310 01380
LEDPOS 080E 00935    00940 01540 01610 01650
MINS   0802 00885    00890
NMIHAN 0066 01030
NOCHR  0823 00960    00970 04070
PROGR  0824 00970    00460
ROW    000F 00280    02550 02590 02630 02670
ROW10  0158 02940    02980
ROW20  0162 03010    02950
ROW30  0164 03030    03000
ROWS   0152 02900    00280
SECS   0803 00890    00900
UPRTC  006E 01120
```

Fig. 10-2 cont'd. Common Area program listing.

100 counts, SECS is incremented by one and HUNDS is set to zero. If SECS equals 60, MINS is incremented by one, SECS is reset to zero, and so forth. At any time, DAYS, HOURS, MINS, SECS, and HUNDS represent the elapsed time from the start of power on. (However, it is up to the applications program to reset all of these variables to zero initially; they have garbage in them on power up.)

The LEDOUT portion of the NMI Interrupt Handler updates the LED display. It simply takes the contents of the LEDBUF and outputs one of the four digits every 1/100 of a second. After 4/100 the entire display has been updated. To the eye it appears that the entire display is on all of the time. Another function that the LEDOUT routine performs is to blink the display. If BLINV is on the display is zeroed for 36/100 out of 100/100 second. This appears as a blinking display. The last thing the NMI routine performs is to switch back the cpu registers and execute a *Ret*urn from *N*on-maskable interrupt (RETN).

KEYBOARD SUBROUTINES

There are four subroutines associated with keyboard input, INPUT, GETCHR, KEYSCN, and ROW. We'll examine them beginning with the most elementary, ROW.

The ROW subroutine takes a keyboard row address of 80H (row 1), 40H (row 2), 20H (row 3), or 10H (row 4), reads the keyboard row and finds a possible column that has a key pressed. If a key is being pressed, the initial value of 3, 6, 9, or 3 is decremented to the proper value for the key (the BS, 0, and ENTER keys become 1, 2, or 3). If no key is being pressed, the returned value becomes 0.

The ROW subroutine is CALLed by the KEYSCN subroutine. The KEYSCN subroutine returns the value of the key that is being pressed or −1 for "BS" or −2 for "ENTER." If no key is being pressed, the 2 flag is set upon return. Normally, an application program would not CALL ROW, but might CALL KEYSCN to see if any key is being pressed. KEYSCN CALLs ROW for each of four rows to test for a key press.

The GETCHR subroutine CALLs KEYSCN. It continues to CALL KEYSCN until a key is pressed. GETCHR is truly a *GET CHaR*acter subroutine. After a character is detected, GETCHR delays 10 milliseconds for key release. If it did not do this, it would appear that the key was being pressed many times.

The main keyboard subroutine is INPUT, which inputs a complete command line. A *command line* is defined as a string of characters making up an applications program command and terminated by an "ENTER." INPUT calls GETCHR, stores the character pressed, and continues until an ENTER is pressed. Up to 16 characters are stored in INBUF by input. Pressing the "BS" key deletes the last character and writes over it with the next character. The number of characters input is returned in the C register. INPUT is called by another subroutine BRANCH, which inputs a line of characters and branches to a processing routine for the function type.

CONVERSION SUBROUTINES

There are two conversion routines BCDBIN and BINBCD. BCDBIN converts a string of bcd digits, typically a string in INBUF, to a binary value. Values of up to 65,535 can be converted. BINBCD works the opposite way. A binary value in HL is converted to a string of bcd values, typically in the LEDBUF for display.

DELAY SUBROUTINE

DELAY delays from 1 to 65,535 milliseconds. This is simply a timing loop that takes 1 millisecond to execute, provided the clock signal to the Z-80 is exactly

1 megahertz. The count in HL determines the delay by DELAY = count × 1 millisecond. This blinks the display for 5 seconds.

BLINK SUBROUTINE

When an input error is encountered, it is convenient to have feedback to the user. BLINK provides this feature by setting the BLINV flag delaying 5 seconds and resetting the flag.

BRANCH SUBROUTINE

The BRANCH subroutine inputs a command string by calling INPUT, puts the number of characters input into NOCHR, and tests for a minimum number input and for a valid "function." The function is arbitrarily defined as the first digit input. By specifying a minimum and maximum function number and a minimum number of characters to be input, this subroutine provides error checking for command lines. If a valid string of characters has been input, then the BRANCH subroutine adds 2 * function + (HL) to find a location for a branch. In fact, HL is set up before the jump to BRANCH to point to a table of relative branches for the appropriate functions. An example of this is:

```
        LD   HL,TABLE   ;BRANCH TABLE ADDR
        LD   DE,0103    ;MIN=1, 0-3 VALID
        JP   BRANCH     ;GO TO BRANCH
TABLE   JR   FUNC00     ;0 FUNCTION=START
                                    TRAIN
        JR   FUNC01     ;1 FUNCTION=STOP
                                    TRAIN
        JR   FUNC02     ;2 FUNCTION=WHISTLE
        JR   FUNC03     ;3 FUNCTION=COLLECT
                                  TICKETS
```

If less than the minimum number of characters is input or if an invalid function is input, then BRANCH blinks the display and waits for the next command line to be input. A typical command line might be:

"0123(ENTER)"

which would start the train (function = 0) and set the speed at 123 miles per hour.

GENERAL USE OF SUBROUTINES

The whole idea behind the subroutines is that before any applications programs are written, one knows there will have to be provision for inputting commands, checking for validity, converting between bcd and binary, and displaying data. The subroutines in the Common Area represent one approach to creating subroutines that will handle these functions.

Each subroutine is described in the listing in terms of *input parameters* and *output parameters.* Certain registers are set up with parameters defining the operation and the subroutine is CALLed. On *exit* from the subroutine, certain registers or variables contain the results of the subroutine processing.

STRUCTURE OF THE APPLICATIONS PROGRAMS

The reader is urged to examine the structure of the applications programs in this section. Each program generally CALLs INIT to move the program variables to RAM. BRANCH is then called to branch out to an input line. Each separate function results in a branch to a different processing routine for the function. The function processing may call other Common Area subroutines, such as BINBCD or BCDBIN, may investigate Common Area variables such as SECS or NOCHR, or may use variables of its own.

RELOCATION OF PROGRAMS

All of the programs in this section are designed to run in certain areas of EPROM. If the code for the programs is moved to another area it will not execute because of direct memory references such as "JP LOCN," which jumps to a specific location in the applications program. Programs may be relocated by the following procedure:

1. Establish the new starting address. Calculate the difference between the old starting address and new and label it BIAS.
2. Relocate all one-byte instructions by using the same value for the byte.
3. Relocate all two-byte instructions by using same values for the bytes.
4. If a three-byte instruction references a Common Area subroutine, use the same values for the bytes.
5. If a three-byte instruction references a RAM variable, use the same values for the bytes.
6. If a three-byte instruction references a location in the applications program (such as JP NEXT), go to Step 9.
7. If a four-byte instruction contains a reference to an EPROM location (such as LD IX,TABLE), go to Step 9.
8. Continue with Step 2 until done.
9. (Add relocation bias.) Add BIAS to the address portion of the instruction data. Go to Step 8.

Review of instruction addressing in Chapter 6 may help to clarify which instruction addresses need to be changed. In general, JPs to locations in the applications programs, or LDs of addresses or data from the applications programs will need to have their address references modified by adding BIAS.

USING SEVERAL APPLICATIONS PROGRAMS AT ONCE

By relocating programs or by using the programs as they are, it is possible to have several different programs in EPROM at one time, especially in the case of a 2716 EPROM. Each program must, of course, be in its own section of EPROM in this case.

Locations 1 and 2 specify the address for the start of the application after power up; these locations are the last two bytes of a "JP." If these locations specify a single applications program, then it will not be possible to enter any other! The solution is as follows: Locations 1 and 2 specify a short program at 200H that "decodes" a single input character. This input character is used to branch out to the proper applications program.

Suppose, for example, three applications programs are resident in a 2758 EPROM, as shown in Fig. 10-3. Their starting addresses are 220H, 2C0H, and 360H. The Microcomputer Educator is arbitrarily assigned code 1, the Combination Lock code 2, and the Burglar Alarm code 3. Locations 1 and 2 are programmed to 00H and 02H, respectively, to specify a start at location 200H. At 200H a short decode program looks for a 1, 2, or 3 entry and branches off to the proper application program as shown in the code of Fig. 10-4.

The stack pointer must be initialized before any CALL is made. GETCHR waits for a key to be pressed. The assumption is that a 1, 2, or 3 key will be pressed. Pressing a key returns to the "CP 1" code and a comparison is made for "1," "2," or "3" with a branch out to the proper application program. Note that any key other than "1" or "2" results in transferring control to the Burglar Alarm program. Once one of the applications programs is entered, it has complete control and another cannot be entered except by a power down and restart to return to the decode program at 200H.

This scheme may be used for any number of applications programs at any number of different areas by adding a "CP N" with a "JP Z,XXX" for each applications program.

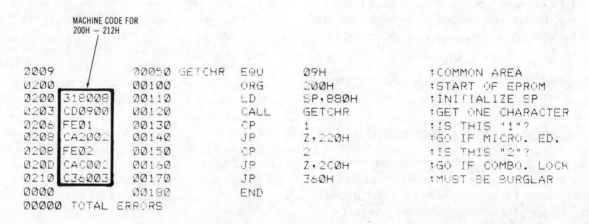

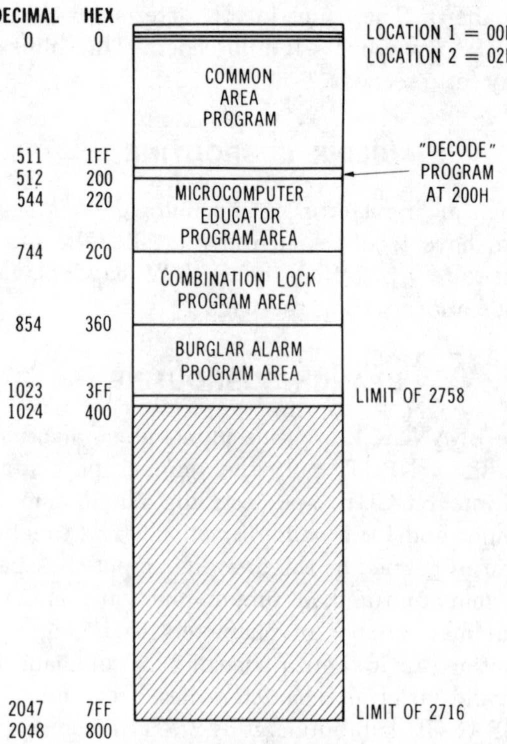

Fig. 10-3. Multiple applications programs.

MACHINE CODE FOR 200H – 212H

```
0009              GETCHR   EQU    09H        ;COMMON AREA
0200                       ORG    200H       ;START OF EPROM
0200 318008                LD     SP,880H    ;INITIALIZE SP
0203 CD0900                CALL   GETCHR     ;GET ONE CHARACTER
0206 FE01                  CP     1          ;IS THIS "1"?
0208 CA2002                JP     Z,220H     ;GO IF MICRO. ED.
020B FE02                  CP     2          ;IS THIS "2"?
020D CAC002                JP     Z,2C0H     ;GO IF COMBO. LOCK
0210 C36003                JP     360H       ;MUST BE BURGLAR
0000                       END
00000 TOTAL ERRORS

GETCHR  0009
```

Fig. 10-4. DECODE program for multiple applications.

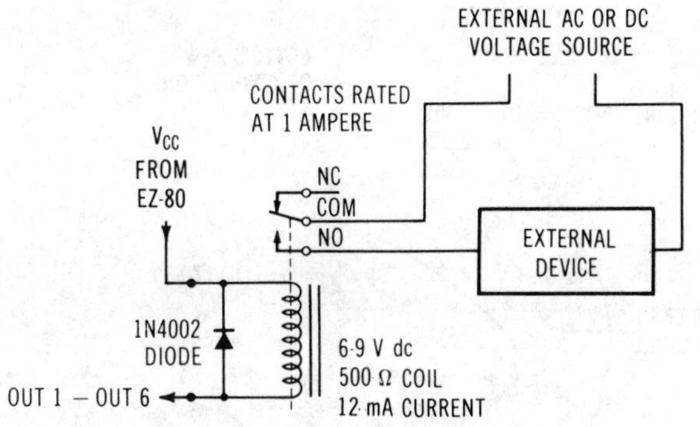

Fig. 10-5. Relay control of external devices.

APPLICATIONS HARDWARE DEVICES

Some applications programs call for control of external devices such as solenoids, others call for input of external data, and other require audio output. We will look at some suggested approaches to accomplishing these functions.

Fig. 10-5 shows a method for controlling external devices using a sensitive miniature relay. The particular one used here is Radio Shack No. 275-004 or equivalent. If this relay cannot be found, then another with similar specifications should be obtained. Look

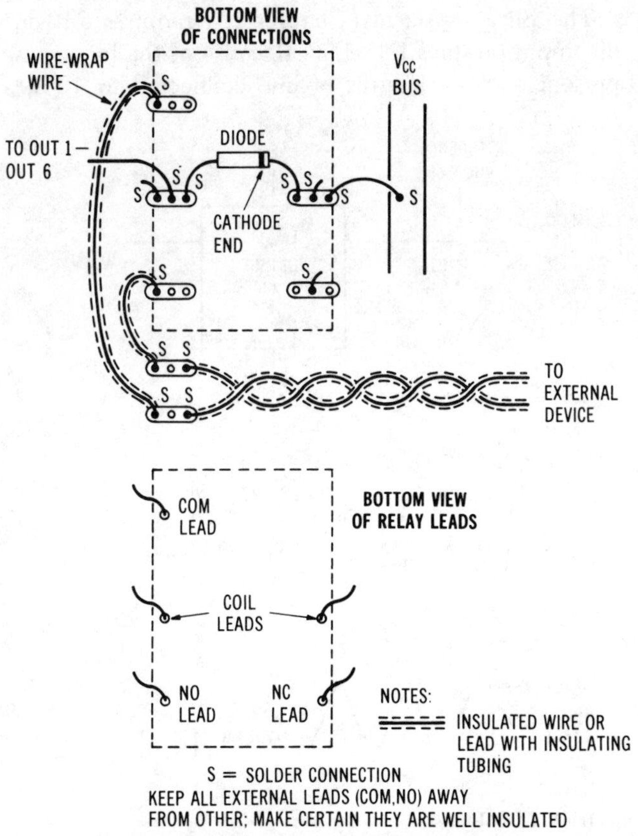

Fig. 10-6. Relay circuitry construction.

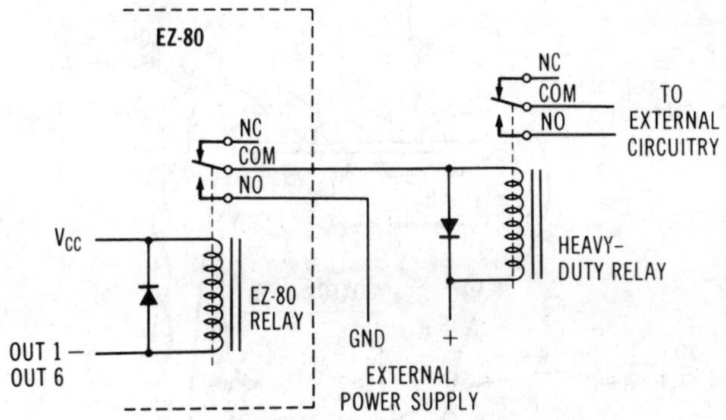

Fig. 10-7. Driving heavy loads.

for a 6-V (or less) dc relay (operates with 6 Vdc) with current less than 30 milliamperes. A relay requiring more than 30 milliamperes may burn out the 74368 driver. The Radio Shack relay will "pull in" with 5 volts dc—this may not always be true with another relay. Another important point: The contacts with this device are rated at 1 ampere at 125 volts ac. This means that the relay will control up to 125 watts, equivalent to a 125-watt bulb. The diode prevents the back voltage associated with inductive loads from damaging the 74368. *If this relay is used to control high voltages, be certain to isolate the high voltage from the microcomputer circuitry.* Do not attempt to overload the relay with air conditioners or milling machines! A suggested physical layout for the relay is shown in Fig. 10-6.

The applications that use such a device are: the Combination Lock (Chapter 12) to control a solenoid for a door or other latch, the Morse Code Sender (Chapter 15) to interface to an existing keyer, the Telephone Dialer (Chapter 16) to interface to the phone lines, and the Timer (Chapter 18) that controls up to six external devices.

If a higher-power device must be controlled, then this relay may be used to control yet another relay as shown in Fig. 10-7, and the process can be repeated until your EZ-80 is controlling the output of Hoover Dam. Remember, do not overload the con-

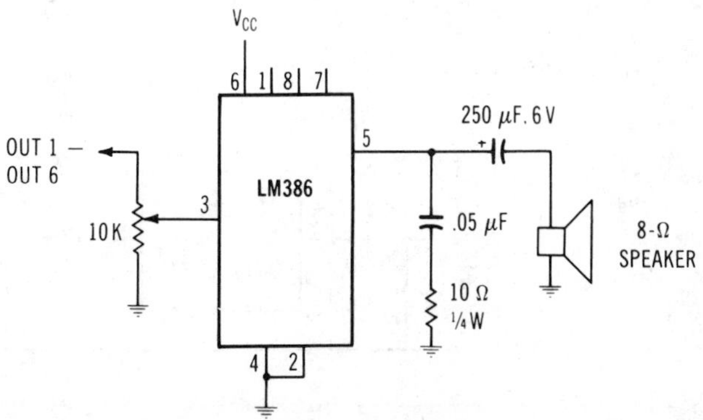

Fig. 10-8. Audio amplifier.

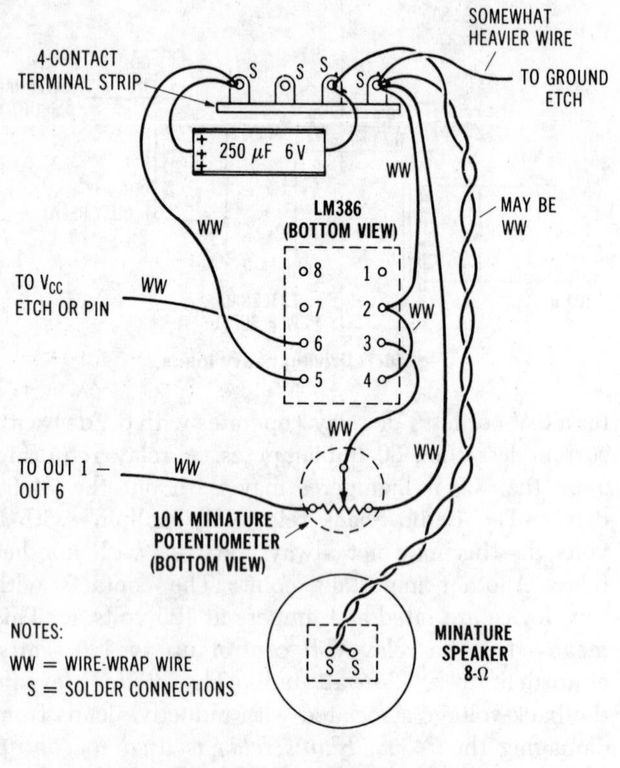

Fig. 10-9. Audio amplifier construction.

tacts and keep high voltage well isolated from other circuitry!

Some of the applications call for an audio output. The Burglar Alarm (Chapter 13) uses an audio signal to signal a broken contact, the Morse Code Generator (Chapter 14) and Sender (Chapter 15) create Morse Code audio, and the Music Synthesizer (Chapter 19), of course, requires audio. A simple audio amplifier can be made from six components as shown in Fig. 10-8.

The LM386 is a low-voltage audio amplifier on an 8-pin chip. It can be constructed along the lines of Fig. 10-9. The 10-kilohm potentiometer should be adjusted for the desired volume. The speaker should be a miniature 8-ohm-impedance speaker.

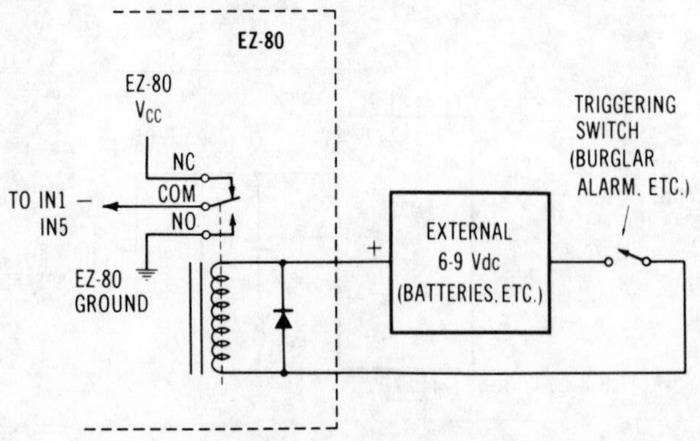

Fig. 10-10. Input using relays.

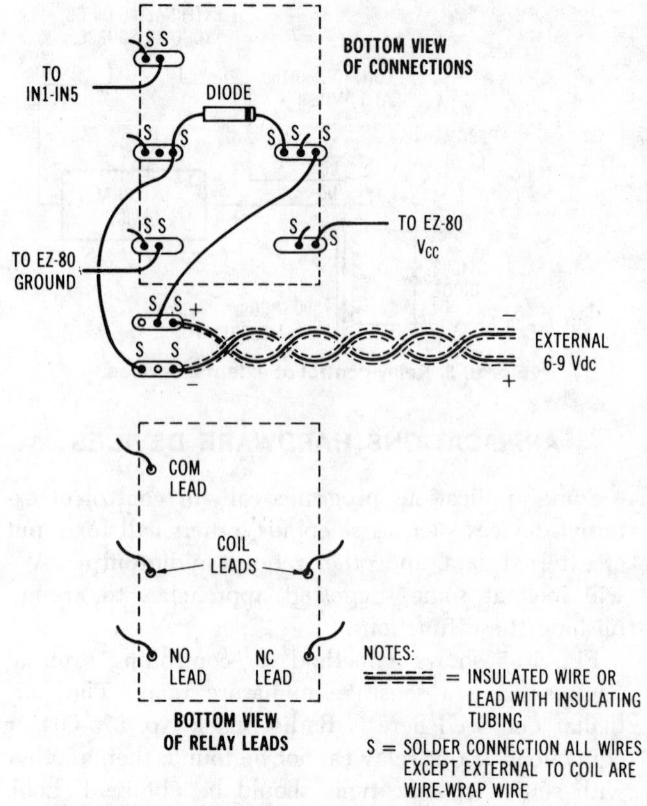

Fig. 10-11. Relay input construction.

The Burglar Alarm (Chapter 13) requires an "on/off" input on lines IN1–IN6. Because of the high noise present on long lengths of line connected to TTL, a

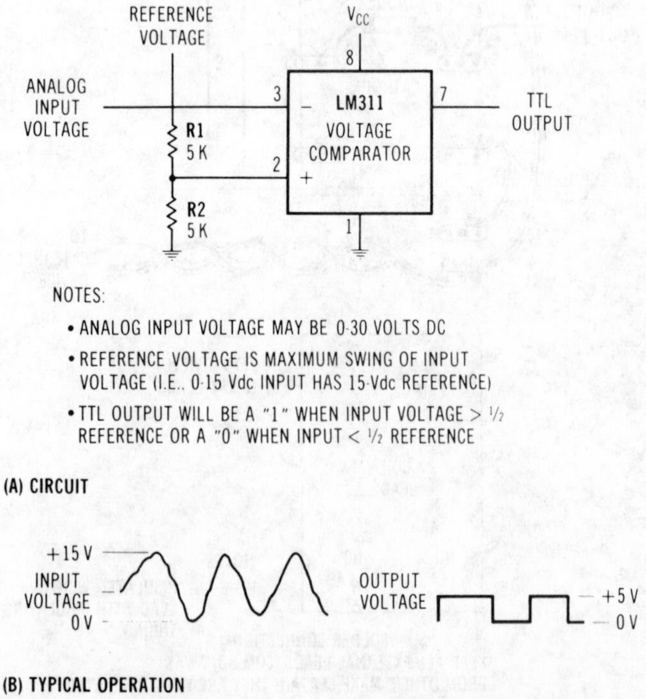

Fig. 10-12. Converting to TTL signals.

connection cannot be made directly to the 74LS04. Fig. 10-10 shows the recommended interface for slow-speed (several times per second) inputs that must be detected by the EZ-80. The lengths of wires from the contacts to IN1–IN5 should be kept short (maximum of several feet). The voltage to drive the relays can be derived from the +5-Vdc power supply of the EZ-80. However, it may be necessary to use a separate voltage source because of voltage drops in long runs of wire. In this case any convenient spdt relay can be used in place of the Radio Shack relay, or a 9-volt power supply may be used instead of the +5 volts. A suggested physical layout for the input devices is shown in Fig. 10-11.

The same input scheme may be used for other applications requiring the detection of on/off signals that are generated at locations which are remote from the EZ-80.

The Frequency Counter/Tachometer application requires an input on IN1. Here, again, it is important to avoid noise on the input lines to prevent false counts. Keep the input line from the signal as short as possible. Shielding (shielded sheath of wire to ground) will help. As described in Chapter 17 the signal itself must be "TTL compatible." A suggested means for converting a periodic external world signal into a TTL-compatible pulse is shown in the illustration of Fig. 10-12.

CHAPTER 11

Microcomputer Educator

This chapter describes the Microcomputer Educator application of the EZ-80. Unlike the other applications the Microcomputer Educator does not connect to the outside world to detect switch closures or to output signals; its sole function is use as a training aid in assembly-language programming. The Microcomputer Educator can be used to enter assembly-language code into the RAM memory area, to check that code, and to execute the small programs that the code represents. In this way the EZ-80 user can teach himself or herself assembly-language programming by hand-assembling short sections of code, keying the code into the EZ-80, and running the programs.

As an example, suppose that the user wants to write a short program to add the numbers from 1 to 100 and display the result on the EZ-80 display. By reference to the instruction types and instruction formats in Appendices D and E of this book, the program in Fig. 11-1 may be generated.

This program accomplishes the following: Instruction number 1 loads the BC register pair with 100. Instruction number 2 loads the HL register pair with 0; HL is used to hold the running total of the numbers from 1 to 100. Instructions 3 through 7 add 100, 99, 98, 97, . . . , 1 to the total in HL, decrease the count in BC from 100, 99, 98, . . . , down to 1, and test the count in BC to see when it reaches 0. If the count has not reached 0, then the add of the next number is performed. If the count reaches 0, then instruction number 8 is executed. Instruction 9 uses a routine in the EZ-80 Common Area (see Chapter 10) that converts a binary value of 0 through 9999 in HL to a "binary-coded decimal" equivalent for display on the LEDs, which can only display decimal values. The value in HL representing the total of the numbers from 100 to 1 is put into the LED display buffer by the routine (instruction 8 loads the IX register with the address of the display buffer). The last instruction simply loops to itself at the end of the program.

The program above is written in convenient assembly-language format, similar to the assembly-language code used in the book. It must be converted to machine-language format before it can be entered into RAM and run. Using Appendix E the assembly-language formats can be converted to machine language. The location of the machine-language code must be in RAM memory from about 830H to 85FH. The first portion of RAM (800–82FH) is used for variable storage (LED buffer, time, and so forth) and the last portion of RAM (860–87FH) is used by the EZ-80 stack. This provides about 30H (48) locations that can be used for simple programs. Fig. 11-2 is the equivalent program above, assembled to start at 830H.

The program code is entered into RAM by running the Microcomputer Educator and entering the data on the keyboard shown in Fig. 11-3. At the end of the entry, "0" starts execution and the answer of 5050 is displayed on the LED display. To reenter the Microcomputer Educator (in this case) the EZ-80 must be powered down and then up, restarting the Microcomputer Educator. When this is done, the contents of RAM will be destroyed. Many simple routines of this type can be implemented with the Microcomputer Educator, and if the reader is interested in learning assembly language for the Z-80 microprocessor he or she is urged to experiment with this application using the code in this book for study and emulation.

OPERATING INSTRUCTIONS

The Microcomputer Educator is programmed into EPROM starting at 220H, as shown in Fig. 11-4. Other applications programs may be programmed into the EPROM if their locations do not conflict with the Microcomputer Educator. Use the techniques described in Chapter 10 to transfer control to the Microcomputer Educator if other programs are coresident in EPROM. If only the Microcomputer Educator is

```
INSTRUCTION
NUMBER

 1           LD      BC,100        ;100
 2           LD      HL,0          ;ZERO RESULT
 3   LOOP    ADD     HL,BC         ;ADD NEXT TO RESULT
 4           DEC     BC            ;COUNT DOWN
 5           LD      A,C           ;GET LS BYTE OF COUNT
 6           OR      B             ;MERGE MS BYTE OF COUNT
 7           JR      NZ,LOOP       ;GO IF COUNT NOT ZERO
 8           LD      IX,LEDBUF     ;POINT TO LED BUFFER
 9           CALL    BINBCD        ;CONVERT TO BCD
10           JR      $
```

Fig. 11-1. Sample Microcomputer Educator program.

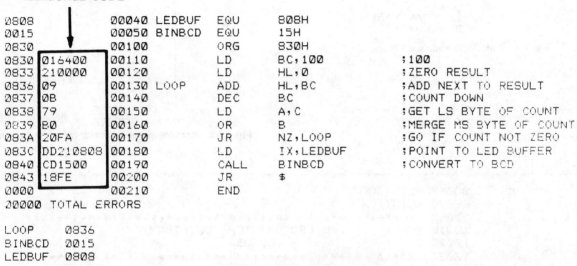

```
       MACHINE
    LANGUAGE CODE

0808            00040 LEDBUF  EQU   808H
0015            00050 BINBCD  EQU   15H
0830            00100         ORG   830H
0830 016400     00110         LD    BC,100      ;100
0833 210000     00120         LD    HL,0        ;ZERO RESULT
0836 09         00130 LOOP    ADD   HL,BC       ;ADD NEXT TO RESULT
0837 0B         00140         DEC   BC          ;COUNT DOWN
0838 79         00150         LD    A,C         ;GET LS BYTE OF COUNT
0839 B0         00160         OR    B           ;MERGE MS BYTE OF COUNT
083A 20FA       00170         JR    NZ,LOOP     ;GO IF COUNT NOT ZERO
083C DD210808   00180         LD    IX,LEDBUF   ;POINT TO LED BUFFER
0840 CD1500     00190         CALL  BINBCD      ;CONVERT TO BCD
0843 18FE       00200         JR    $
0000            00210         END
00000 TOTAL ERRORS

LOOP     0836
BINBCD   0015
LEDBUF   0808
```

Fig. 11-2. Machine language code.

resident, locations 1 and 2 of the EPROM will hold a 20H and 02H, respectively.

The Microcomputer Educator accepts three inputs, defined by a 0, 1, 2, or 3 (see Table 11-1). Entering "3nnnn" changes a pointer called the "current location pointer" to nnnn, where nnnn is the value 0 through 2175. The location counter points to the location to be displayed or into which data (instructions) will be entered.

Entering "2" displays the contents of the current location on the EZ-80 display. Entering "0100" followed by "2," for example, sets the current location counter to decimal 100 and then displays the contents of location 100 (in the Common Area). Before display, the current location counter is incremented by one, so that it points to the next location, in this case 101. Entering "2" again (or simply "ENTER") displays the contents of 101, entering "2" again displays the contents of 102, and so forth. Note that both ROM and RAM locations may be examined.

Entering "1nnn" enters nnn into the current location and increments the current location pointer by one. Entering "32096," "123," "150," for example, sets the current location pointer to RAM location 2096 and then stores 23 into location 2096 and 50 into location 2097. Note that no data can be stored in EPROM! This command can be used to enter machine code into RAM for experimentation.

Another point that is extremely important to remember is the following: It is easy to cause erroneous results or "program bombing" by destroying data in the variable area (800H–82FH) or the stack area (860H and up), so do not change these locations unless you are aware of the consequences!

Entering "0" starts execution at the current location. Typically all machine code will be entered by using "1" commands, the current location pointer will be reset to start at the beginning of the entered program, and a "0" will then start execution, as shown in Fig. 11-3.

COMMAND STRINGS	COMMENT
32076	SET LOCATION COUNTER = 830H
11	01
1100	64
10	00
133	21
10	00
10	00
19	09
111	0B
1121	79
1176	B0
132	20
1250	FA
1221	DD
133	21
18	08
18	08
1205	CD
121	15
10	00
124	18
1254	FE
32076	SET LOCATION COUNTER = 850H
0	START EXECUTION

Fig. 11-3. Entering a simple program.

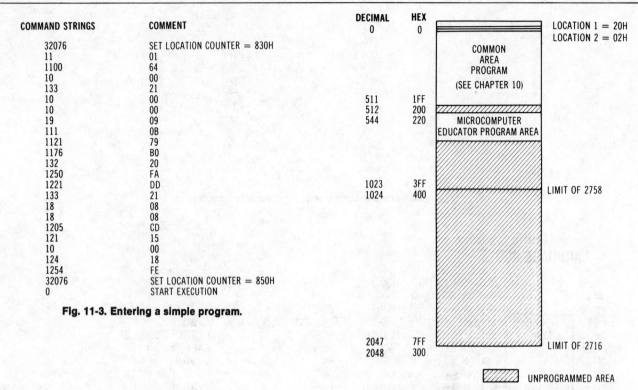

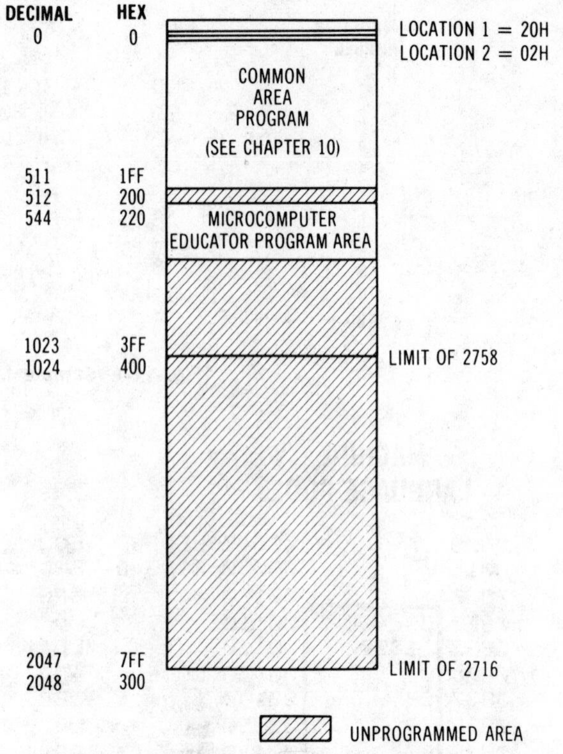

Fig. 11-4. Microcomputer Educator memory mapping.

```
                00099 *LIST OFF
                09999 *LIST ON
                10000 ;*****************************************************
                10010 ;                 MICROCOMPUTER EDUCATOR              *
                10020 ;                         00-05                       *
                10030 ;*****************************************************
                10040 ;
0220            10050         ORG     220H            ;NEXT EPROM AREA
0220            10060 MICRO   EQU     $               ;START OF MICR EDUC
0220 318008     10070         LD      SP,880H         ;INITIALIZE STACK
0223 21A402     10080         LD      HL,PDATA        ;START OF RAM DATA
0226 010300     10090         LD      BC,PDATAS       ;SIZE OF DATA
0229 CD0300     10100         CALL    INIT            ;INITIALIZE
022C 210000     10110 MICR90  LD      HL,0            ;ZERO HL
022F 220808     10120         LD      (LEDBUF),HL     ;ZERO LEFT DIGITS
0232 220A08     10130         LD      (LEDBUF+2),HL   ;ZERO RIGHT DIGITS
0235 213E02     10140         LD      HL,MICRT        ;FUNCTION TABLE ADDR
0238 110300     10150         LD      DE,0003H        ;0=MINIMUM,0-3 VALID
023B C31E00     10160         JP      BRANCH          ;BRANCH OUT
023E 1806       10170 MICRT   JR      MICR00          ;0=START EXECUTION
0240 1808       10180         JR      MICR10          ;1=SET DATA
0242 183B       10190         JR      MICR20          ;2=DISPLAY DATA
0244 184E       10200         JR      MICR30          ;3=SET LOCN COUNTER
                10210 ;
                10220 ;MICR00. START EXECUTION FROM CURRENT LOCATION.
                10230 ;
0246 2A2408     10240 MICR00  LD      HL,(PNTR)       ;GET CURRENT LOCATION
0249 E9         10250         JP      (HL)            ;JUMP OUT
                10260 ;
                10270 ;MICR10.SET LOCATION TO SPECIFIED DATA
                10280 ;
```

Fig. 11-5. Microcomputer Educator

```
024A 110001   10290 MICR10  LD      DE,256           ;MAXIMUM
024D AF       10300         XOR     A                ;ZERO FLAG
024E 322608   10310         LD      (MFLG),A         ;SET ONE BYTE
0251 DD211408 10320 MICR11  LD      IX,INBUF+1       ;START OF DATA
0255 3A2308   10330         LD      A,(NOCHR)        ;GET # OF CHARS INPUT
0258 47       10340         LD      B,A              ;MOVE TO B
0259 05       10350         DEC     B                ;ADJUST FOR FUNCTION CODE
025A CD1200   10360         CALL    BCDBIN           ;CONVERT
025D 3805     10370         JR      C,MICR12         ;GO IF OK
025F CD1B00   10380         CALL    BLINK            ;OVER LIMIT-BLINK
0262 18C8     10390         JR      MICR90           ;GO FOR NEXT FUNCTION
0264 DD2A2408 10400 MICR12  LD      IX,(PNTR)        ;GET CURRENT LOCATION
0268 DD7500   10410         LD      (IX),L           ;STORE VALUE
026B 3A2608   10420         LD      A,(MFLG)         ;GET 1/2 BYTE FLAG
026E B7       10430         OR      A                ;TEST
026F 2805     10440         JR      Z,MICR13         ;GO IF 1 BYTE
0271 DD7401   10450         LD      (IX+1),H         ;TWO BYTES
0274 18B6     10460         JR      MICR90           ;DON'T BUMP LOCATION
0276 2A2408   10470 MICR13  LD      HL,(PNTR)        ;GET CURRENT LOCATION
0279 23       10480         INC     HL               ;BUMP BY 1
027A 222408   10490         LD      (PNTR),HL        ;STORE
027D 18AD     10500         JR      MICR90           ;GET NEXT COMMAND
              10510 ;
              10520 ;MICR20.DISPLAY CURRENT LOCATION.
              10530 ;
027F 2A2408   10540 MICR20  LD      HL,(PNTR)        ;GET CURRENT LOCATION
0282 7E       10550         LD      A,(HL)           ;GET CONTENTS
0283 6F       10560         LD      L,A              ;NOW IN L
0284 2600     10570         LD      H,0              ;NOW IN HL
0286 DD210708 10580         LD      IX,LEDBUF-1      ;LED BUFFER
028A CD1500   10590         CALL    BINBCD           ;CONVERT AND DISPLAY
028D CD0C00   10600 MICR25  CALL    KEYSCN             ;TEST KEY PUSH
0290 28FB     10610         JR      Z,MICR25           ;GO IF NONE
0292 18E2     10620         JR      MICR13           ;GO TO UPDATE
              10630 ;
              10640 ;MICR30.SET LOCATION COUNTER.
              10650 ;
0294 212408   10660 MICR30  LD      HL,PNTR          ;LOCATION COUNTER LOCN
0297 222408   10670         LD      (PNTR),HL        ;TO ITSELF!
029A 118008   10680         LD      DE,880H          ;RAM+1
029D 3E01     10690         LD      A,1              ;ONE TO A
029F 322608   10700         LD      (MFLG),A         ;SET TWO-BYTE FLAG
02A2 18AD     10710         JR      MICR11           ;GO TO STORE
              10720 ;
              10730 ;DATA AREA
              10740 ;
02A4          10750 PDATA   EQU     $                ;START OF PROGRAM RAM
02A4 0000     10760         DEFW    0                ;(PNTR)
02A6 00       10770         DEFB    0                ;(MFLG)
              10780 ;********END OF LOCATIONS TO BE PROGRAMMED********
0003          10790 PDATAS  EQU     $-PDATA          ;SIZE
0824          10800 PNTR    EQU     PROGR            ;LOCATION OF (PNTR)
0826          10810 MFLG    EQU     PNTR+2           ;LOCATION OF MFLG
0000          10820         END
00000 TOTAL ERRORS
```

program listing.

Table 11-1. Microcomputer Educator Commands

Command	Description
0E	Start execution at location defined by current location counter.
1nnnE	Enter data nnn (0–255) into current location counter. Then increment location counter by one.
2E	Display data at current location and increment location counter by one. Pressing E again displays next location.
3nnnnE	Set location counter to nnnnn (0 to 2175). E = "ENTER"

The "default" start of the location pointer is 0. No check is made for altering the location pointer.

THEORY OF OPERATION

Refer to Fig. 11-5. The first part of the program initializes the stack and CALLs INIT to move the RAM data variables to RAM. A JP to BRANCH is then made to get the next command. The 0, 1, 2, and 3 commands are processed at MICR00, MICR10, MICR20, and MICR30, respectively.

MICR00 simply jumps out to the location pointed to by PNTR, the current location pointer. MICR10 converts the input value to binary (CALL BCDBIN). If the value is less than 256, it is stored in the current location and PNTR is incremented by 1; if the value is greater than 255, the LED display blinks to denote an error. MICR20 displays the contents of the current location and increments PNTR by one. The contents is displayed until the next key is pushed (CALL KEYSCN). MICR30 stores the value input into PNTR instead of the current location.

PNTR is a two-byte variable representing the current location. MFLG is a one-byte variable that denotes a one-byte store (0) or two-byte store (1). One byte is stored in the case of a "1" command, while two bytes are stored in the case of a "3" command, as the current location pointer may be a value up to 2175.

CHAPTER 12

Combination Lock

This chapter describes the Combination Lock of the EZ-80. Up to six outputs may be controlled by this application. Each output may control a lock solenoid or other action. A code sequence of digits is defined. For example, the code may be the (Fibonacci) series: 0112358. When this code is properly entered, the selected output energizes for 5 seconds. If the code is not entered properly, the display will blink. As the number of digits is of variable length, the result is a coded sequence that cannot be broken in a reasonable time, making this an ideal application for combination locks.

OPERATING INSTRUCTIONS

The Combination Lock is programmed into EPROM starting at 2C0H, as shown in Fig. 12-1. Other applications programs may be programmed into the EPROM if their locations do not conflict with the Combination Lock. Use the techniques in Chapter 10 to transfer control to the Combination Lock if other programs are coresident in EPROM. If only the Combination Lock is resident, locations 1 and 2 of the EPROM will hold a C0H and 02H, respectively.

The default code in EPROM is defined to be 11235. This code is used for all outputs directly upon power up, which occurs for initial start, manual restart, or power failure restart. A new code may be defined by keyboard input at any time. An alternative way to define a new code is to change the CODEP table in

Table 12-1. Combination Lock Commands

Command	Description
0mmmmnnnnnE	Change the code from mmmm to nnnnn. mmmm must be current code. nnnnn may be any string of digits for new code.
1mnnnnE	Energize output M (1–6). nnnn must be current code.
	E = "ENTER"

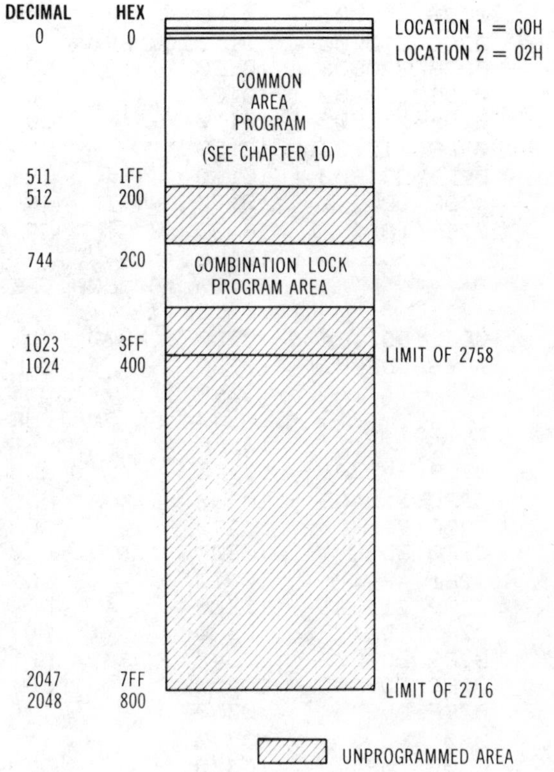

Fig. 12-1. Combination Lock memory mapping.

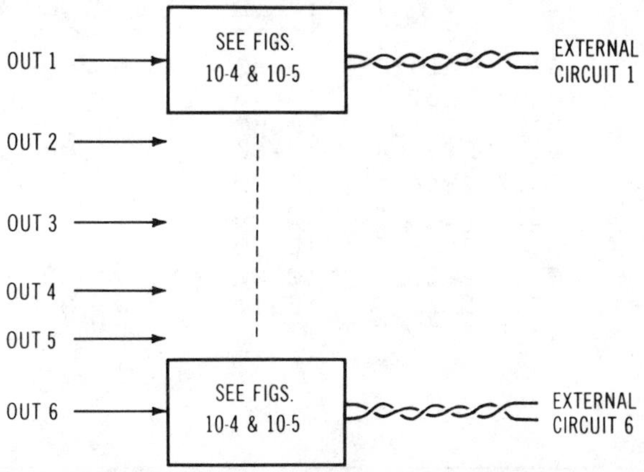

Fig. 12-2. Combination Lock relay outputs.

```
                00050 *LIST OFF
                09999 *LIST ON
                10000 ;*****************************************
                10010 ;*            COMBINATION LOCK           *
                10020 ;*                 00-01                 *
                10030 ;*****************************************
                10040 ;
02C0            10050           ORG     2C0H            ;NEXT EPROM AREA
02C0            10060 COMBO     EQU     $               ;START OF COMB LOCK
02C0 318008     10070           LD      SP,880H         ;INITIALIZE STACK
02C3 215903     10080           LD      HL,CODEP        ;START OF RAM DATA
02C6 010600     10090           LD      BC,CODEL        ;SIZE OF DATA
02C9 CD0300     10100           CALL    INIT            ;INITIALIZE
02CC 210000     10110 COMB90    LD      HL,0            ;ZERO HL
02CF 220808     10120           LD      (LEDBUF),HL     ;ZERO LEFT DIGITS
02D2 220A08     10130           LD      (LEDBUF+2),HL   ;ZERO RIGHT DIGITS
02D5 21DE02     10140           LD      HL,COMBT        ;FUNCTION TABLE ADDR
02D8 110103     10150           LD      DE,0301H        ;3 MINIMUM,0-1 VALID
02DB C31E00     10160           JP      BRANCH          ;BRANCH OUT
02DE 1802       10170 COMBT     JR      COMB00          ;0=REDEFINE
02E0 1825       10180           JR      COMB10          ;1=ENABLE
                10190 ;
                10200 ;COMB00. REDEFINE THE LOCK CODE
                10210 ;
02E2 DD211408   10220 COMB00    LD      IX,INBUF+1      ;POINT TO INPUT CODE
02E6 CD3B03     10230           CALL    COMCMP          ;COMPARE
                10240 ;
                10250 ;KEY MATCHES HERE
                10260 ;
02E9 3A2308     10270           LD      A,(NOCHR)       ;GET # OF CHARS INPUT
02EC 212408     10280           LD      HL,CODES        ;POINT TO CODE LENGTH
02EF 96         10290           SUB     (HL)            ;# IN NEW KEY+1
02F0 3D         10300           DEC     A               ;# IN NEW KEY
02F1 47         10310           LD      B,A             ;SETUP FOR STORE
02F2 322408     10320           LD      (CODES),A       ;STORE
02F5 FD212508   10330           LD      IY,CODER        ;START OF RAM KEY
02F9 DD7E00     10340 COMB02    LD      A,(IX)            ;GET NEW DIGITS
02FC FD7700     10350           LD      (IY),A            ;STORE IN RAM
02FF DD23       10360           INC     IX                ;BUMP DIGIT PNTR
0301 FD23       10370           INC     IY                ;BUMP RAM PNTR
0303 10F4       10380           DJNZ    COMB02            ;CONTINUE TIL ALL
0305 18C5       10390           JR      COMB90          ;GET NEXT COMMAND
                10400 ;
                10410 ;COMB10. ENABLE OUTPUT N.
                10420 ;
0307 3A1408     10430 COMB10    LD      A,(INBUF+1)     ;GET N
030A FE07       10440           CP      7               ;TEST FOR 1-6
030C F25303     10450           JP      P,COMCM3        ;ERROR, GT 6
030F B7         10460           OR      A               ;TEST FOR 0
0310 2841       10470           JR      Z,COMCM3        ;GO IF ZERO
0312 DD211508   10480           LD      IX,INBUF+2      ;START OF KEY
0316 CD3B03     10490           CALL    COMCMP          ;COMPARE
0319 3A2308     10500           LD      A,(NOCHR)       ;GET # INPUT
031C D602       10510           SUB     2               ;FIND # IN CODE
```

Fig. 12-3. Combination Lock

EPROM. The first digit is the number of digits in the code string. The sequence may be as long as desired (within limits of the input buffer).

There are two commands that may be input from the keyboard, "0" or "1" (see Table 12-1). Entering "0mmmmnnnnn" changes the code sequence from the EPROM value of "mmm" to the new value of "nnnnn." "mmmm" must be the current code sequence, and the new code sequence of "nnnnn" may be any length. If the incorrect value of the current code se-

quence is input, the display will blink for 5 seconds.

Entering "1mnnnnn" energizes output m if the entered code sequence "nnnnn" matches the current code. M may be 1–6, corresponding to OUT1–OUT6. Output m will be on for 5 seconds; this duration may be changed if locations "TIME+1" and "TIME+2" are changed to a value of other than 5000 (location TIME+1 holds the least significant byte of the value, while TIME+2 holds the most significant byte of the value).

```
031E 47        10520          LD    B,A            ;# IN CURRENT CODE
031F 3A2408    10530          LD    A,(CODES)
0322 90        10540          SUB   B              ;TEST FOR EQUAL
0323 202E      10550          JR    NZ,COMCM3      ;GO IF NOT EQUAL
               10560 ;
               10570 ;KEY MATCHES HERE
               10580 ;
0325 3A1408    10590          LD    A,(INBUF+1)    ;GET N
0328 47        10600          LD    B,A            ;TRANSFER TO B
0329 3E40      10610          LD    A,40H          ;BIT FOR OUTPUT LINE
032B 0F        10620 COMB12   RRCA                 ;ALIGN BIT
032C 10FD      10630          DJNZ  COMB12         ;LOOP TIL ALIGNED
032E D301      10640          OUT   (1),A          ;ENABLE OUTPUT LINE
0330 218813    10650 TIME     LD    HL,5000        ;5 SECONDS
0333 CD1800    10660          CALL  DELAY          ;DELAY
0336 AF        10670          XOR   A              ;ZERO A
0337 D301      10680          OUT   (1),A          ;DISABLE OUTPUT LINE
0339 1891      10690          JR    COMB90         ;GET NEXT COMMAND
               10700 ;
               10710 ;COMPARE SR. COMPARES TWO STRINGS
               10720 ;
033B FD212508  10730 COMCMP   LD    IY,CODER       ;START OF RAM CODE
033F 3A2408    10740          LD    A,(CODES)      ;LENGTH OF CODE
0342 47        10750          LD    B,A            ;TRANSFER TO B
0343 DD7E00    10760 COMCM1   LD    A,(IX)         ;INPUT CODE
0346 FDBE00    10770          CP    (IY)           ;COMPARE CODES
0349 2007      10780          JR    NZ,COMCM2      ;GO IF NOT EQUAL
034B DD23      10790          INC   IX             ;BUMP INPUT PNTR
034D FD23      10800          INC   IY             ;BUMP RAM PNTR
034F 10F2      10810          DJNZ  COMCM1         ;CONTINUE TIL ALL CHKD
0351 C9        10820          RET                  ;RETURN
0352 E1        10830 COMCM2   POP   HL             ;RESET STACK
0353 CD1800    10840 COMCM3   CALL  BLINK          ;BLINK DISPLAY
0356 C3CC02    10850          JP    COMB90         ;TRY AGAIN
               10860 ;
               10870 ;DATA AREA
               10880 ;
0359           10890 CODEP    EQU   $              ;START OF PROGRAM RAM
0359 05        10900          DEFB  5              ;CODE SIZE
035A 01        10910          DEFB  1              ;CODE=11235
035B 01        10920          DEFB  1
035C 02        10930          DEFB  2
035D 03        10940          DEFB  3
035E 05        10950          DEFB  5
               10960 ;*******END OF LOCATIONS TO BE PROGRAMED**********
0006           10970 CODEL    EQU   $-CODEP        ;SIZE
0824           10980 CODES    EQU   PROGR          ;LOCATION OF (CODES)
0825           10990 CODER    EQU   CODES+1        ;START OF KEY
0000           11000          END
00000 TOTAL ERRORS
```

program listing.

APPLICATIONS HARDWARE

The basic applications hardware required for this application is one *relay* for every output. The relays are physically small (1⅛ × ¾ × 1-inch) and may be mounted on the applications area of the wire-wrapped E-80 or on a separate board. The connections required for up to six outputs on OUT1 through OUT6 are shown in Fig. 12-2. Each relay uses a *diode* to reduce the reverse voltage developed as the relay coil is energized. The contacts of the relay will handle an ampere, so be careful not to attach to a heavy load on the relay contacts. It may be necessary to drive another relay with the relay. One way of doing this is shown in Fig. 10-6.

THEORY OF OPERATION

The Combination Lock Program (Fig. 12-3) is made up of four parts, initialization, "0" command processing, "1" command processing, and a compare subroutine.

Initialization (COMBO) initializes the stack and then moves the variables to RAM (CALL INIT). The BRANCH routine is then entered to input the next command. If the command is a "0," the code at COMB00 is entered. The compare subroutine is CALLed to compare the code sequence to the current code sequence. If the codes compare, the new code is substituted for the old in RAM and a jump is made to COMB90 to get the next command. (If the codes do not compare, the display blinks.) If the command input is a "1" and the input code matches the current code, the code at COMB10 is entered. The output number is converted to the proper one bit to be sent to the 8255, resulting in an output on PB5–PB0 (OUT1–OUT6). This output is enabled for 5 seconds, after which it is reset and a jump made to COMB90 to get the next command.

Subroutine COMCMP is a general-purpose subroutine that compares two strings of digits, one string located in RAM, and the other the input string. If each digit of the two strings does not compare, the display is blinked for 5 seconds and a jump is made to COMB90 for the next command. If the strings do compare, a RET(urn) is made to the instruction after the CALL is made.

The main variable in this application is the code sequence itself. This sequence is moved from EPROM to RAM during initialization. Any redefinition of the code results in a new sequence being stored in the RAM variable area. The first byte of the code sequence is always the number of bytes in the code sequence to follow.

CHAPTER 13

Burglar Alarm

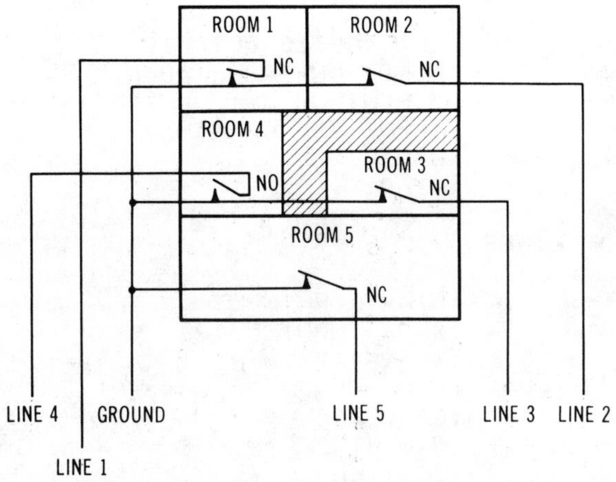

Fig. 13-1. Burglar Alarm application.

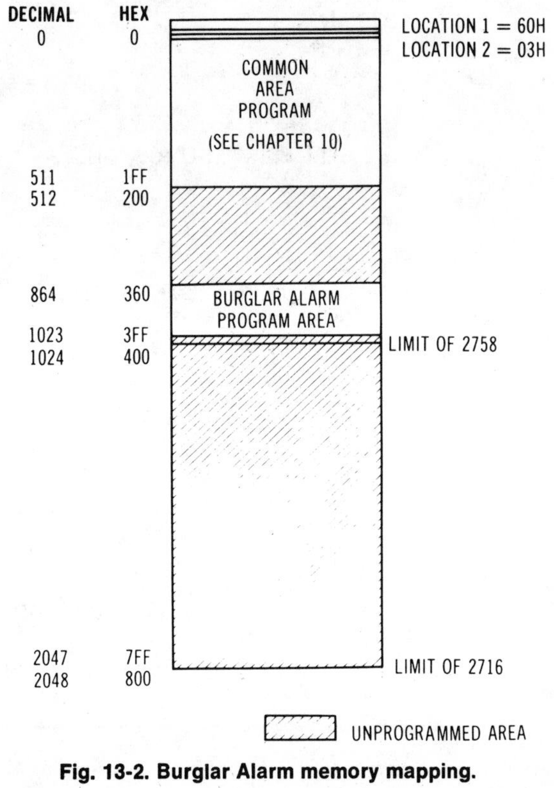

Fig. 13-2. Burglar Alarm memory mapping.

This chapter describes the Burglar Alarm application of the EZ-80. Up to five inputs are tested thousands of times per second. The five inputs represent either a normally open or normally closed switch or set of switches that comprise a burglar alarm system. The state of the inputs may be redefined at any time. If input number 1 is normally closed, but must be opened for some reason, input number 1 may be redefined as "open." When the burglar alarm application is active, an input that becomes "open" when it should be closed or one that becomes "closed" when

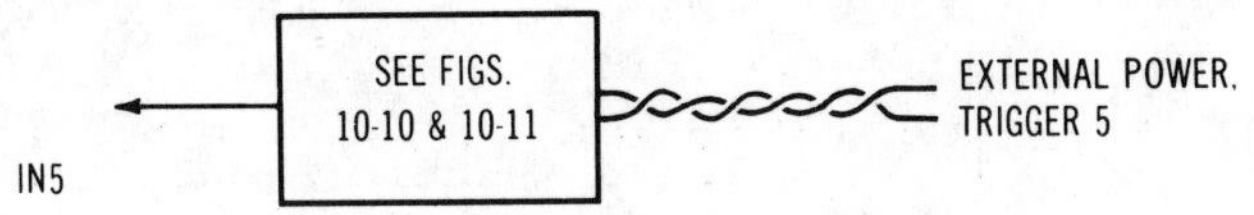

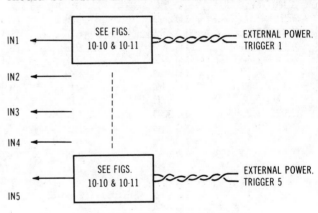

Fig. 13-3. Burglar Alarm relay inputs.

Table 13-1. Burglar Alarm Commands

Command	Description
OnnE	Define state of input lines IN1–IN5 to be nn, where nn is 0–31 (0–11111).
1E	Start burglar alarm. Continuously check state of input lines for match to defined state. If different, display failing number, output audio alarm, and turn on corresponding output line.
	E = "ENTER"

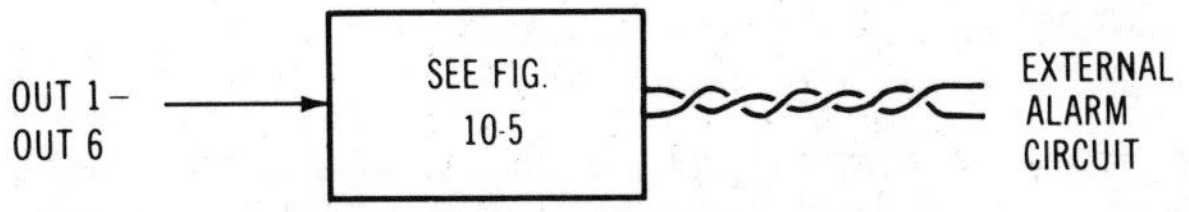

Fig. 13-4. Output line connections.

```
                00099 *LIST OFF
                09999 *LIST ON
                10000 ;*******************************************
                10010 ;              BURGLAR ALARM              *
                10020 ;                 00-04                   *
                10030 ;*******************************************
                10040 ;
0360            10050          ORG     360H             ;NEXT EPROM AREA
0360            10060 BURGLR   EQU     $                ;START OF BURGLAR ALARM
0360 318008     10070          LD      SP,880H          ;INITIALIZE STACK
0363 21FA03     10080          LD      HL,PDATA         ;START OF RAM DATA
0366 010100     10090          LD      BC,PDATAS        ;SIZE OF DATA
0369 CD0300     10100          CALL    INIT             ;INITIALIZE
036C 210000     10110 BURG90   LD      HL,0             ;0 TO HL
036F 220808     10120          LD      (LEDBUF),HL      ;ZERO FOR DISPLAY
0372 220A08     10130          LD      (LEDBUF+2),HL    ;ZERO LS DIGITS
0375 7D         10131          LD      A,L              ;ZERO A
0376 D301       10132          OUT     (1),A            ;INITIALIZE OUTPUTS
0378 218103     10140          LD      HL,BURGT         ;FUNCTION TABLE ADDR
037B 110100     10150          LD      DE,0001H         ;0 MINIMUM,0-1 VALID
037E C31E00     10160          JP      BRANCH           ;INPUT AND BRANCH
0381 1802       10170 BURGT    JR      BURG00           ;0=DEFINE
0383 1820       10180          JR      BURG10           ;START
                10190 ;
                10200 ;BURG00. DEFINE STATES OF LINES
                10210 ;
0385 DD211408   10220 BURG00   LD      IX,INBUF+1       ;START OF INPUT
0389 3A2308     10230          LD      A,(NOCHR)        ;# OF INPUT CHARS
038C 47         10240          LD      B,A              ;TRANSFER TO B
038D 05         10250          DEC     B                ;# OF CHARS TO CONVERT
038E CD1200     10260          CALL    BCDBIN           ;CONVERT
0391 7D         10270          LD      A,L              ;GET #
0392 D620       10280          SUB     32               ;TEST FOR LT 32
0394 FA9C03     10290          JP      M,BURG01         ;GO IF LT 32
0397 CD1B00     10300          CALL    BLINK            ;OVER LIMIT-BLINK
039A 18D0       10310          JR      BURG90           ;GO FOR NEXT FUNCTION
039C 7D         10320 BURG01   LD      A,L              ;GET N
039D 07         10330          RLCA                     ;ALIGN
039E 07         10340          RLCA
039F 07         10350          RLCA
03A0 322408     10360          LD      (CODE),A         ;SAVE FOR TEST
03A3 18C7       10370          JR      BURG90           ;GO FOR NEXT FUNCTION
                10380 ;
                10390 ;BURG10.START ALARM
                10400 ;
03A5 DB02       10410 BURG10   IN      A,(02)           ;GET LINES
03A7 E6F8       10420          AND     0F8H             ;GET INPUT LINES ONLY
03A9 47         10430          LD      B,A              ;NOW IN B
03AA 3A2408     10440          LD      A,(CODE)         ;GET CODE
03AD A8         10450          XOR     B                ;TEST FOR EQUAL
03AE 2014       10460          JR      NZ,BURG11        ;NOT EQUAL
03B0 2600       10461          LD      H,0              ;ZERO MSB
03B2 3A0308     10462          LD      A,(SECS)         ;GET SECONDS
03B5 6F         10463          LD      L,A              ;TRANSFER TO HL
03B6 DD210708   10464          LD      IX,LEDBUF-1      ;LED DISPLAY BUFFER
03BA CD1500     10465          CALL    BINBCD           ;DISPLAY SOMETHING
03BD CD0C00     10470          CALL    KEYSCN           ;TEST FOR KEY
03C0 28E3       10480          JR      Z,BURG10         ;GO IF NONE
03C2 18A8       10490          JR      BURG90           ;KEY PUSH-GO FOR COMMAND
03C4 0F         10500 BURG11   RRCA                     ;ALIGN
03C5 0F         10510          RRCA
03C6 4F         10520          LD      C,A              ;SAVE FAILING BIT
```

Fig. 13-5. Burglar Alarm

it should be open causes a blinking display of the input that is incorrect, generation of an audio tone on output line 6, and closure of the associated output line 1 to 5.

Fig. 13-1 shows a typical application of this system. There are five rooms involved, and they are connected to input lines 1–5. Lines 1, 2, 3, and 5 represent normally closed inputs. Line 4 is normally open. If a switch is broken in room 3 (metal foil on a window, or other such switch), output line 3 goes high, a tone is generated on output line 6 which is fed into a small audio amplifier, and the number 3 flashes on the EZ-80 LED display.

OPERATING INSTRUCTIONS

The Burglar Alarm is programmed into EPROM starting at 360H, as shown in Fig. 13-2. Other applications programs may be programmed into the EPROM if their locations do not conflict with the Burglar Alarm. Use the techniques described in Chapter 10 to transfer control to the Burglar Alarm if other programs are to be coresident in EPROM. If only the Burglar Alarm is resident, locations 1 and 2 of the EPROM will hold a 60H and a 03H, respectively.

There are two commands that may be input from the keyboard, "0" or "1" (see Table 13-1). Entering "0nn" defines the state of the five input lines. Here "nn" is a number from 0 to 31, representing the state of input lines 1–5.

Entering "1" starts the burglar alarm. The program takes the current definition of the five lines and compares it to the instantaneous values of the five lines tens of thousands of times per second. If no "0" input to define the lines has occurred, the Burglar Alarm program assumes that all five lines are normally open.

APPLICATIONS HARDWARE

The basic applications hardware required for this application is five relay sets, one for each input line. They are connected as shown in Fig. 13-3. When an

```
03C7 0607     10530          LD     B,7            ;# OF FAILING LINE
03C9 05       10540 BURG12   DEC    B                 ;BUMP #
03CA CB3F     10550          SRL    A                 ;SHIFT
03CC 20FB     10560          JR     NZ,BURG12         ;GO IF NOT SHIFTED OUT
03CE 320808   10570          LD     (LEDBUF),A     ;ZERO LEDBUF
03D1 320908   10580          LD     (LEDBUF+1),A
03D4 320A08   10590          LD     (LEDBUF+2),A
03D7 78       10600          LD     A,B            ;GET # FOR DISPLAY
03D8 320B08   10610          LD     (LEDBUF+3),A   ;STORE #
03DB 3EFF     10620          LD     A,0FFH         ;ALL ON FOR BLINK
03DD 320F08   10630          LD     (BLINV),A      ;SET BLINK FLAG
03E0 79       10640          LD     A,C            ;RESTORE FAILING BIT
03E1 EE01     10650 BURG13   XOR    1                 ;SET FOR ALARM
03E3 D301     10660          OUT    (01),A            ;OUTPUT TO LINE & ALARM
03E5 210100   10670          LD     HL,1              ;DELAY 1 MS
03E8 CD1800   10680          CALL   DELAY             ;DELAY
03EB F5       10690          PUSH   AF                ;SAVE A
03EC CD0C00   10700          CALL   KEYSCN            ;TEST FOR KEYPUSH
03EF E1       10702          POP    HL                ;GET A
03F0 7C       10704          LD     A,H               ;DON'T DISTURB CARRY
03F1 28EE     10710          JR     Z,BURG13          ;GO IF NONE
03F3 AF       10721          XOR    A                 ;0 TO A
03F4 320F08   10722          LD     (BLINV),A         ;RESET BLINK
03F7 C36C03   10730          JP     BURG90          ;GO TO INPUT
              10740 ;
              10750 ;DATA AREA
              10760 ;
03FA          10770 PDATA    EQU    $              ;START OF PROGRAM RAM
03FA F8       10780          DEFB   0F8H           ;(CODE)-ALL ON
              10790 ;*******END OF LOCATIONS TO BE PROGRAMED*********
0001          10800 PDATAS   EQU    $-PDATA        ;SIZE
0824          10810 CODE     EQU    PROGR          ;LOCATION OF (CODE)
0000          10820          END
00000 TOTAL ERRORS
```

program listing.

input becomes active, the corresponding output line goes high. This line may be used to trigger an additional alarm associated with one of the five circuits, driven by a relay or solenoid as shown in Fig. 13-4. Output line 6 is used to generate an audio tone, which may be fed into a small audio amplifier which is mounted on the EZ-80 as shown in Figs. 10-8 and 10-9.

THEORY OF OPERATION

The Burglar Alarm application program (Fig. 13-5) is made up of three parts: the initialization area (BURGLR), processing of the "0" command (BURG00), and processing of the 1 command (BURG10).

The initialization portion initializes the stack and then moves the variable (CODE) into the RAM area. CODE is predefined to be all ones (all lines open). A CALL is then made to the common area BRANCH routine to input the next command.

The code at BURG00 processes a "0" command. The nn value is converted from keyboard BCD to binary (BCDBIN). If the value is 0–31, it is saved in variable CODE for comparison to the states of the five input lines. If the value is not 0–31, the LED display blinks to signal erroneous input.

The code at BURG10 starts the alarm. The five input lines are read and compared to the CODE value. If the values are identical, the inputs are read again. If at any time the inputs do not equal the CODE definition, the failing input is converted to a digit of 1–5 and displayed on the LED display. The blink flag (BLINV) is then set to blink the display. The associated output line is then set to 1 and a tone is output on line 6. This condition continues until a key is pressed.

The sole variable in this program is CODE, used to hold the definition of the input lines.

CHAPTER 14

Morse Code Generator

This chapter describes the Morse Code Generator application of the EZ-80. This chapter and the next one use some of the same coding. The generator generates a continuous stream of random Morse code characters at user selectable rates from 1 to 99 words per minute. The characters are "pseudo-random," that is, they are random, but *repeatable* from the same point, to allow for verification of copied code characters at a slower speed. Ten different sequences, 0–9, may be chosen. The characters are sent in eight-letter groupings.

The output of the generator is a tone on the OUT6 line which can be fed into an external audio amplifier or used with an "on-board" audio amplifier with a small speaker.

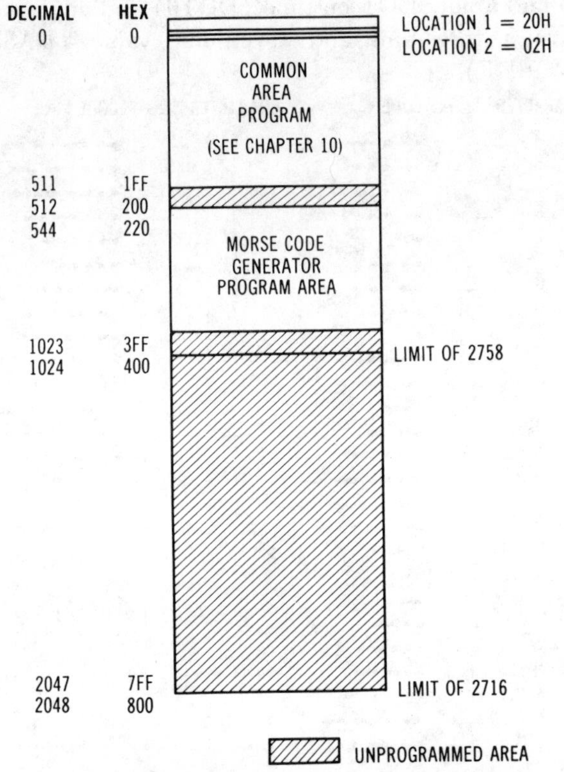

Fig. 14-1. Morse Code Generator memory mapping.

Table 14-1. Morse Code Generator Commands

Command	Description
OnE	Send random code characters A–Z, 0–9, ".", ",", "?", and "/" at speed currently defined in 8-letter groups based on "seed" n.
1nnE	Set speed of transmission to nn (0–99) words per minute.
	E = "ENTER"

OPERATING INSTRUCTIONS

The generator is programmed into EPROM starting at 220H, as shown in Fig. 14-1. The generator takes up the majority of a 1K (2758) EPROM; other programs could be used in the same 2716 EPROM. Set locations 1 and 2 of the EPROM to 20H and 02H, respectively, for an EPROM with only the generator present.

The generator uses two commands as shown in Table 14-1. The "On" command starts the generation of Morse code characters. The sequence used is defined by n, whose values are 0–9. Restarting the generator with the same value of n will result in the same

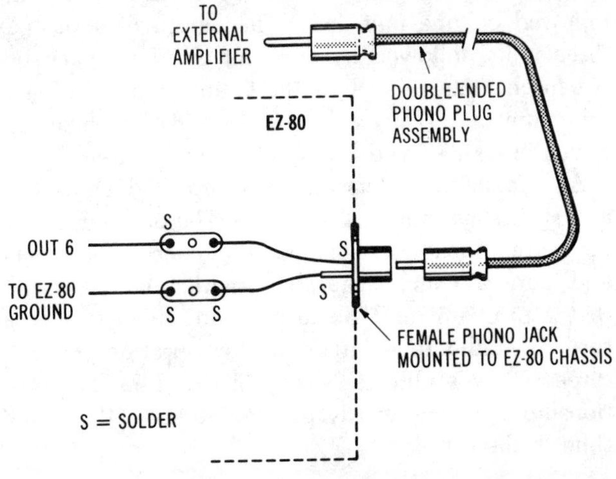

Fig. 14-2. Morse Code Generator external audio.

sequence being generated for each restart. The speed of transmission will be the speed specified by the user for the "1" command. If no speed has been input, the code will be sent at one word per minute. Pressing any key stops the transmission.

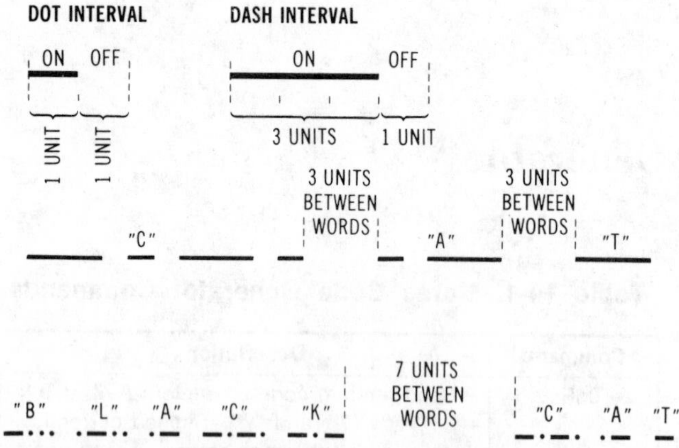

Fig. 14-3. Morse code intervals.

The "1nn" command allows the user to specify the speed in steps of one word per minute. Limited input checking for invalid characters is done, but extensive checking is not performed to save space in EPROM.

APPLICATIONS HARDWARE

The basic applications hardware required for this application is an audio amplifier chip and speaker for output OUT6, connected as shown in Fig. 10-8 and 10-9. Alternatively, the output on OUT6 could be fed into an external amplifier as shown in Fig. 14-2.

THEORY OF OPERATION

Morse code characters are standardized as shown in Fig. 14-3. The length of a dot is one unit "on," followed by one unit "off." The length of a dash is three units, followed by one unit off. The space between characters (such as the C and A in "CAT") is three units. The space between words (such as between "BLACK" and "CAT") is seven units long.

All Morse characters are made up of dots, dashes, and spaces, as shown in Fig. 14-4. The ones generated here are alphabetic characters, numeric characters, and period, comma, question mark, and slash. All that a program must do to generate characters is to turn an audio tone on or off for durations of one, three, or seven units, as shown in Fig. 14-3. The relationship between words per minute and the "unit" time of the dot is:

$$\text{words/minute} = \text{dots per second} \times 2.4$$

making a one word per minute dot about 1.2 seconds and a 99 word-per-minute dot about 12 milliseconds (12/1000 second) for the "on" time. Fig. 14-4 is the complete Morse code.

The Morse Code Generator is made up of several parts (see Fig. 14-5). On the bottom level is the TOGGLE subroutine which creates an audio tone for a specified duration. The tone is created by turning on OUT6 and then turning it off. The on/off toggle is done about 1000 times per second, creating a 1000-hertz tone on the output of OUT6. This toggle is done continuously for a duration determined by a count in HL. For each cycle, one count is subtracted from HL. The count specified determines whether the tone will be on for a dot interval or a dash interval, or whether there will simply be a time delay (no tone) for a dot, dash, or space interval.

The TONE subroutine CALLs the TOGGLE subroutine with two counts. The first (in HL) is the "on" time count, and the second (in DE) is the off time count. TONE is in turn called by the subroutines to send a dot (MORST), a dash (MORSH), a character space (MORSC), or a word space (MORSW). These routines simply pick up the right counts for on times and off times for these functions. As the counts change with speed, the counts are adjusted to the speed every time the speed is changed by command "1." The basic unit time (ONE WPM), representing the length of a dot for one word per minute is divided by the speed to find a new DOT on time (DOT0) and adjusted to give a three-unit and seven-unit value (DASH0, WORDF).

CHARACTER	CODE	CHARACTER	CODE
A	.-	0	-----
B	-...	1	.----
C	-.-.	2	..---
D	-..	3	...--
E	.	4	....-
F	..-.	5	.....
G	--.	6	-....
H	....	7	--...
I	..	8	---..
J	.---	9	----.
K	-.-		
L	.-..	.	.-.-.-
M	--	,	--..--
N	-.	?	..--..
O	---	/	-..-.
P	.--.		
Q	--.-		
R	.-.		
S	...		
T	-		
U	..-		
V	...-		
W	.--		
X	-..-		
Y	-.--		
Z	--..		

Fig. 14-4. Morse code characters.

```
                 00099 *LIST OFF
                 09999 *LIST ON
                 10000 ;******************************************
                 10010 ;           MORSE CODE GENERATOR            *
                 10020 ;                 00-03                     *
                 10030 ;******************************************
                 10040 ;
0220             10050          ORG     220H          ;START EPROM AREA
0220             10060 MORSE    EQU     $             ;START OF MORSE PROGRAM
0220 318008      10070          LD      SP,880H       ;INITIALIZE STACK
0223 21A903      10080          LD      HL,PDATA      ;START OF RAM DATA
0226 010700      10090          LD      BC,PDATAS     ;SIZE OF DATA
0229 CD0300      10100          CALL    INIT          ;INITIALIZE
022C 210000      10110 MQRS90   LD      HL,0          ;0 TO HL
022F 220808      10120          LD      (LEDBUF),HL   ;ZERO FOR MS DISPLAY
0232 220A08      10130          LD      (LEDBUF+2),HL ;ZERO LS DIGITS
0235 213E02      10140          LD      HL,MORTB      ;FUNCTION TABLE ADDDR
0238 110101      10150          LD      DE,0101H      ;1 MINIMUM,0-1 VALID
023B C31E00      10160          JP      BRANCH        ;INPUT AND BRANCH
023E 1803        10170 MORTB    JR      MORS10        ;0=SEND RANDOM
0240 C39902      10180          JP      MORS20        ;1=SET SPEED(MUST BE LAST)
                 10190 ;
                 10200 ;MORS10.SEND RANDOM CHARACTERS.
                 10210 ;
0243 AF          10220 MORS10   XOR     A             ;0
0244 322408      10230          LD      (MNUM),A      ;INITIALIZE CHAR COUNT
0247 3A1408      10240          LD      A,(INBUF+1)   ;GET SEED
024A 3C          10242          INC     A             ;FOR NON-ZERO MULTIPLY
024B 67          10244          LD      H,A           ;PUT IN MSB
024C 6F          10246          LD      L,A           ;PUT IN LSB
024D E5          10250          PUSH    HL            ;SAVE FOR NEXT RANDOM
024E CD0C00      10260 MORS1A   CALL    KEYSCN          ;TEST FOR KEY DEPRESS
0251 CA5802      10270          JP      Z,MORS1B        ;GO IF KEY NOT PRESSED
0254 E1          10280          POP     HL              ;RESET STACK
0255 C32C02      10290          JP      MORS90          ;GO FOR NEXT COMMAND
0258 D1          10300 MORS1B   POP     DE              ;GET SEED
0259 210000      10310          LD      HL,0            ;GENERATE NEW RANDOM #
025C 0605        10320          LD      B,5
025E 19          10330 MORS1E   ADD     HL,DE
025F 10FD        10340          DJNZ    MORS1E
0261 E5          10350          PUSH    HL              ;SAVE FOR NEXT TIME
0262 7C          10355          LD      A,H             ;GET MS BYTE
0263 E67E        10360          AND     07EH            ;GET 0-126
0265 4F          10370          LD      C,A             ;NOW IN C
0266 0600        10380          LD      B,0             ;NOW IN B
0268 DD212903    10390          LD      IX,MCHRT        ;CHARACTER TABLE ADDRESS
026C DD09        10400          ADD     IX,BC           ;POINT TO CHAR
026E DD4601      10410          LD      B,(IX+1)        ;GET # BITS
0271 DD4E00      10420          LD      C,(IX)          ;GET CONFIGURATION
0274 CB01        10430 MORS11   RLC     C               ;SHIFT OUT BIT
0276 C5          10440          PUSH    BC                ;SAVE #, CONFIG
0277 381B        10450          JR      C,MORS12          ;GO IF DASH
0279 CDDB02      10460          CALL    MORST             ;SEND DOT
```

Fig. 14-5. Morse Code Generator program listing.

```
027C C1       10470 MORS1C  POP     BC              ;RESTORE #,CONFIG
027D 10F5     10480         DJNZ    MORS11          ;CONTINUE IF MORE
027F 212408   10482         LD      HL,MNUM         ;CONTINUE IF MORE
0282 34       10484         INC     (HL)            ;BUMP CHAR CNT
0283 3A2408   10490         LD      A,(MNUM)        ;GET CHAR COUNT
0286 E607     10500         AND     7               ;GET 3 LS BITS
0288 2005     10510         JR      NZ,MORS1D
028A CDF402   10520         CALL    MORSW           ;SEND WORD SPACE
028D 18BF     10530         JR      MORS1A          ;NEXT CHARACTER
028F CDE402   10540 MORS1D  CALL    MORSC           ;SEND CHAR SPACE
0292 18BA     10550         JR      MORS1A          ;NEXT CHARACTER
0294 CDD002   10560 MORS12  CALL    MORSH           ;SEND DASH
0297 18E3     10570         JR      MORS1C          ;GO TO OUTPUT
              10580 ;
              10590 ;MORS20.SET SPEED.
              10600 ;
0299 DD211408 10610 MORS20  LD      IX,INBUF+1      ;START OF INPUT
029D 3A2308   10620         LD      A,(NOCHR)       ;GET # OF INPUT CHARS
02A0 47       10630         LD      B,A             ;TRANSFER TO B
02A1 05       10640         DEC     B               ;# OF CHARS TO CONVERT
02A2 CD1200   10650         CALL    BCDBIN          ;CONVERT
02A5 4D       10660         LD      C,L             ;SPEED IN C
02A6 79       10661         LD      A,C             ;GET SPEED FOR 0 TEST
02A7 B7       10662         OR      A               ;TEST FOR 0
02A8 2006     10663         JR      NZ,MORS21       ;GO IF NOT 0
02AA CD1B00   10664         CALL    BLINK           ;ERROR-BLINK
02AD C32C02   10665         JP      MORS90          ;GET NEXT COMMAND
02B0 21C704   10670 MORS21  LD      HL,ONEWPM       ;1 WPM UNIT
02B3 0600     10680         LD      B,0             ;SPEED IN BC
02B5 11FFFF   10690         LD      DE,-1           ;QUOTIENT
02B8 B7       10700 MORS22  OR      A                  ;RESET CARRY
02B9 ED42     10710         SBC     HL,BC              ;DIVIDE BY SPEED
02BB 13       10720         INC     DE                 ;BUMP QUOTIENT
02BC F2B802   10730         JP      P,MORS22           ;CONTINUE TIL NEGATIVE
02BF D5       10740         PUSH    DE              ;SAVE QUOTIENT
02C0 E1       10750         POP     HL              ;TRANSFER TO HL
02C1 222508   10760         LD      (DOTO),HL       ;DOT ON TIME
02C4 29       10770         ADD     HL,HL           ;UNIT*2
02C5 19       10780         ADD     HL,DE           ;UNIT*3
02C6 222708   10790         LD      (DASHO),HL      ;DASH ON TIME
02C9 29       10800         ADD     HL,HL           ;UNIT*6
02CA 222908   10810         LD      (WORDF),HL      ;WORD OFF TIME
02CD C32C02   10820         JP      MORS90          ;GO FOR NEXT COMMAND
              10830 ;
              10840 ;MORSH.SEND DASH.
              10850 ;
02D0 2A2708   10860 MORSH   LD      HL,(DASHO)      ;DASH ON TIME
02D3 ED5B2508 10870         LD      DE,(DASHF)      ;DASH OFF TIME
02D7 CDFA02   10880 MORSH1  CALL    TONE            ;OUTPUT
02DA C9       10890         RET                     ;RETURN
              10900 ;
              10910 ;MORST.SEND DOT.
              10920 ;
```

Fig. 14-5 cont'd. Morse Code

```
02FD 2808     11170          JR     Z,TONE1        ;GO IF NO ON TIME
02FF 0E03     11180          LD     C,3            ;OUTPUT MASK
0301 CD0E03   11190          CALL   TOGGLE         ;OUTPUT TONE AND DELAY
0304 AF       11200          XOR    A              ;0
0305 D301     11210          OUT    (1),A          ;TURN OFF OUT5,OUT6
0307 E1       11220 TONE1    POP    HL             ;GET OFF TIME
0308 0E00     11230          LD     C,0            ;OUTPUT MASK
030A CD0E03   11240          CALL   TOGGLE         ;DELAY ONLY
030D C9       11250          RET                   ;RETURN
              11260 ;
              11270 ;TOGGLE.OUTPUT TONE ON OUT6 AND DELAY.
              11280 ;
030E 11FFFF   11290 TOGGLE   LD     DE,-1          ;-1 FOR DECREMENT
0311 3E03     11300          LD     A,3            ;FOR OUTPUT
0313 19       11310 TOGG1    ADD    HL,DE          ;HL-1 TO HL
0314 D0       11320          RET    NC             ;RETURN IF DONE
0315 A1       11330          AND    C              ;AND ACTIVE BIT WITH MASK
0316 D301     11340          OUT    (1),A          ;OUTPUT
0318 0624     11350          LD     B,36           ;ON CNT
031A 10FE     11360          DJNZ   $                 ;LOOP HERE
031C EE01     11370          XOR    1              ;TOGGLE OUT6
031E A1       11380          AND    C              ;AND ACTIVE BIT WITH MASK
031F D301     11390          OUT    (1),A          ;OUTPUT
0321 0623     11400          LD     B,35           ;OFF CNT
0323 10FE     11410          DJNZ   $                 ;LOOP HERE
0325 EE01     11415          XOR    1              ;TOGGLE OUT6
0327 18EA     11420          JR     TOGG1          ;CONTINUE
              11430 ;

02DB 2A2508   10930 MORST    LD     HL,(DOTO)      ;DOT ON TIME
02DE ED5B2508 10940          LD     DE,(DOTF)      ;DOT OFF TIME
02E2 18F3     10950          JR     MORSH1         ;OUTPUT
              10960 ;
              10970 ;MORSC.SEND CHARACTER SPACE.
              10980 ;
02E4 2A2708   10990 MORSC    LD     HL,(CHARF)     ;CHARACTER SPACE OFF TIME
02E7 ED5B2508 11000          LD     DE,(DOTO)      ;DOT ON TIME
02EB B7       11010          OR     A              ;CLEAR C
02EC ED52     11020          SBC    HL,DE          ;TWO UNITS
02EE EB       11030          EX     DE,HL          ;OFF TO DE
02EF 210000   11040 MORSC1   LD     HL,0           ;CHARACTER SPACE ON TIME
02F2 18E3     11050          JR     MORSH1         ;OUTPUT
              11060 ;
              11070 ;MORSW.SEND WORD SPACE.
              11080 ;
02F4 ED5B2908 11090 MORSW    LD     DE,(WORDF)     ;WORD SPACE OFF TIME(6)
02F8 18F5     11100          JR     MORSC1         ;OUTPUT
              11110 ;
              11120 ;OUTPUT DOT,DASH,SPACE
              11130 ;
02FA D5       11140 TONE     PUSH   DE             ;SAVE OFF TIME
02FB 7D       11150          LD     A,L            ;GET ON TIME LSB
02FC B4       11160          OR     H              ;MERGE ON TIME MSB
```

Generator program listing.

```
                11440 ;CHARACTER TABLE.
                11450 ;
0329            11460 MCHRT    EQU     $              ;TABLE OF CHARACTERS
0329 4002       11470          DEFW    240H           ;A
032B 8004       11480          DEFW    480H           ;B
032D A004       11490          DEFW    4A0H           ;C
032F 8003       11500          DEFW    380H           ;D
0331 0001       11510          DEFW    100H           ;E
0333 2004       11520          DEFW    420H           ;F
0335 C003       11530          DEFW    3C0H           ;G
0337 0004       11540          DEFW    400H           ;H
0339 0002       11550          DEFW    200H           ;I
033B 7004       11560          DEFW    470H           ;J
033D A003       11570          DEFW    3A0H           ;K
033F 4004       11580          DEFW    440H           ;L
0341 C002       11590          DEFW    2C0H           ;M
0343 8002       11600          DEFW    280H           ;N
0345 E003       11610          DEFW    3E0H           ;O
0347 6004       11620          DEFW    460H           ;P
0349 D004       11630          DEFW    4D0H           ;Q
034B 4003       11640          DEFW    340H           ;R
034D 0003       11650          DEFW    300H           ;S
034F 8001       11660          DEFW    180H           ;T
0351 2003       11670          DEFW    320H           ;U
0353 1004       11680          DEFW    410H           ;V
0355 6003       11690          DEFW    360H           ;W
0357 9004       11700          DEFW    490H           ;X
0359 B004       11710          DEFW    4B0H           ;Y
035B C004       11720          DEFW    4C0H           ;Z
035D 7805       11730          DEFW    578H           ;1
035F 3805       11740          DEFW    538H           ;2
0361 1805       11750          DEFW    518H           ;3
0363 0805       11760          DEFW    508H           ;4
0365 0005       11770          DEFW    500H           ;5
0367 8005       11780          DEFW    580H           ;6
0369 C005       11790          DEFW    5C0H           ;7
036B E005       11800          DEFW    5E0H           ;8
036D F005       11810          DEFW    5F0H           ;9
036F F805       11820          DEFW    5F8H           ;0
0371 3006       11830          DEFW    630H           ;?
0373 5406       11840          DEFW    654H           ;.
0375 CC06       11850          DEFW    6CCH           ;,
0377 9005       11860          DEFW    590H           ;/
0379 0001       11870          DEFW    100H           ;E
037B 8001       11880          DEFW    180H           ;T
037D 0002       11890          DEFW    200H           ;I
037F C002       11900          DEFW    2C0H           ;M
0381 4002       11910          DEFW    240H           ;A
0383 8002       11920          DEFW    280H           ;N
0385 0003       11930          DEFW    300H           ;S
0387 E003       11940          DEFW    3E0H           ;O
0389 C003       11950          DEFW    3C0H           ;G
038B A003       11960          DEFW    3A0H           ;K
```

Fig. 14-5 cont'd. Morse Code

The MORS10 routine generates and sends random characters. An 8-bit value is generated by the input value for the "0n" command, or by the last random value. This value is used to find an even index of 1, 2, 4, . . . , 126. The index is then used to find a character in the MCHRT character table. Each character in the table is made up of two bytes, as shown in Fig. 14-6. The second byte contains the number of dots and dashes in the character. For example "E" has 1 (dot), while "P" has four (dot dash dash dot). The first byte is the sequence of dots and dashes from left to right. The first byte of "P," for example, is 60H, or 01100000. If 0 is a dot and 1 is a dash, then the first 4 bits are dot dash dash dot, and this is how the MORSIO routine generates the P character. The bits are stripped off the left end of the value one at a time, and the number stripped off is the number contained in the second byte of the character code. After each character is sent, either a character or word space is sent, the word space being sent after every eight characters.

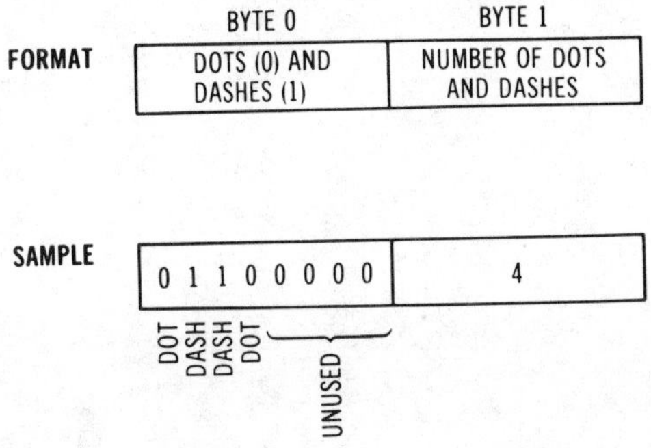

Fig. 14-6. Morse Code Generator code table format.

Variables in this program include default values for one, three, and seven units at one word per minute (DOTO, ONEWPM, DASHO, and WORDF), MNUM, which holds the number of characters output, and the character table, MCHRT, 64 characters long.

```
038D 8003       11970          DEFW    380H                 ;D
038F 6003       11980          DEFW    360H                 ;W
0391 4003       11990          DEFW    340H                 ;R
0393 2003       12000          DEFW    320H                 ;U
0395 2004       12010          DEFW    420H                 ;F
0397 A003       12020          DEFW    3A0H                 ;K
0399 B004       12030          DEFW    4B0H                 ;Y
039B A004       12040          DEFW    4A0H                 ;C
039D 8004       12050          DEFW    480H                 ;B
039F 7004       12060          DEFW    470H                 ;J
03A1 6004       12070          DEFW    460H                 ;P
03A3 4004       12080          DEFW    440H                 ;L
03A5 1004       12090          DEFW    410H                 ;V
03A7 0004       12100          DEFW    400H                 ;H
                12110 ;
                12120 ;DATA AREA
                12130 ;
03A9            12140 PDATA    EQU     $                    ;START OF PROGRAM RAM
03A9 00         12150          DEFB    0                    ;(MNUM)
03AA C704       12160          DEFW    1223                 ;(DOTO)
03AC 560E       12170          DEFW    3670                 ;(DASHO)
03AE AA1C       12180          DEFW    7338                 ;(WORDF)
                12190 ;********END OF LOCATIONS TO BE PROGRAMMED*****
0007            12200 PDATAS   EQU     $-PDATA
0824            12210 MNUM     EQU     PROGR
0825            12220 DOTO     EQU     MNUM+1
0825            12230 DOTF     EQU     DOTO
0827            12240 DASHO    EQU     DOTF+2
0825            12250 DASHF    EQU     DOTF
0827            12260 CHARF    EQU     DASHO
0829            12270 WORDF    EQU     CHARF+2
04C7            12280 ONEWPM   EQU     1223
0000            12290          END
00000 TOTAL ERRORS
```

Generator program listing.

CHAPTER 15

Morse Code Sender

This chapter describes the Morse Code Sender application of the EZ-80. This application differs from the last chapter in that the user can program messages into EPROM for use in amateur radio or other applications. Up to ten messages may be included, with lengths of over 1000 characters in the case of a 2096-byte 2716 EPROM. Pressing a keyboard entry outputs the message in audible form (OUT6) and also provides an on/off condition suitable for keying a transmitter. Speeds of 1 to 99 words per minute are selectable.

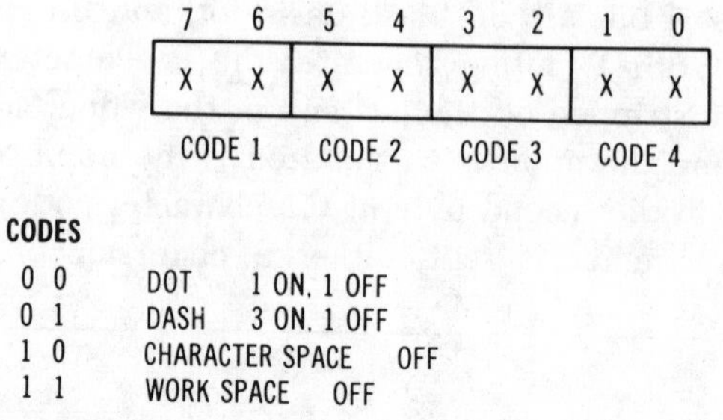

Fig. 15-2. Code arrangement for message bytes.

Table 15-1. Morse Code Sender Commands

Command	Description
0nE	Send message n (0–9) at speed currently defined.
1nnE	Set speed of transmission to nn (0–99) words per minute.
	E = "ENTER"

OPERATING INSTRUCTIONS

The Sender is programmed into EPROM starting at 220H as shown in Fig. 15-1. The Sender provides room for about 150 characters in the 2758 version at the top of EPROM. Each byte of the message area contains four codes as shown in Fig. 15-2. A 00

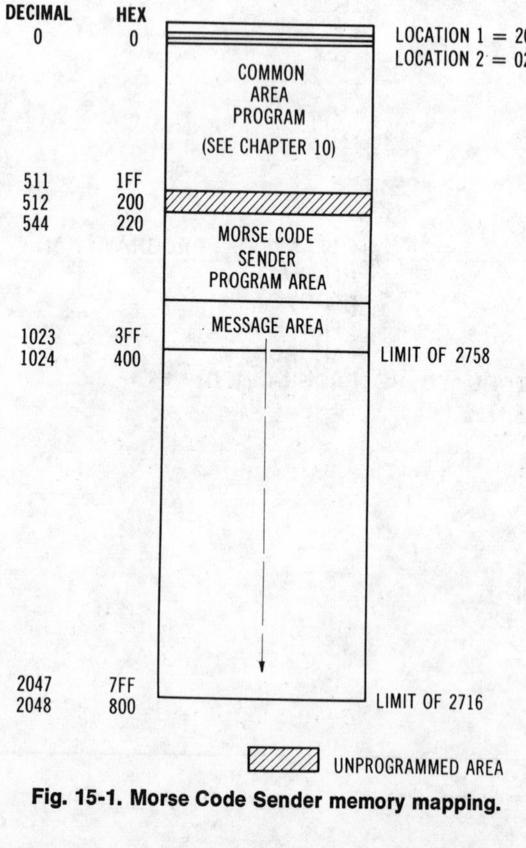

Fig. 15-1. Morse Code Sender memory mapping.

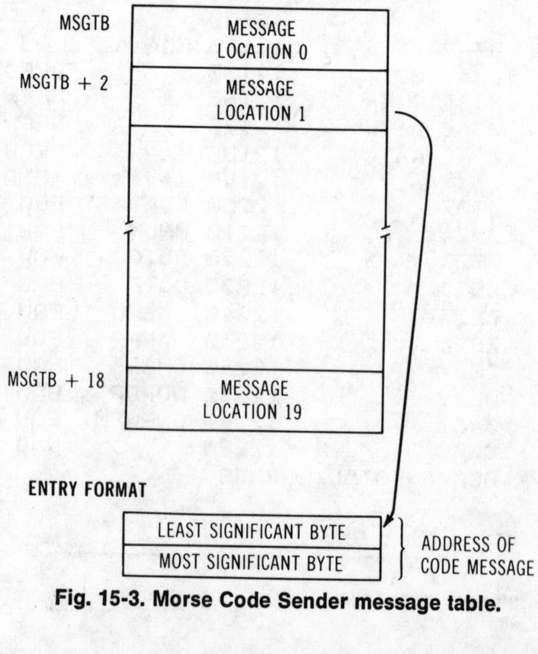

Fig. 15-3. Morse Code Sender message table.

```
                  00099 *LIST OFF
                  09999 *LIST ON
                  10000 ;*******************************************
                  10010 ;          MORSE CODE SENDER                *
                  10020 ;               00-03                       *
                  10030 ;*******************************************
                  10040 ;
0220              10050           ORG     220H              ;START EPROM AREA
0220              10060 MORSE     EQU     $                 ;START OF MORSE PROGRAM
0220 318008       10070           LD      SP,880H           ;INITIALIZE STACK
0223 214C03       10080           LD      HL,PDATA          ;START OF RAM DATA
0226 011E00       10090           LD      BC,PDATAS         ;SIZE OF DATA
0229 CD0300       10100           CALL    INIT              ;INITIALIZE
022C 210000       10110 MORS90    LD      HL,0              ;0 TO HL
022F 220808       10120           LD      (LEDBUF),HL       ;ZERO FOR MS DISPLAY
0232 220A08       10130           LD      (LEDBUF+2),HL     ;ZERO LS DIGITS
0235 213E02       10140           LD      HL,MORTB          ;FUNCTION TABLE ADDDR
0238 110100       10150           LD      DE,0001H          ;0 MINIMUM,0-1 VALID
023B C31E00       10160           JP      BRANCH            ;INPUT AND BRANCH
023E 1803         10170 MORTB     JR      MORS00            ;0=SEND MSG N
0240 C39502       10180           JP      MORS20            ;1=SET SPEED(MUST BE LAST)
                  10190 ;
                  10200 ;MORS00.SEND MSG N.
                  10210 ;
0243 CDCC02       10220 MORS00    CALL    MORMT             ;POINT TO MSG N
0246 222408       10230           LD      (MPNTR),HL        ;INITIALIZE MSG PNTR
0249 3EC0         10240 MORS01    LD      A,0C0H             ;INITIAL MASK
024B 322608       10250           LD      (MMASK),A          ;INITIALIZE MSG MASK
024E 3E07         10260           LD      A,7                ;SHIFT COUNT
0250 322708       10270           LD      (MSHFT),A          ;INITIALIZE SHIFT #
0253 2A2408       10280 MORS02    LD      HL,(MPNTR)         ;GET LOC OF MSG
0256 3A2608       10290           LD      A,(MMASK)          ;GET MASK
0259 4F           10300           LD      C,A                ;TRANSFER TO C
025A 3A2708       10310           LD      A,(MSHFT)          ;GET SHIFT #
025D 47           10320           LD      B,A                ;TRANSFER TO B
025E 7E           10330           LD      A,(HL)             ;GET BYTE
025F 3C           10340           INC     A                 ;TEST FOR -1
0260 28CA         10350           JR      Z,MORS90          ;GO IF END
0262 3D           10360           DEC     A                 ;READJUST
0263 A1           10370           AND     C                  ;MASK OUT UNWANTED
0264 05           10380 MORS03    DEC     B                  ;DEC SHIFT #
0265 2803         10384           JR      Z,MORS3C           ;GO IF DONE
0267 0F           10388           RRCA                       ;SHIFT RIGHT
0268 18FA         10392           JR      MORS03             ;CONTINUE
026A B7           10396 MORS3C    OR      A                 ;TEST FOR DOT
026B 2011         10400           JR      NZ,MORS05          ;GO IF NOT DOT
026D CDEB02       10410           CALL    MORST              ;SEND DOT
0270 CD0A03       10420 MORS04    CALL    MORAM              ;ADJUST MASK AND SHIFT
0273 20DE         10430           JR      NZ,MORS02          ;GO FOR NEXT DOT & DASH
0275 2A2408       10440           LD      HL,(MPNTR)         ;GET POINTER
0278 23           10450           INC     HL                 ;POINT TO NEXT BYTE
0279 222408       10460           LD      (MPNTR),HL         ;STORE FOR NEXT ACCESS
027C 18CB         10470           JR      MORS01             ;GO TO INITIALIZE MASK,SHF
027E FE01         10480 MORS05    CP      1                 ;TEST FOR 1
0280 2005         10490           JR      NZ,MORS06          ;GO IF NOT DASH
0282 CDE002       10500           CALL    MORSH              ;SEND DASH
0285 18E9         10510           JR      MORS04             ;GO FOR ADJUSTMENT
0287 FE02         10520 MORS06    CP      2                 ;TEST FOR 2
0289 2005         10530           JR      NZ,MORS07          ;GO IF NOT CHAR SPACE
028B CDF402       10540           CALL    MORSC              ;SEND CHAR SPACE
028E 18E0         10550           JR      MORS04             ;CONTINUE
0290 CD0403       10560 MORS07    CALL    MORSW              ;SET WORD SPACE
```

Fig. 15-4. Morse Code Sender program listing.

```
0293 18DB        10570           JR      MORS04              ;GO TO OUTPUT
                 10580   ;
                 10590   ;MORS20.SET SPEED.
                 10600   ;
0295 DD211408    10610   MORS20  LD      IX,INBUF+1          ;START OF INPUT
0299 3A2308      10620           LD      A,(NOCHR)           ;GET # OF INPUT CHARS
029C 47          10630           LD      B,A                 ;TRANSFER TO B
029D 05          10640           DEC     B                   ;# OF CHARS TO CONVERT
029E CD1200      10650           CALL    BCDBIN              ;CONVERT
02A1 4D          10660           LD      C,L                 ;SPEED IN C
02A2 79          10661           LD      A,C                 ;GET SPEED FOR 0 TEST
02A3 B7          10662           OR      A                   ;TEST FOR 0
02A4 2006        10663           JR      NZ,MORS21           ;GO IF NOT 0
02A6 CD1B00      10664           CALL    BLINK               ;ERROR-BLINK
02A9 C32C02      10665           JP      MORS90              ;GET NEXT COMMAND
02AC 21C704      10670   MORS21  LD      HL,ONEWPM           ;1 WPM UNIT
02AF 0600        10680           LD      B,0                 ;SPEED IN BC
02B1 11FFFF      10690           LD      DE,-1               ;QUOTIENT
02B4 B7          10700   MORS22  OR      A                   ;RESET CARRY
02B5 ED42        10710           SBC     HL,BC               ;DIVIDE BY SPEED
02B7 13          10720           INC     DE                  ;BUMP QUOTIENT
02B8 F2B402      10730           JP      P,MORS22            ;CONTINUE TIL NEGATIVE
02BB D5          10740           PUSH    DE                  ;SAVE QUOTIENT
02BC E1          10750           POP     HL                  ;TRANSFER TO HL
02BD 222808      10760           LD      (DOTO),HL           ;DOT ON TIME
02C0 29          10770           ADD     HL,HL               ;UNIT*2
02C1 19          10780           ADD     HL,DE               ;UNIT*3
02C2 222A08      10790           LD      (DASHO),HL          ;DASH ON TIME
02C5 29          10800           ADD     HL,HL               ;UNIT*6
02C6 222C08      10810           LD      (WORDF),HL          ;WORD OFF TIME
02C9 C32C02      10820           JP      MORS90              ;GO FOR NEXT COMMAND
                 10830   ;
                 10840   ;MORMT.POINTS TO MESSAGE N.
                 10850   ;
02CC 3A1408      10860   MORMT   LD      A,(INBUF+1)         ;GET N
02CF 07          10870           RLCA                        ;N*2
02D0 4F          10880           LD      C,A                 ;N*2 IN C
02D1 0600        10890           LD      B,0                 ;N*2 IN BC
02D3 DD212E08    10900           LD      IX,MSGTB            ;MESSAGE TABLE ADDR
02D7 DD09        10910           ADD     IX,BC               ;POINT TO MESSAGE
02D9 DD6E00      10920           LD      L,(IX)              ;GET LS BYTE
02DC DD6601      10930           LD      H,(IX+1)            ;GET MS BYTE
02DF C9          10940           RET                         ;RETURN
                 10950   ;
                 10960   ;MORSH.SEND DASH.
                 10970   ;
02E0 2A2A08      10980   MORSH   LD      HL,(DASHO)          ;DASH ON TIME
02E3 ED5B2808    10990           LD      DE,(DASHF)          ;DASH OFF TIME
02E7 CD1D03      11000   MORSH1  CALL    TONE                ;OUTPUT
02EA C9          11010           RET                         ;RETURN
                 11020   ;
                 11030   ;MORST.SEND DOT.
                 11040   ;
02EB 2A2808      11050   MORST   LD      HL,(DOTO)           ;DOT ON TIME
02EE ED5B2808    11060           LD      DE,(DOTF)           ;DOT OFF TIME
02F2 18F3        11070           JR      MORSH1              ;OUTPUT
                 11080   ;
                 11090   ;MORSC.SEND CHARACTER SPACE.
                 11100   ;
02F4 2A2A08      11110   MORSC   LD      HL,(CHARF)          ;CHARACTER SPACE OFF TIME
02F7 ED5B2808    11120           LD      DE,(DOTO)           ;DOT ON TIME
02FB B7          11130           OR      A                   ;CLEAR C
```

Fig. 15-4 cont'd. Morse Code

```
02FC  ED52      11140            SBC     HL,DE           ;TWO UNITS
02FE  EB        11150            EX      DE,HL           ;OFF TO DE
02FF  210000    11160  MORSC1    LD      HL,0            ;CHARACTER SPACE ON TIME
0302  18E3      11170            JR      MORSH1          ;OUTPUT
                11180  ;
                11190  ;MORSW.SEND WORD SPACE.
                11200  ;
0304  ED5B2C08  11210  MORSW     LD      DE,(WORDF)      ;WORD SPACE OFF TIME
0308  18F5      11220            JR      MORSC1          ;OUTPUT
                11230  ;
                11240  ;MORAM.ADJUST MASK AND SHIFT COUNT.
                11250  ;
030A  3A2708    11260  MORAM     LD      A,(MSHFT)       ;GET SHIFT #
030D  D602      11270            SUB     2               ;ADJUST
030F  322708    11280            LD      (MSHFT),A       ;STORE FOR NEXT
0312  3A2608    11290            LD      A,(MMASK)       ;GET MASK
0315  CB3F      11300            SRL     A               ;ALIGN DOWN 2
0317  CB3F      11310            SRL     A
0319  322608    11320            LD      (MMASK),A       ;STORE FOR NEXT
031C  C9        11330            RET                     ;RETURN
                11340  ;
                11350  ;OUTPUT DOT,DASH,SPACE
                11360  ;
031D  D5        11370  TONE      PUSH    DE              ;SAVE OFF TIME
031E  7D        11380            LD      A,L             ;GET ON TIME LSB
031F  B4        11390            OR      H               ;MERGE ON TIME MSB
0320  2808      11400            JR      Z,TONE1         ;GO IF NO ON TIME
0322  0E03      11410            LD      C,3             ;OUTPUT MASK
0324  CD3103    11420            CALL    TOGGLE          ;OUTPUT TONE AND DELAY
0327  AF        11430            XOR     A               ;0
0328  D301      11440            OUT     (1),A           ;TURN OFF OUT5,OUT6
032A  E1        11450  TONE1     POP     HL              ;GET OFF TIME
032B  0E00      11460            LD      C,0             ;OUTPUT MASK
032D  CD3103    11470            CALL    TOGGLE          ;DELAY ONLY
0330  C9        11480            RET                     ;RETURN
                11490  ;
                11500  ;TOGGLE.OUTPUT TONE ON OUT6 AND DELAY.
                11510  ;
0331  11FFFF    11520  TOGGLE    LD      DE,-1           ;-1 FOR DECREMENT
0334  3E03      11530            LD      A,3             ;FOR OUTPUT
0336  19        11540  TOGG1     ADD     HL,DE           ;HL-1 TO HL
0337  D0        11550            RET     NC              ;RETURN IF DONE
0338  A1        11560            AND     C               ;AND ACTIVE BIT WITH MASK
0339  D301      11570            OUT     (1),A           ;OUTPUT
033B  0624      11580            LD      B,36            ;ON CNT
033D  10FE      11590            DJNZ    $                   ;LOOP HERE
033F  EE01      11600            XOR     1               ;TOGGLE OUT6
0341  A1        11610            AND     C               ;AND ACTIVE BIT WITH MASK
0342  D301      11620            OUT     (1),A           ;OUTPUT
0344  0623      11630            LD      B,35            ;OFF CNT
0346  10FE      11640            DJNZ    $                   ;LOOP HERE
0348  EE01      11645            XOR     1               ;FLIP OUT6
034A  18EA      11650            JR      TOGG1           ;CONTINUE
                11660  ;
                11670  ;DATA AREA
                11680  ;
034C            11690  PDATA     EQU     $               ;START OF PROGRAM RAM
034C  0000      11700            DEFW    0               ;(MPNTR)
034E  00        11710            DEFB    0               ;(MMASK)
034F  00        11720            DEFB    0               ;(MSHFT)
0350  C704      11730            DEFW    1223            ;(DOTO)
0352  560E      11740            DEFW    3670            ;(DASHO)
```

Sender program listing.

code generates a dot. A 01 code generates a dash. A 10 code generates a character space and a 11 code generates a word space. A message is terminated by a byte of all ones. (This means that up to three codes before the byte of all ones may contain a code of 10 to generate "nulls.") The location of each message is placed into a Message Table (MSGTB). Each entry in the message table is in the standard Z-80 address format, last significant byte followed by most significant byte (see Fig. 15-3).

There are two commands in the Sender (see Table 15-1). The "1nn" command sets the speed, as in the case of the Morse Code Generator of the last chapter. From 1 to 99 words per minute may be specified with the default (reset) value being one word per minute.

The "0n" command starts transmission of message n, 0–9. No check is made on the validity of the message; that is, if there is "garbage" in the specified

message area, garbage will be sent! Upon completion, the program returns to await the next keyboard command, either next message or set speed.

APPLICATIONS HARDWARE

Monitoring the output is possible by feeding the output of OUT6 into either an on-board amplifier and speaker or into external audio (see Fig. 14-2). Output line OUT5 is the actual keying line that can be used with a relay or solid-state keying device. (Note that the sense of OUT5 is inverted, that is, "on" is a logic 0, and off is a logic 1.)

THEORY OF OPERATION

Parts of the Sender (see Fig. 15-4) are identical with the application of the last chapter. The genera-

```
0354 AA1C    11750        DEFW   7338              ;(WORDF)
0356 6A03    11760        DEFW   SAMPLE            ;(MSGTB)
0358 0000    11770        DEFW   0
035A 0000    11780        DEFW   0
035C 0000    11790        DEFW   0
035E 0000    11800        DEFW   0
0360 0000    11810        DEFW   0
0362 0000    11820        DEFW   0
0364 0000    11830        DEFW   0
0366 0000    11840        DEFW   0
0368 0000    11850        DEFW   0
001E         11860 PDATAS EQU    $-PDATA
             11870 ;
             11880 ;MESSAGE AREA HERE TIL END OF EPROM
             11890 ;
036A 42      11900 SAMPLE DEFB   42H               ;DE WD6CTY
036B 31      11901        DEFB   31H
036C 64      11902        DEFB   64H
036D 24      11903        DEFB   24H
036E 02      11904        DEFB   02H
036F 44      11905        DEFB   44H
0370 99      11906        DEFB   99H
0371 16      11907        DEFB   16H
0372 FF      11908        DEFB   0FFH
             11930 ;*******END OF LOCATIONS TO BE PROGRAMMED********
0824         11940 MPNTR  EQU    PROGR
0826         11950 MMASK  EQU    MPNTR+2
0827         11960 MSHFT  EQU    MMASK+1
0828         11970 DOTO   EQU    MSHFT+1
0828         11980 DOTF   EQU    DOTO
082A         11990 DASHO  EQU    DOTF+2
0828         12000 DASHF  EQU    DOTF
082A         12010 CHARF  EQU    DASHO
082C         12020 WORDF  EQU    CHARF+2
082E         12030 MSGTB  EQU    WORDF+2
04C7         12040 ONEWPM EQU    1223
0000         12050        END
00000 TOTAL ERRORS
```

Fig. 15-4 cont'd. Morse Code Sender program listing.

tion of dots, dashes, and intervals, and the processing of the speed input are the same. The "0n" command entry, however, works with a predetermined message rather than generating random characters. The "n" of the input (0–9) is used to access the *n*th entry of the Message Table (MSGTB). Each entry should hold a 16-bit address that points to a code message. Each byte of this message is picked up and stripped of its four 2-bit codes. Each code results in either a dot (00), dash (01), character space (10), or word space (11) being sent. Every byte is first checked to see whether it contains all ones; if this is the case, the routine terminates by transferring control back to MORS90 to get the next keyboard command.

Variables used in this program are the variables for intervals (ONEWPM, DOTO, DASHO, and WORDF), the Message Table pointers (MSGTB to MSGTB+19), and three variables used in stripping the codes: MPNTR, MMASK, and MSHFT. MPNTR points to the next byte of the message being transmitted. MMASK holds the current mask for the code position (11000000, 00110000, 00001100, or 00000011). MSHFT holds a count that specifies how far to the right the code must be shifted to right justify it into a value of 00, 01, 10, or 11.

CHAPTER 16

Telephone Dialer

This chapter describes a Telephone Dialer application for the EZ-80. Up to 100 telephone numbers of 1 to 11 digits can be stored in the EZ-80 (2716 version). To call any of the 100, the appropriate number 0–99 is entered on the keyboard of the EZ-80, and the EZ-80 automatically dials the number. Another function implemented in the EZ-80 is an "elapsed time" capability; the EZ-80 displays a running count of minutes and seconds that have elapsed since the beginning of the call. Five of the numbers are temporary numbers that are stored in RAM and thus volatile (power down destroys the data); 95 of the numbers are permanently stored in EPROM (up to 10 in the 2758 or 95 in the 2716 version).

OPERATING INSTRUCTIONS

The Dialer is programmed into EPROM starting at 220H, as shown in Fig. 16-1. There are four functions that can be entered for the Dialer as in Table 16-1.

Entering a "0n123 . . . m" records the string of digits "123 . . m" as telephone number n. Up to 11 digits may be entered as the number, or as few as one. The entry number n may be 0–4, representing the five locations in EZ-80 RAM. Any entry number over 4 is reserved for numbers that are permanently stored in EPROM. Entry errors cause the usual blinking display.

Entering a "2nn" displays the current telephone number for nn on the LED display. Valid entry numbers are 0–99, representing five numbers in RAM (0–4) and 95 numbers in EPROM. This function enables a check on the validity of any temporary (RAM) or permanent number (EPROM).

Entering "3nn" automatically dials number nn and displays it on the LED display as the number is dialed. If an incorrect number is present in RAM or EPROM, the program will not check for validity.

Once the number is dialed, function "1" may be entered. This function displays elapsed time in minutes and seconds from the start of the function entry. Pressing any key terminates the function.

Table 16-1. Telephone Dialer Commands

Command	Description
0nmmmmmmmE	Record number mmmmmmm as telephone number n (0–5) in RAM.
1E	Start display of elapsed minutes and seconds from 0. Pressing any key returns to next command.
2nnE	Display number nn (0–99) on LED display for validity check.
3nnE	Automatically dial number nn (0–99). Pressing ENTER again redials the same number.
	E = "ENTER"

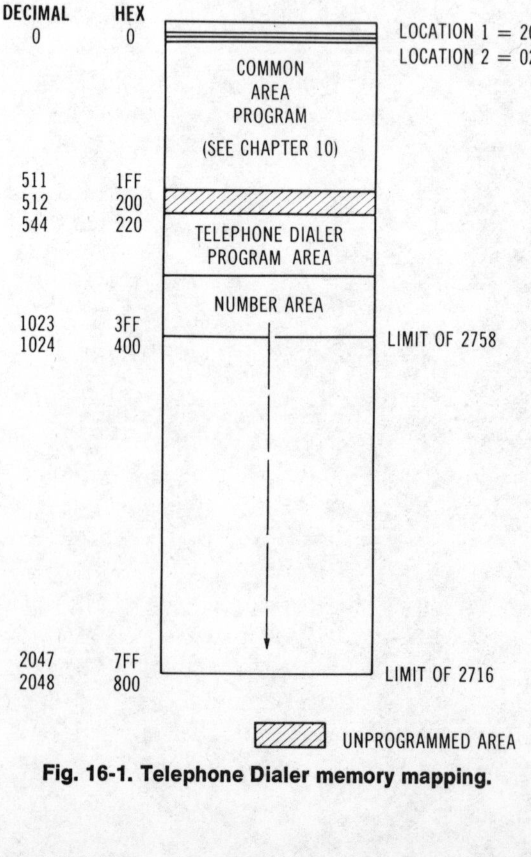

Fig. 16-1. Telephone Dialer memory mapping.

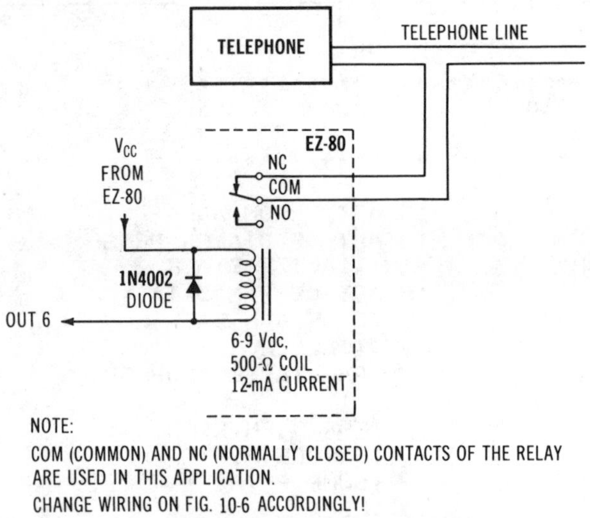

Fig. 16-2. Telephone line interface.

	7 6 5 4	3 2 1 0		
BYTE 0	0 0 0 0	0 0 0 1	1	TELEPHONE NO. 1-714-555-1212
1	0 0 0 0	0 1 1 1	7	
2	0 0 0 0	0 0 0 1	1	
3	0 0 0 0	0 1 0 0	4	
4	0 0 0 0	0 1 0 1	5	
5	0 0 0 0	0 1 0 1	5	
6	0 0 0 0	0 1 0 1	5	
7	0 0 0 0	0 0 0 1	1	
8	0 0 0 0	0 0 1 0	2	
9	0 0 0 0	0 0 0 1	1	
10	0 0 0 0	0 0 1 0	2	
11	1 1 1 1	1 1 1 1	−1	TERMINATOR

Fig. 16-3. Telephone Dialer number storage.

APPLICATIONS HARDWARE

Most telephone numbers may be dialed by interrupting the circuit. A rotary dial phone does exactly that by means of a commutator switch, outputting ten pulses for 0, five for 5, and so forth. This application interfaces to a phone line as shown in Fig. 16-2. The relay is controlled by output line 6 (OUT6) of the EZ-80 and breaks the circuit the appropriate number of times for each digit. Bear in mind that the voltages may be somewhat high (during ringing) and that the phone circuit should be very well isolated from the EZ-80. The phone company will undoubtedly agree!

NOTE:

FCC RULES FORBID DIRECT CONNECTION OF UNAPPROVED EQUIPMENT TO PHONE LINES. A "COUPLER" MUST BE USED BETWEEN THE LINE AND SUCH EQUIPMENT. CHECK WITH YOUR LOCAL PHONE COMPANY TO INSTALL SUCH A COUPLER.

THEORY OF OPERATION

Numbers are stored in both RAM and EPROM as shown in Fig. 16-3. Each number is stored as a single bcd digit in one byte. The number is terminated by a −1 in the last byte. The RAM table is located at the start of program RAM (PRLOC) and is five entries of 12 bytes each, or 72 bytes. This provides enough room for variable storage (800H to PRLOC −1) and the stack at top of RAM. The EPROM table starts at the last program location (PROMT). A sample number has been entered to illustrate the coding. Remember that each number burned into the EPROM must be terminated by a −1 (0FFH) and must start at the first byte of the table entry. Each entry must be 12 bytes even if the last are unused. There is enough room in EPROM (2758) for 10 (2758) or 95 (2716) entries. Unused entries must be filled with −1s (normal initial state of EPROM).

The program (Fig. 16-4) is made up of five sections—initialization, and processing for the four functions. In the case of the Dialer, there are no variables in RAM storage and therefore no CALL is made to INITialize. The CALL to BRANCH inputs the command and branches out to one of the four functions.

The "0" function records a number from the input string. The entry number is checked for validity. If it is valid, the location of the entry in RAM is computed. Entry number 0 is at the start of the RAM table, entry 1 is at start + 12, entry 2 is at start + 24, and so forth. Before the number is filled into the RAM table, the 12 bytes of the entry are filled with −1 to mark the termination for the number. The number is then moved to the table entry, starting at the first byte of the RAM entry (LDIR).

The "1" function zeros the real-time-clock variables, HUNS, SECS, and MINS, to enable a start from elapsed time of 0. This function continually displays the MINS and SECS value on the LED display after conversion to bcd (two calls to BINBCD).

The "3" function displays the current number in RAM or EPROM and dials the number. The entry number is first checked to see whether it is in RAM (0–4) or EPROM (5–99). The location of the RAM or EPROM table is established as a result of this test. The displacement of the entry from the start of the table is then computed by multiplying the RAM entry number by 12 or by multiplying the EPROM entry number − 5 by 12. It is then added to the location of the table to locate the proper entry.

Once the entry has been located, each digit of the entry is simultaneously displayed and dialed. Dialing is implemented by turning on OUT6 for 1/20 of a second and then turning it off for 1/20 of a second for each pulse required. Dialing of each digit continues until a −1 is detected as the terminating character.

```
                 00099 *LIST OFF
                 09999 *LIST ON
                 10000 ;*****************************************
                 10010 ;          TELEPHONE DIALER              *
                 10020 ;               00-09                    *
                 10030 ;*****************************************
                 10040 ;
0220             10050          ORG     220H              ;START EPROM AREA
0220             10060 DIALER   EQU     $                 ;START OF DIALER PROG
0220 318008      10070          LD      SP,880H           ;INITIALIZE STACK
0223 217803      10071          LD      HL,PDATA          ;START OF RAM DATA
0226 010700      10072          LD      BC,PDATAS         ;SIZE OF RAM DATA
0229 CD0300      10073          CALL    INIT              ;INITIALIZE
022C 212B08      10074          LD      HL,RAMT             ;RAM TABLE ADDRESS
022F 3EFF        10075          LD      A,0FFH              ;-1
0231 063C        10076          LD      B,60                ;FOR 5 ENTRIES
0233 77          10077 DIAL99   LD      (HL),A              ;STTORE -1
0234 23          10078          INC     HL                  ;BUMP PNTR
0235 10FC        10079          DJNZ    DIAL99              ;LOOP
0237 210000      10080 DIAL90   LD      HL,0              ;0
023A 220808      10090          LD      (LEDBUF),HL       ;ZERO MS DISPLAY
023D 220A08      10100          LD      (LEDBUF+2),HL     ;ZERO LS DISPLAY
0240 214902      10110          LD      HL,DIALTB         ;FUNCTION TABLE ADDRESS
0243 110300      10120          LD      DE,03H            ;0=MINIMUM,0-3 VALID
0246 C31E00      10130          JP      BRANCH            ;INPUT AND BRANCH
0249 180A        10140 DIALTB   JR      DIAL00            ;0=RECORD#
024B 1851        10150          JR      DIAL10            ;1=ELAPSED TIME
024D 1803        10160          JR      DIAL2B            ;2=DISPLAY#
024F C37303      10170          JP      DIAL30            ;3=DIAL NUMBER N(LAST!)
0252 C3D602      10175 DIAL2B   JP      DIAL20            ;LINK
                 10180 ;
                 10190 ;DIAL00. RECORD #.
                 10200 ;
0255 DD211408    10210 DIAL00   LD      IX,INBUF+1        ;START OF N
0259 0601        10220          LD      B,1               ;# INPUT
025B 110500      10250          LD      DE,5              ;LIMIT OF 5
025E CD1200      10260          CALL    BCDBIN            ;CONVERT
0261 3805        10270          JR      C,DIAL01          ;GO IF N OK
0263 CD1B00      10280 DIAL0A   CALL    BLINK             ;N SPECIFIES EPROM
0266 18CF        10290          JR      DIAL90            ;GO AGAIN
0268 3A2308      10295 DIAL01   LD      A,(NOCHR)         ;GET # OF CHARS INPUT
026B FE0E        10296          CP      14                ;TEST FOR LT 14
026D F26302      10297          JP      P,DIAL0A          ;ERROR IF 14 OR 14+
0270 FE03        10298          CP      3                 ;TEST FOR 0-2
0272 FA6302      10299          JP      M,DIAL0A          ;ERROR IF 0-2
0275 110000      10300          LD      DE,0              ;0 TO DE
0278 EB          10310          EX      DE,HL             ;N IN DE,0 IN HL
0279 19          10320          ADD     HL,DE             ;N*1
027A 19          10330          ADD     HL,DE             ;N*2
027B 19          10340          ADD     HL,DE             ;N*3
027C 29          10350          ADD     HL,HL             ;N*6
027D 29          10360          ADD     HL,HL             ;N*12
027E 112B08      10370          LD      DE,RAMT           ;START OF RAM TABLE
0281 19          10380          ADD     HL,DE             ;START+N*12
0282 3EFF        10390          LD      A,0FFH            ;-1 FOR FILL
0284 060C        10400          LD      B,12              ;# OF BYTES
0286 77          10410 DIAL02   LD      (HL),A              ;STORE -1
0287 23          10420          INC     HL                  ;BUMP POINTER
0288 10FC        10430          DJNZ    DIAL02              ;CONTINUE
028A 01F4FF      10440          LD      BC,-12            ;DECREMENT
028D 09          10450          ADD     HL,BC             ;POINT TO #
028E 111508      10460          LD      DE,INBUF+2        ;POINT TO #
```

Fig. 16-4. Telephone Dialer

```
0291 3A2308   10470          LD     A,(NOCHR)       ;GET # INPUT
0294 4F       10480          LD     C,A             ;TRANSFER TO C
0295 0D       10490          DEC    C               ;ADJUST FOR "0N"
0296 0D       10510          DEC    C
0297 0600     10520          LD     B,0             ;INPUT # IN BC
0299 EB       10525          EX     DE,HL           ;SWAP FOR LDIR
029A EDB0     10530          LDIR                   ;MOVE TO TABLE
029C 1899     10540          JR     DIAL90          ;GO FOR NEXT INPUT
              10550 ;
              10560 ;DIAL10.DISPLAY ELAPSED TIME.
              10570 ;
029E AF       10580 DIAL10   XOR    A               ;ZERO A
029F 320408   10590          LD     (HUNDS),A       ;0 TO 100THS
02A2 320308   10600          LD     (SECS),A        ;0 TO SECS
02A5 320208   10610          LD     (MINS),A        ;0 TO MINS
02A8 3A0308   10620 DIAL11   LD     A,(SECS)        ;GET SECONDS
02AB 6F       10630          LD     L,A             ;NOW IN L
02AC 2600     10640          LD     H,0             ;NOW IN HL
02AE DD212408 10650          LD     IX,BUFR         ;TEMP BUFFER
02B2 CD1500   10660          CALL   BINBCD          ;CONVERT AND STORE
02B5 2A2708   10665          LD     HL,(BUFR+3)     ;GET SECS
02B8 220A08   10666          LD     (LEDBUF+2),HL   ;DISPLAY
02BB 3A0208   10670          LD     A,(MINS)        ;GET MINUTES
02BE 6F       10680          LD     L,A             ;NOW IN L
02BF 2600     10690          LD     H,0             ;NOW IN HL
02C1 DD212408 10700          LD     IX,BUFR         ;TEMP BUFFER
02C5 CD1500   10710          CALL   BINBCD          ;CONVERT AND STORE
02C8 2A2708   10715          LD     HL,(BUFR+3)     ;GET MINS
02CB 220808   10716          LD     (LEDBUF),HL     ;DISPLAY
02CE CD0C00   10720          CALL   KEYSCN          ;TEST FOR KEYPUSH
02D1 28D5     10730          JR     Z,DIAL11        ;GO IF NONE
02D3 C33702   10740          JP     DIAL90          ;GO FOR NEXT INPUT
              10750 ;
              10760 ;DIAL20.DISPLAY #.
              10770 ;
02D6 0600     10780 DIAL20   LD     B,0             ;SET DISPLAY MODE
02D8 210000   10790 DIAL29   LD     HL,0            ;0 TO HL
02DB 220808   10800          LD     (LEDBUF),HL     ;ZERO MS DISPLAY
02DE 220A08   10810          LD     (LEDBUF+2),HL   ;ZERO LS DISPLAY
02E1 C5       10820          PUSH   BC              ;SAVE FLAG
02E2 DD211408 10830          LD     IX,INBUF+1      ;START OF N
02E6 3A2308   10840          LD     A,(NOCHR)       ;# OF CHARS INPUT
02E9 FE02     10841          CP     2               ;TEST FOR 0 OR 1
02EB F2F302   10842          JP     P,DIAL28        ;GO IF 2 OR 2+
02EE 2A2908   10843          LD     HL,(PRLOC)      ;GET PREVIOUS LOCN
02F1 1824     10844          JR     DIAL27          ;DON'T COMPUTE LOC
02F3 47       10850 DIAL28   LD     B,A             ;TRANSFER TO B
02F4 05       10860          DEC    B               ;ADJUST FOR "2"
02F5 110500   10870          LD     DE,5            ;RAM LIMIT
02F8 CD1200   10880          CALL   BCDBIN          ;CONVERT
02FB 112B08   10890          LD     DE,RAMT         ;RAM TABLE ADDRESS
02FE 380D     10900          JR     C,DIAL21        ;GO IF RAM
0300 7D       10901          LD     A,L             ;GET #
0301 FE64     10902          CP     100             ;TEST FOR GE 100X
0303 F26302   10903          JP     P,DIAL0A        ;GO IF GE 100
0306 117F03   10910          LD     DE,PROMT        ;PROM TABLE ADDRESS
0309 01FBFF   10920          LD     BC,-5           ;FOR ADD
030C 09       10930          ADD    HL,BC           ;ADJUST FOR PROM
030D 29       10940 DIAL21   ADD    HL,HL           ;N*2
030E 29       10950          ADD    HL,HL           ;N*4
030F E5       10960          PUSH   HL              ;SAVE N*4
0310 29       10970          ADD    HL,HL           ;N*8
```

program listing.

```
0311 C1       10980         POP   BC              ;GET N*4
0312 09       10990         ADD   HL,BC           ;N*12
0313 19       11000         ADD   HL,DE           ;TABLE START+N*12
0314 222908   11002         LD    (PRLOC),HL      ;SAVE LOCATION
0317 DD210808 11005 DIAL27  LD    IX,LEDBUF       ;POINT TO FIRST DIGIT
031B D1       11010 DIAL22  POP   DE                ;GET FLAG
031C 7E       11020         LD    A,(HL)            ;GET DIGIT
031D 23       11025         INC   HL                ;BUMP PNTR
031E D5       11030         PUSH  DE                ;SAVE FLAG
031F FEFF     11040         CP    0FFH              ;TEST FOR END
0321 2846     11050         JR    Z,DIAL25          ;GO IF END
0323 F5       11055         PUSH  AF                ;SAVE DIGIT
0324 DD7E00   11056         LD    A,(IX)            ;GET DIGIT #
0327 3C       11057         INC   A                 ;BUMP BY ONE
0328 FE0A     11058         CP    10                ;TEST FOR 10
032A 2001     11059         JR    NZ,DIAL2A         ;GO IF NOT 10
032C AF       11060         XOR   A                 ;10-START AT 0
032D DD7700   11061 DIAL2A  LD    (IX),A            ;STORE
0330 F1       11062         POP   AF                ;RESTORE DIGIT
0331 320B08   11063         LD    (LEDBUF+3),A      ;DISPLAY
0334 CB42     11070         BIT   0,D               ;TEST MODE
0336 200A     11080         JR    NZ,DIAL23         ;GO IF DIAL MODE
0338 E5       11090         PUSH  HL
0339 21E803   11100         LD    HL,1000           ;ONE SECOND VALUE
033C CD1800   11110         CALL  DELAY             ;GO FOR NEXT DIGIT
033F E1       11120         POP   HL                ;SAVE POINTER
0340 18D9     11130         JR    DIAL22            ;GO FOR NEXT DIGIT
0342 47       11140 DIAL23  LD    B,A               ;GET NUMBER
0343 E5       11150         PUSH  HL                ;SAVE POINTER
0344 B7       11160         OR    A                 ;TEST FOR 0
0345 2002     11170         JR    NZ,DIAL24         ;GO IF 1-9
0347 060A     11175         LD    B,10              ;0=10 PULSES
0349 C5       11180 DIAL24  PUSH  BC                  ;SAVE COUNT
034A 3EFF     11190         LD    A,0FFH              ;ALL ON
034C D301     11200         OUT   (1),A               ;TURN ON PULSE
034E 213200   11210         LD    HL,50               ;1/20TH SEC
0351 CD1800   11220         CALL  DELAY               ;DELAY
0354 AF       11230         XOR   A                   ;ALL OFF
0355 D301     11240         OUT   (1),A               ;TURN OFF PULSE
0357 213200   11250         LD    HL,50               ;1/20TH SEC
035A CD1800   11260         CALL  DELAY               ;DELAY
035D C1       11270         POP   BC                  ;GET COUNT
035E 10E9     11280         DJNZ  DIAL24              ;GO IF MORE
0360 21EE02   11300         LD    HL,750            ;3/4 SEC CNT
0363 CD1800   11310         CALL  DELAY             ;DELAY
0366 E1       11315         POP   HL                ;RESTORE POINTER
0367 18B2     11320         JR    DIAL22            ;GO FOR NEXT DIGIT
0369 D1       11330 DIAL25  POP   DE              ;RESET STACK
036A 21E803   11340         LD    HL,1000         ;1 SECOND DELAY
036D CD1800   11350         CALL  DELAY           ;DELAY
0370 C33702   11360         JP    DIAL90          ;GO FOR NEXT FUNCTION
              11370 ;
              11380 ;DIAL30. DIAL #.
              11390 ;
0373 0601     11400 DIAL30  LD    B,1             ;SET DIAL MODE
0375 C3D802   11410         JP    DIAL29          ;GO TO DIAL
              11490 ;
              11491 ;DATA AREA
              11492 ;
0378          11493 PDATA   EQU   $               ;START OF PROGRAM RAM
0378 00       11494         DEFB  0               ;(BUFFR)
0379 00       11495         DEFB  0
```

Fig. 16-4 cont'd. Telephone Dialer program listing.

```
037A 00         11496          DEFB    0
037B 00         11497          DEFB    0
037C 00         11498          DEFB    0
037D 2B08       11499          DEFW    RAMT              ;(PRLOC)
0007            11500 PDATAS   EQU     $-PDATA
                11501 ;****EPROM NUMBER AREA. HERE TO END OF EPROM****
037F            11502 PROMT    EQU     $                 ;START OF EPROM NUMBERS
037F 0104       11503          DEFW    0401H
0381 0104       11504          DEFW    0401H
0383 0505       11505          DEFW    0505H
0385 0501       11506          DEFW    0105H
0387 0201       11507          DEFW    0102H
0389 02FF       11508          DEFW    0FF02H
                11513 ;********END OF LOCATIONS TO BE PROGRAMMED******
0824            11520 BUFR     EQU     PROGR             ;LOCATION OF (BUFR)
0829            11521 PRLOC    EQU     BUFR+5            ;LOCATION OF (PRLOC)
082B            11522 RAMT     EQU     PRLOC+2           ;LOCATION OF RAM AREA
0000            11560          END
00000 TOTAL ERRORS
```

Fig. 16-4 cont'd. Telephone Dialer program listing.

The "2" function is identical with the "3" function except that it does not dial the number. A "flag" (contained in the B register) is maintained so that the dialing function may be skipped for a display only.

No variables are contained within the RAM area except for the RAM table entries and a temporary buffer of five bytes, BUFR.

CHAPTER 17

Frequency Counter/Tachometer

This chapter describes a frequency counter/tachometer application for the EZ-80. In this application the EZ-80 monitors the IN1 line to count pulses. Whenever the line changes from 0 to 1 or from 1 to 0, an interval count is incremented by 1. If the IN1 is connected to a source of pulses such as is shown in Fig. 17-1, the Frequency Counter can be used as either a tachometer or frequency counter and will count as few as one pulse per minute up to 50,000 pulses per minute.

The *period* or time interval over which pulses may be counted is user selectable; 0.1 second, 1 second, 1 minute, or manual operation may be specified. A "debounce" time in increments of 1 millisecond is also selectable by keyboard input. Many signals have "bounce" associated with them as shown in Fig. 17-2. By delaying the proper time before testing the signal again, this bounce may be disregarded in accumulating counts. Debounce delay times of 1 millisecond to 0.255 second are possible.

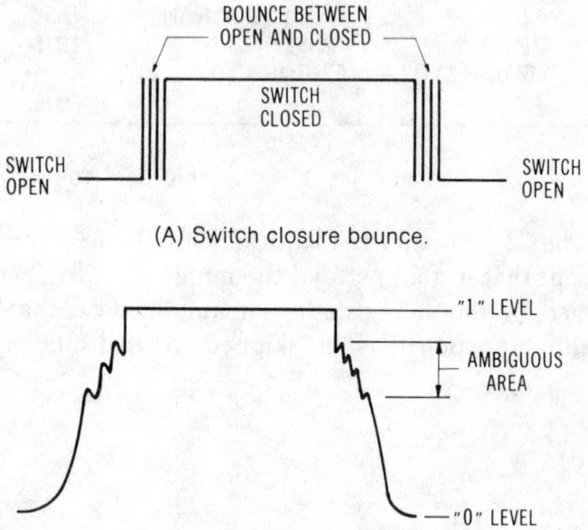

(A) Switch closure bounce.

(B) Signal from transducer.

Fig. 17-2. Bounce in signals.

OPERATING INSTRUCTIONS

The Frequency Counter is programmed into EPROM starting at 220H as shown in Fig. 17-3. Other applications programs may be programmed into EPROM if their locations do not conflict with the Frequency Counter. Use the techniques described in Chapter 10 to transfer control to the Frequency Counter if other programs are coresident in EPROM.

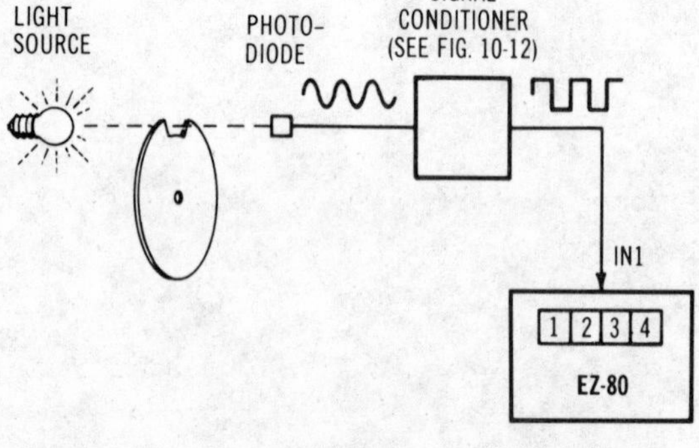

Fig. 17-1. Frequency Counter/Tachometer use.

Table 17-1. Frequency Counter/ Tachometer Commands

Command	Description
0nE	Set counting interval. 0.1 second = 0; 1 second = 1, 1 minute = 2; manual = 3.
1E	Start counting over currently defined interval. If not manual, continually display number of counts received during each interval. If manual, count pulses until key depressed at which time display will be made.
2nnnE	Specify a debounce delay of nnn * 1 milliseconds (1 millisecond to 0.255 second). If n = 0, do not debounce.
	E = "ENTER"

If only the Frequency Counter is resident, locations 1 and 2 of the EPROM will hold 20H and 2, respectively.

There are three functions that may be input from the keyboard for the Frequency Counter (see Table 17-1). Entering a "0n" sets the period (interval) for counting. N=0 specifies ⅒ second, N=1 is 1 second, N=2 specifies 1 minute, and N=3 designates manual operation.

Entering a "2nnn" specifies the debounce time delay. If a 2 function is not input, there will be no (appreciable) delay in counting pulses. If the 2 function is specified, the program will delay nnn * 1 milliseconds after each change in signal level (see Fig. 17-4). The debounce delay should be chosen when the signal is not "monotonically increasing or decreasing" as shown in the figure.

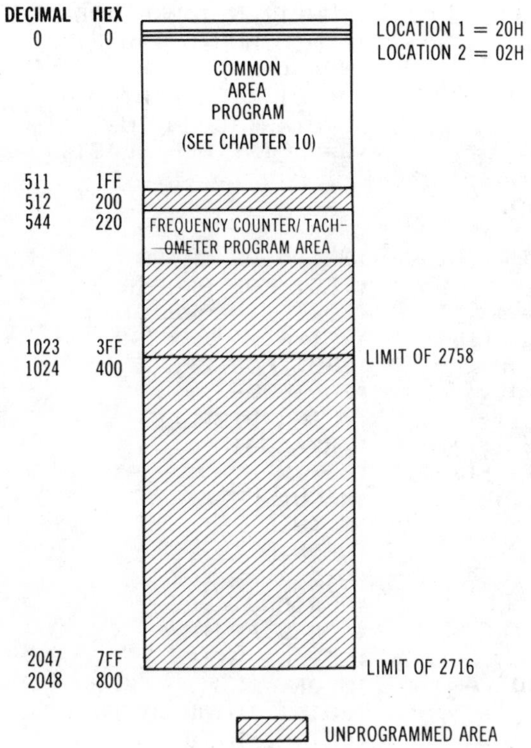

Fig. 17-3. Frequency Counter/Tachometer memory mapping.

Entering a "1" starts the count. If automatic (nonmanual) mode is selected, the program will count over the interval specified and display the results on the LED display. The display will change every ⅒, 1, or 60 seconds depending upon the interval. If manual mode is selected, the program will count pulses until any key is depressed, at which time it will stop with the count accumulated over the manual interval displayed. Pushing the key for the next command reenters command processing.

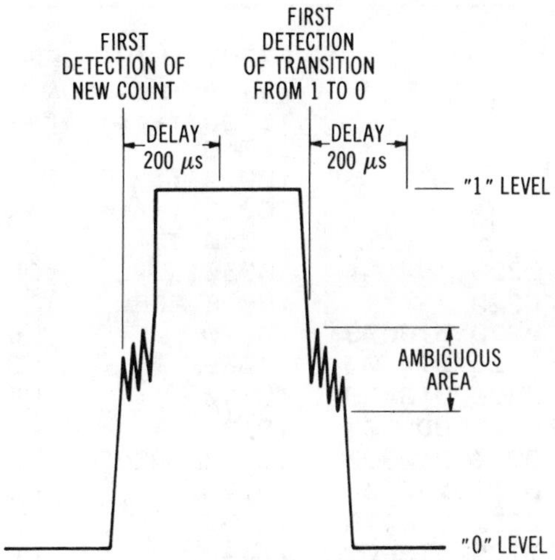

Fig. 17-4. Use of delay.

APPLICATIONS HARDWARE

No applications hardware is required for this application. The input signal to IN1, however, must be within voltage limits of +0 to +5 volts. It must be a digital signal varying from a nominal 0 to over +3.0 volts for a 0 to 1, or 1 to 0 transition. A method for converting a digital signal of different voltage levels is shown in Fig. 10-12. Note that pulses are counted for every complete transition from 0 to 1 and back to 0 again.

THEORY OF OPERATION

The Frequency Counter (Fig. 17-5) is made up of four sections: initialization and the processing of the 0, 1, and 2 commands (FREQ00, FREQ10, and FREQ20). Initialization moves the program variables down to program RAM and then looks for the next command input.

The FREQ00 routine processes the time period specified. A check is made for a valid input of 0 to 3 for 0.1 second, 1 second, 1 minute, or manual, respectively. If a valid input is present, the variable PERIOD is loaded with 2 bytes from the period table PTABLE. There are four entries in the period table, one for each interval. Each entry is two bytes long. The first byte represents the initial hundreds count, and the next byte represents the initial seconds count. At the start of each counting interval, these counts are put into the HUNDS and MINS real-time-clock locations. The real-time-clock then increments each variable automatically. The end of the interval is defined by a MINS value of 1. The entries in PTABLE represent values that will take 0.1 second, 1 second, or 1 minute to reach MINS = 1. The last value for manual operation is a dummy.

```
                    00099 *LIST OFF
                    09999 *LIST ON
                    10000 ;*******************************************
                    10010 ;                FREQUENCY COUNTER           *
                    10020 ;                      00-05                 *
                    10030 ;*******************************************
                    10040 ;
0220                10050        ORG    220H            ;NEXT EPROM AREA
0220                10060 FREQR  EQU    $               ;START OF FREQ COUNTER
0220 318008         10070        LD     SP,880H         ;INITIALIZE STACK
0223 214303         10080        LD     HL,PDATA        ;START OF RAM DATA
0226 010400         10090        LD     BC,PDATAS       ;SIZE OF DATA
0229 CD0300         10100        CALL   INIT            ;INITIALIZE
022C 210000         10110 FREQ90 LD     HL,0            ;ZERO HL
022F 220808         10120        LD     (LEDBUF),HL     ;ZERO MS DISPLAY
0232 220A08         10130        LD     (LEDBUF+2),HL   ;ZERO LS DISPLAY
0235 213E02         10140        LD     HL,FREQT        ;FUNCTION TABLE ADDR
0238 110201         10150        LD     DE,0102H        ;1 MINIMUM,0-2 VALID
023B C31E00         10160        JP     BRANCH          ;BRANCH OUT
023E 1805           10170 FREQT  JR     FREQ00          ;0=SET TIME PERIOD
0240 1830           10180        JR     FREQ10          ;1=START COUNTING
0242 C30803         10190        JP     FREQ20          ;2=DEFINE DEB (LAST!)
                    10200 ;
                    10210 ;FREQ00.SET TIME PERIOD.
                    10220 ;
0245 3A2308         10221 FREQ00 LD     A,(NOCHR)       ;GET # OF CHARS
0248 FE02           10222        CP     2               ;TEST FOR PROPER #
024A 2008           10223        JR     NZ,FREQ0A       ;GO IF INCORRECT
024C 3A1408         10230        LD     A,(INBUF+1)     ;GET N
024F FE04           10240        CP     4               ;TEST FOR 0-3
0251 FA5902         10250        JP     M,FREQ01        ;GO IF 0-3
0254 CD1B00         10260 FREQ0A CALL   BLINK           ;BLINK DISPLAY
0257 18D3           10270        JR     FREQ90          ;TRY AGAIN
0259 3A1408         10280 FREQ01 LD     A,(INBUF+1)     ;GET N
025C 322708         10290        LD     (MFLG),A        ;MANUAL FLAG
025F 6F             10300        LD     L,A             ;N IN L
0260 2600           10310        LD     H,0             ;N IN HL
0262 29             10320        ADD    HL,HL           ;N*2
0263 013B03         10330        LD     BC,PTABLE       ;PERIOD TABLE
0266 09             10340        ADD    HL,BC           ;ADD START+N*2
0267 7E             10350        LD     A,(HL)          ;GET LS BYTE
0268 322508         10360        LD     (PERIOD),A      ;STORE
026B 23             10370        INC    HL              ;POINT TO MS BYTE
026C 7E             10380        LD     A,(HL)          ;GET MS BYTE
026D 322608         10390        LD     (PERIOD+1),A    ;STORE
0270 18BA           10400        JR     FREQ90          ;GO FOR NEXT FUNCTION
                    10410 ;
                    10420 ;FREQ10.START COUNTING.
                    10430 ;
0272 AF             10440 FREQ10 XOR    A               ;0 TO A
0273 320408         10441        LD     (HUNDS),A       ;ZERO 100THS
0276 320308         10442        LD     (SECS),A        ;ZERO SECS
0279 320208         10445        LD     (MINS),A        ;ZERO MINUTES
027C 320108         10446        LD     (HOURS),A       ;ZERO HRS
027F 320008         10447        LD     (DAYS),A        ;ZERO DAYS
0282 110000         10500        LD     DE,0            ;INITIALIZE COUNT
0285 0680           10510        LD     B,80H           ;MASK
0287 210208         10520        LD     HL,MINS         ;POINTER TO MINUTES
028A 3A2608         10521        LD     A,(PERIOD+1)    ;GET SECONDS
028D 320308         10522        LD     (SECS),A        ;INITIALIZE SECS
0290 3A2508         10523        LD     A,(PERIOD)      ;GET 100THS
```

Fig. 17-5. Frequency Counter/

```
0293 320408   10524          LD    (HUNDS),A       ;INITIALIZE 100THS
0296 3A2708   10530          LD    A,(MFLG)        ;GET MANUAL FLAG
0299 FE03     10540          CP    3               ;TEST FOR MANUAL
029B 2830     10550          JR    Z,FREQ1A        ;GO IF MANUAL
029D CB46     10551 FREQ12   BIT   0,(HL)                 ;TEST DONE
029F C2BD02   10552          JP    NZ,FREQ14              ;GO IF DONE
02A2 DB02     10560          IN    A,(2)                  ;GET INPUT
02A4 A0       10570          AND   B                      ;TEST INPUT
02A5 CA9D02   10580          JP    Z,FREQ12               ;GO IF ZERO INPUT
02A8 CD2803   10590          CALL  DEB                  ;DEBOUNCE
02AB CB46     10591 FREQ13   BIT   0,(HL)                 ;TEST DONE
02AD C2BD02   10592          JP    NZ,FREQ14              ;GO IF DONE
02B0 DB02     10600          IN    A,(2)                  ;GET INPUT
02B2 A0       10610          AND   B                      ;TEST INPUT
02B3 C2AB02   10620          JP    NZ,FREQ13              ;GO IF ONE INPUT
02B6 CD2803   10630          CALL  DEB                  ;DEBOUNCE
02B9 13       10640          INC   DE                   ;BUMP COUNT
02BA C39D02   10660          JP    FREQ12               ;GO IF NOT DONE
02BD EB       10670 FREQ14   EX    DE,HL           ;COUNT TO HL
02BE DD210708 10680          LD    IX,LEDBUF-1     ;LED BUFFER
02C2 CD1500   10690          CALL  BINBCD          ;CONVERT AND DISPLAY
02C5 CD0C00   10700          CALL  KEYSCN          ;TEST KEY PUSH
02C8 28A8     10710          JR    Z,FREQ10        ;CONTINUE IF NONE
02CA C32C02   10720          JP    FREQ90          ;KEY PUSH
02CD 3E10     10721 FREQ1A   LD    A,10H                  ;ROW 4 ADDRESS
02CF DB02     10722          IN    A,(2)                  ;GET INPUT
02D1 E601     10723          AND   1                      ;TEST ENTER KEY
02D3 281D     10724          JR    Z,FREQ1D               ;GO IF KEY PUSH
02D5 DB02     10730          IN    A,(2)                  ;GET INPUT
02D7 A0       10740          AND   B                      ;TEST INPUT
02D8 CACD02   10750          JP    Z,FREQ1A               ;GO IF ZERO INPUT
02DB CD2803   10760          CALL  DEB                  ;DEBOUNCE
02DE 3E10     10761 FREQ1B   LD    A,10H                  ;ROW 4 ALDDRESS
02E0 DB02     10762          IN    A,(2)                  ;GET INPUT
02E2 E601     10763          AND   1                      ;TEST ENTER KEY
02E4 280C     10764          JR    Z,FREQ1D               ;GO IF KEY PUSH
02E6 DB02     10770          IN    A,(2)                  ;GET INPUT
02E8 A0       10780          AND   B                      ;TEST INPUT
02E9 C2DE02   10790          JP    NZ,FREQ1B              ;GO IF ONE INPUT
02EC CD2803   10800          CALL  DEB                  ;DEBOUNCE
02EF 13       10810          INC   DE                   ;BUMP COUNT
02F0 18DB     10820          JR    FREQ1A               ;CONTINE
02F2 EB       10860 FREQ1D   EX    DE,HL           ;COUNT TO HL
02F3 DD210708 10870          LD    IX,LEDBUF-1     ;LED BUFFER
02F7 CD1500   10880          CALL  BINBCD          ;CONVERT AND DISPLAY
02FA 21E803   10890          LD    HL,1000         ;1 SECOND
02FD CD1800   10900          CALL  DELAY           ;DELAY
0300 CD0C00   10910 FREQ1C   CALL  KEYSCN          ;TEST NEXT KEY PUSH
0303 28FB     10920          JR    Z,FREQ1C        ;LOOP IF NONE
0305 C32C02   10930          JP    FREQ90          ;GO FOR NEXT COMMAND
              10960 ;
              10970 ;FREQ20.DEFINE DEBOUNCE.
              10980 ;
0308 3A2308   10981 FREQ20   LD    A,(NOCHR)       ;GET # OF CHARS
030B FE02     10982          CP    2               ;TEST #
030D FA5402   10983          JP    M,FREQ0A        ;GO IF INVALID
0310 DD211408 10990          LD    IX,INBUF+1      ;BYPASS "2"
0314 3A2308   11000          LD    A,(NOCHR)       ;GET # INPUT CHARS
0317 47       11010          LD    B,A             ;TRANSFER TO B
0318 05       11020          DEC   B               ;ADJUST FOR "2"
0319 CD1200   11030          CALL  BCDBIN          ;CONVERT
```

Tachometer program listing.

```
031C 7C         11031          LD     A,H              ;GET MSB
031D B7         11032          OR     A                ;TEST
031E C25402     11033          JP     NZ,FREQ0A        ;GO IF GT 255 MS
0321 7D         11034          LD     A,L              ;GET DEBOUNCE VALUE
0322 322408     11040          LD     (DEBNC),A        ;STORE DEBOUNCE DLY
0325 C32C02     11050          JP     FREQ90           ;GO FOR NEW FUNCTION
                11051 ;
                11052 ;DEBOUNCE SUBROUTINE
                11053 ;
0328 3A2408     11054 DEB      LD     A,(DEBNC)        ;GET DEBOUNCE DELAY
032B B7         11055          OR     A                ;TEST FOR 0
032C C8         11056          RET    Z                ;GO IF NO DEBOUNCE
032D 6F         11057          LD     L,A              ;NOW IN L
032E 2600       11058          LD     H,0              ;NOW IN HL
0330 D5         11059          PUSH   DE               ;SAVE COUNT
0331 CD1800     11060          CALL   DELAY            ;DELAY
0334 D1         11061          POP    DE               ;RESTORE COUNT
0335 210208     11062          LD     HL,MINS          ;RESTORE ADDRESS
0338 0680       11063          LD     B,80H            ;RESTORE MASK
033A C9         11064          RET                     ;RETURN
                11065 ;
                11070 ;PERIOD TABLE.
                11080 ;
033B 5A3B       11090 PTABLE   DEFW   15194            ;0=10THS OF SECONDS
033D 003B       11100          DEFW   15104            ;1=SECONDS
033F 0000       11110          DEFW   0                ;2=MINUTES
0341 0000       11120          DEFW   0                ;3=MANUAL
                11130 ;
                11140 ;DATA AREA
                11150 ;
0343            11160 PDATA    EQU    $                ;START OF PROGRAAM RAM
0343 00         11170          DEFB   0                ;(DEBNC)
0344 0000       11180          DEFW   0                ;(PERIOD)
0346 00         11190          DEFB   0                ;(MFLG)
                11200 ;*******END OF LOCATIONS TO BE PROGRAMMED*******
0004            11210 PDATAS   EQU    $-PDATA          ;SIZE
0824            11220 DEBNC    EQU    PROGR            ;LOCATION OF (DEBNC)
0825            11230 PERIOD   EQU    DEBNC+1          ;LOCATION OF (PERIOD)
0827            11240 MFLG     EQU    PERIOD+2         ;LOCATION OF (MFLG)
0000            11250          END
00000 TOTAL ERRORS
```

Fig. 17-5 cont'd. Frequency Counter/Tachometer program listing.

The FREQ20 routine processes the debounce time by storing it into variable DEBNC.

The FREQ10 routine controls the actual counting. First, the HUNDS and SECS variables of the real-time clock are initialized with the value from PTABLE. Then the input line IN1 is checked. Every time it changes from 0 to 1 or from 1 to 0, the frequency count is incremented by 1. After any change a delay is performed based on the value of DEBNC. The MINS count is checked for 1 if the mode is nonmanual. If the MINS count is not 0, then the interval is not over and a new check is made of IN1. If the MINS count = 1 (or if a key has been pressed in manual mode), the accumulated count is displayed on the LED display. After the display the counting interval is again entered for nonmanual operation; if manual operation is taking place, another key push restarts keyboard entry.

The accuracy of the counter is dependent primarily upon the proper setting of the NMI interrupt frequency. This must be adjusted accurately to give 100 cycles per second (100 hertz) for accurate frequency counting (see Chapter 9).

No "outflow" indication is provided and the shortest interval (1/10 second) should be used initially on unknown frequencies to determine the appropriate interval. Counts above 50,000 pulses per minute (833 per second or 8.3 per 1/10 second) will become increasingly inaccurate as the input frequency rises. Counts below 50,000 per second are accurate to within ±1 count, assuming perfect NMI adjustment.

CHAPTER 18

Timer

This chapter describes the Timer application of the EZ-80. Unlike a mechanical clock timer this Timer allows a cycle of from 2 minutes to 100 days. Up to six outputs can be controlled with the Timer, which controls external devices using output lines OUT1–OUT6. Eighteen different "events" at eighteen different times within the cycle may be programmed. Reprogramming may be done at any time. To turn on line 6 at day 23, hour 5, and minute 23 and to turn it off at day 23, hour 5, and minute 24, for example, the following commands would be entered:

```
00123052301
00223052400
3
```

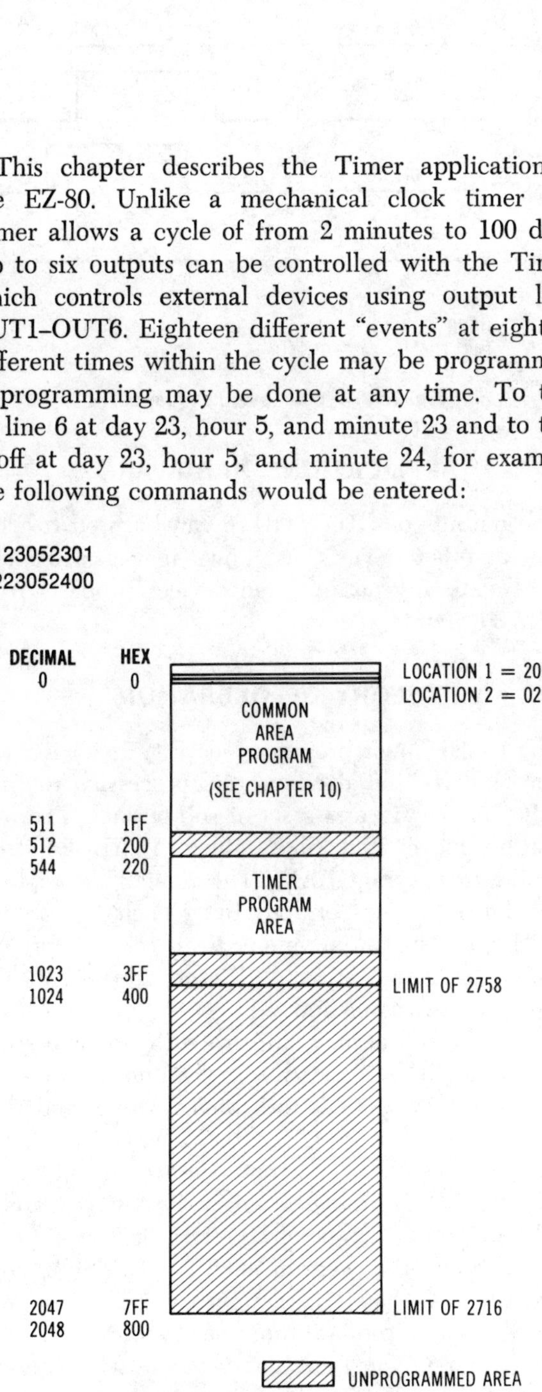

Fig. 18-1. Timer memory mapping.

Controlling any combination of the six outputs is just about as simple. The external devices controlled may be sprinkler valves, solenoids, or even electrical appliances, provided the proper interface is present.

OPERATING INSTRUCTIONS

The Timer is programmed into EPROM starting at 220H as shown in Fig. 18-1. The Timer uses most of the 512 bytes available for program storage in EPROM and other programs cannot be programmed in EPROM in the 2758 version of the Timer. Set EPROM locations 1 and 2 to 20H and 2 respectively.

The Timer has four commands (see Table 18-1). Command "0" is of the form "0nnDDHHMMmm." Here "nn" is the number 00 to 17 and represents all of 18 event definitions that can be programmed. Each set of events must have a different nn number. DD, HH, MM are days, hours, and minutes; each event number must be two decimal digits such as 12. DD may be 00 to 99, HH is 00 to 23, and MM is 00 to 59. The mm characters are a two-digit value representing the state of the six output lines OUT1–OUT6, as shown in Fig. 18-2. In programming a sequence of events the numbers of the events need not be consecutive in

Table 18-1. Timer Commands

Command	Description
0nnDDHHMMmmE	Set event nn (00–19) at day = DD, hour = HH, minute = MM, and output mm (00–63 or binary 000000-111111). If nn = 00, define cycle.
1nnE	Display event number nn (00–19) on LED display in days, hours, minutes, and output value.
2nnE	Kill (delete) event nn (00–19).
3E	Start timing from DD = 0, HH = 0, MM = 0, with a cycle defined by event number 0 and output as specified by time table.
	E = "ENTER"

time. Fig. 18-3 shows a sequence of four events. Lines 1 and 4 are turned on at day 1, hour 12, minute 23, and turned off at day 1, hour 12, minute 53. Lines 2 and 5 are turned on at day 1, hour 12, minute 30 and off at day 1, hour 13, minute 0. Note that if a line is on (or off), it must retain that state if another event occurs during the time it is active, as shown in the figure.

If a "0" command with event 00 is specified, the cycle time is defined. "000010000" defines a cycle time of one day, "000070000" defines a cycle time of one week, and "000001200" defines a cycle time of twelve hours, for example. At the end of a cycle, the program starts counting again from 0 after outputting value mm.

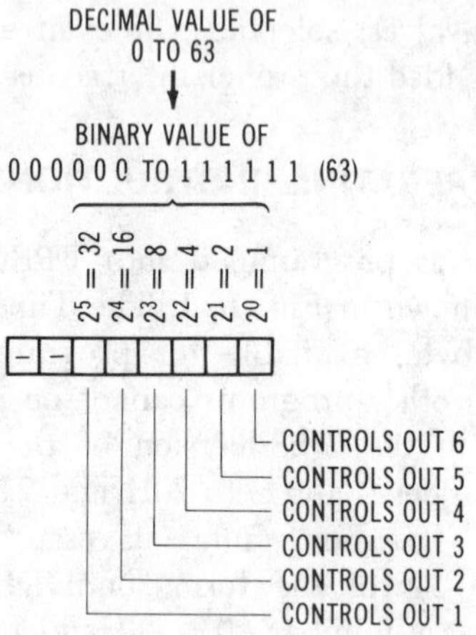

Fig. 18-2. Timer output coding.

Command "1nn" reads the state of even number nn and displays it on the display as DD, pause, HH, pause, MM, pause, and mm. As unused even numbers are filled with a −1 value, they will display "255." This command allows the user to verify the events or cycle that have been programmed.

Command "2nn" kills (deletes) the nn event program by filling with all ones.

Command "3" starts the timer from 0 and repeats the cycles programmed. The program continuously tests the real-time-clock value and compares it with all entries in the time table. If the "DDHHMM" entry in the time table is the same as the real-time HHMMSS value, the event definition mm is output to lines OUT1–OUT6. A delay of one second is then performed and another set of comparisons is done. Comparisons and outputs are done over the entire cycle. At the end of the cycle the real-time-clock values are reset and the cycle repeats.

Note that for any given minute more than one set of events can be defined but it is most efficient to incorporate actions for all 6 lines in one entry.

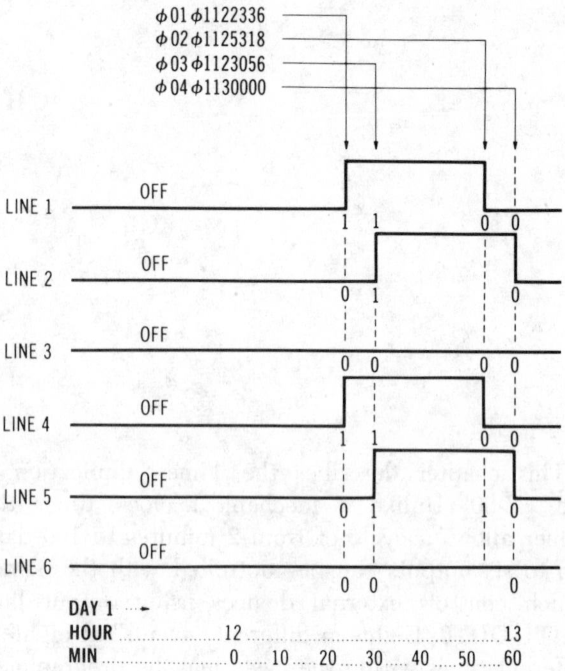

Fig. 18-3. Typical event sequence.

APPLICATIONS HARDWARE

The outputs of OUT1–OUT6 can be used to close relays or other devices, as shown in Figs. 10-5 and 10-6. Isolate any high-voltage devices properly from the EZ-80 circuits.

THEORY OF OPERATION

The EZ-80 Timer program (see Fig. 18-4) is made up of six parts: initialization, four processing routines for the commands, and a set of subroutines. The initialization moves the time table (TTABLE) from EPROM to program RAM. The time table contains space for 18 entries of four bytes each, for a total of 72 bytes. The initial value for all is a −1, or "unused." After initialization, a JP is made to BRANCH to get the next command.

The three subroutines are primarily to save space in EPROM. FINDN gets the "nn" value from a command string, converts it to a binary value, and then points IX to the proper TTABLE location. CONPUS converts two characters from the command string (DD, HH, MM, or mm) to binary. SEARCH searches the TTABLE for a value of DD, HH, or MM.

TIME00 sets the event in the TTABLE. Subroutine CONPUS is CALLed to get binary values for DD, HH, MM, and mm. Subroutine FINDN finds the location of nn. The four binary values are then put in the entry at byte 0, byte 1, byte 2, and byte 3, respectively.

```
                    00099 *LIST OFF
                    09999 *LIST ON
                    10000 ;*****************************************
                    10010 ;                  TIMER                      *
                    10020 ;                  00-06                      *
                    10030 ;*****************************************
                    10040 ;
0220                10050          ORG     220H            ;NEXT EPROM AREA
0220                10060 TIMER    EQU     $               ;START OF TIMER
0220 318008         10070          LD      SP,880H         ;INITIALIZE STACK
0223 217603         10080          LD      HL,PDATA        ;START OF RAM DATA
0226 014800         10090          LD      BC,PDATAS       ;SIZE OF DATA
0229 CD0300         10100          CALL    INIT            ;INITIALIZE
022C 210000         10110 TIME90   LD      HL,0            ;ZERO HL
022F AF             10111          XOR     A               ;ZERO A
0230 D301           10112          OUT     (1),A           ;RESET LINES
0232 220808         10120          LD      (LEDBUF),HL     ;ZERO MS DISPLAY
0235 220A08         10130          LD      (LEDBUF+2),HL   ;ZERO LS DISPLAY
0238 214102         10140          LD      HL,TIMET        ;FUNCTION TABLE ADDRESS
023B 110301         10150          LD      DE,0103H        ;1=MINIMUM,0-3 VALID
023E C31E00         10160          JP      BRANCH          ;BRANCH OUT
0241 180A           10170 TIMET    JR      TIME00          ;0=SET EVENT
0243 1842           10180          JR      TIME10          ;1=READ EVENT
0245 1803           10190          JR      TIME2A          ;2=KILL EVENT
0247 C3DA02         10200          JP      TIME30          ;3=START(MUST BE LAST)
024A C3C702         10201 TIME2A   JP      TIME20          ;LINK
                    10210 ;
                    10220 ;TIME00.SET EVENT IN TTABLE.
                    10230 ;
024D 3A2308         10231 TIME00   LD      A,(NOCHR)       ;GET NO CHARS INPUT
0250 FE0B           10232          CP      11              ;TEST FOR PROPER #
0252 C24403         10233          JP      NZ,CON11        ;GO IF NOT CORRECT
0255 CD1A03         10240          CALL    FINDN           ;FIND LOCATION
0258 DDE5           10244          PUSH    IX              ;TRANSFER TO IY
025A FDE1           10248          POP     IY
025C DD211608       10252          LD      IX,INBUF+3      ;START OF DAYS
0260 116400         10256          LD      DE,100          ;LIMIT OF 99 DAYS
0263 CD3603         10260          CALL    CONPUS          ;FIND DAYS
0266 FD7500         10264          LD      (IY),L          ;STORE
0269 111800         10268          LD      DE,24           ;LIMIT OF 24 HOURS
026C CD3603         10272          CALL    CONPUS          ;FIND HOURS
026F FD7501         10276          LD      (IY+1),L        ;STORE
0272 113C00         10280          LD      DE,60           ;LIMIT OF 59 MINUTES
0275 CD3603         10284          CALL    CONPUS          ;FIND MINUTES
0278 FD7502         10288          LD      (IY+2),L        ;STORE
027B 114000         10292          LD      DE,64           ;LIMIT OF 63 VALUE
027E CD3603         10296          CALL    CONPUS          ;FIND VALUE
0281 FD7503         10300          LD      (IY+3),L        ;STORE
0284 C32C02         10420          JP      TIME90          ;RETURN FOR NEXT CMND
                    10430 ;
                    10440 ;TIME10.DISPLAY EVENT TABLE ENTRY.
                    10450 ;
0287 3A2308         10451 TIME10   LD      A,(NOCHR)       ;GET NO CHARS INPUT
028A FE03           10452          CP      3               ;TEST FOR 3
028C C24403         10453          JP      NZ,CON11        ;GO IF NOT CORRECT
028F CD1A03         10460          CALL    FINDN           ;POINT TO ENTRY
0292 0E04           10470          LD      C,4             ;FOR DISPLAY OF VALUES
0294 DD2B           10480          DEC     IX              ;ADJUST FOR LOOP
0296 DDE5           10490          PUSH    IX              ;SAVE LOCATION
0298 DD210708       10500 TIME11   LD      IX,LEDBUF-1     ;FOR DISPLAY
029C FDE1           10510          POP     IY              ;GET LOCATION
029E FD23           10520          INC     IY              ;BUMP BY ONE
```

Fig. 18-4. Timer program listing.

```
02A0 FDE5      10530         PUSH   IY              ;SAVE
02A2 210000    10540         LD     HL,0            ;ZERO HL
02A5 220808    10550         LD     (LEDBUF),HL     ;ZERO MS DISPLAY
02A8 220A08    10560         LD     (LEDBUF+2),HL   ;ZERO LS DISPLAY
02AB FD6E00    10570         LD     L,(IY)          ;GET VALUE FOR L
02AE 2600      10580         LD     H,0             ;NOW IN HL
02B0 CD1500    10590         CALL   BINBCD          ;DISPLAY
02B3 3E05      10591         LD     A,5             ;CONSTANT
02B5 91        10592         SUB    C               ;GET 5-B=# OF VARIABLE
02B6 320808    10593         LD     (LEDBUF),A      ;DISPLAY AT LEFT
02B9 21F401    10600         LD     HL,500          ;1/2 SECOND CONSTANT
02BC CD1800    10610         CALL   DELAY           ;DELAY TO READ DISPLAY
02BF 0D        10620         DEC    C               ;DECREMENT COUNT
02C0 20D6      10630         JR     NZ,TIME11       ;GO IF NOT END
02C2 FDE1      10640         POP    IY              ;RESET STACK
02C4 C32C02    10650         JP     TIME90          ;GO FOR NEXT CMND
               10660 ;
               10670 ;TIME20.KILL EVENT NN.
               10680 ;
02C7 3A2308    10681 TIME20  LD     A,(NOCHR)       ;GET NO CHARS INPUT
02CA FE03      10682         CP     3               ;TEST FOR 3
02CC C24403    10683         JP     NZ,CON11        ;GO IF NOT CORRECT
02CF CD1A03    10690         CALL   FINDN           ;POINT TO ENTRY
02D2 3EFF      10700         LD     A,0FFH          ;DUMMY FOR NO MATCH
02D4 DD7700    10710         LD     (IX),A          ;RESET DAYS
02D7 C32C02    10720         JP     TIME90          ;RETURN FOR NEXT CMND
               10730 ;
               10740 ;TIME30.START TIMER AND PROCESS.
               10750 ;
02DA AF        10760 TIME30  XOR    A               ;0 TO A
02DB 320408    10770         LD     (HUNDS),A       ;ZERO 100THS
02DE 320308    10780         LD     (SECS),A        ;ZERO SECS
02E1 320208    10790         LD     (MINS),A        ;ZERO MINS
02E4 320108    10800         LD     (HOURS),A       ;ZERO HOURS
02E7 320008    10810         LD     (DAYS),A        ;ZERO DAYS
02EA CD0C00    10811 TIME31  CALL   KEYSCN            ;TEST KEY
02ED C22C02    10812         JP     NZ,TIME90         ;GO IF KEY
02F0 2600      10820         LD     H,0               ;0 TO MSB
02F2 3A0308    10824         LD     A,(SECS)          ;GET CURRENT SECS
02F5 6F        10828         LD     L,A               ;NOW IN HL
02F6 DD210708  10832         LD     IX,LEDBUF-1       ;POINT TO LED BUFFER
02FA CD1500    10836         CALL   BINBCD            ;DISPLAY RUNNING
02FD CD4A03    10920         CALL   SEARCH            ;SEARCH TABLE
0300 20E8      10930         JR     NZ,TIME31         ;GO IF NOT FOUND
               10940 ;ENTRY FOUND HERE.
0302 DDE5      10942         PUSH   IX                ;SAVE ADDRESS
0304 E1        10943         POP    HL                ;FOR COMPARE
0305 012408    10950         LD     BC,TTABLE         ;TABLE ADDRESS
0308 B7        10960         OR     A                 ;CLEAR CARRY
0309 ED42      10970         SBC    HL,BC             ;TEST FOR 0TH ENTRY
030B DD7E03    10990         LD     A,(IX+3)          ;GET CONFIGURATION
030E D301      11000         OUT    (1),A             ;OUTPUT TO OUT1-OUT6
0310 28C8      11001         JR     Z,TIME30          ;START NEXT CYCLE
0312 21E803    11010         LD     HL,1000           ;DELAY
0315 CD1800    11020         CALL   DELAY             ;ONE SECOND
0318 18D0      11030         JR     TIME31            ;GO FOR NEXT TEST
               11040 ;
               11050 ;SUBROUTINE TO FIND NEXT ENTRY LOCATION.
               11060 ;
031A DD211408  11070 FINDN   LD     IX,INBUF+1      ;POINT TO NN
031E 0602      11080         LD     B,2             ;2 CHARACTERS
0320 111200    11090         LD     DE,18           ;LIMIT OF 17
```

Fig. 18-4 cont'd. Timer

```
0323 CD1200   11100            CALL    BCDBIN          ;CONVERT TO BINARY
0326 D23E03   11110            JP      NC,CON10        ;GO IF INVALID
0329 E5       11120            PUSH    HL              ;TRANSFER TO IX
032A DDE1     11130            POP     IX
032C DD29     11140            ADD     IX,IX           ;N*2
032E DD29     11150            ADD     IX,IX           ;N*4
0330 012408   11160            LD      BC,TTABLE       ;ADDRESS OF TIME TABLE
0333 DD09     11170            ADD     IX,BC           ;POINT TO ENTRY
0335 C9       11180            RET                     ;RETURN
              11190 ;
              11200 ;SUBROUTINE TO CONVERT 2 CHARS TO BINARY & PUSH.
              11210 ;
0336 0602     11220 CONPUS     LD      B,2             ;2 CHARACTERS
0338 CD1200   11230            CALL    BCDBIN          ;CONVERT
033B 3001     11240            JR      NC,CON10        ;GO IF INVALID
033D C9       11260            RET                     ;RETURN
033E E1       11270 CON10      POP     HL              ;RESET STACK
033F 3EFF     11271            LD      A,0FFH          ;-1
0341 FD7700   11272            LD      (IY),A          ;RESET ENTRY
0344 CD1B00   11280 CON11      CALL    BLINK           ;INVALID-BLINK
0347 C32C02   11290            JP      TIME90          ;GET NEXT CMND
              11300 ;
              11310 ;SUBROUTINE TO SEARCH TABLE FOR MATCH.
              11320 ;
034A DD212408 11330 SEARCH     LD      IX,TTABLE       ;START OF TABLE
034E 110400   11350            LD      DE,4            ;4 BYTES PER ENTRY
0351 0612     11360            LD      B,18            ;18 ENTRIES
0353 3A0408   11361 SEAR10     LD      A,(HUNDS)       ;GET 1/100THS
0356 FE63     11362            CP      99              ;TEST FOR PENDING CHANGE
0358 28F9     11363            JR      Z,SEAR10        ;WAIT 'TIL QUIET
035A 3A0208   11364            LD      A,(MINS)        ;CURRENT MINUTES
035D DDBE02   11365            CP      (IX+2)          ;COMPARE TO TABLE
0360 200F     11366            JR      NZ,SEAR11       ;GO IF NO MATCH
0362 3A0108   11367            LD      A,(HOURS)       ;CURRENT HOURS
0365 DDBE01   11368            CP      (IX+1)          ;COMPARE TO TABLE
0368 2007     11369            JR      NZ,SEAR11       ;GO IF NO MATCH
036A 3A0008   11370            LD      A,(DAYS)        ;CURRENT DAYS
036D DDBE00   11371            CP      (IX+0)          ;COMPARE TO TABLE
0370 C8       11372            RET     Z               ;RETURN IF MATCH
0371 DD19     11390 SEAR11     ADD     IX,DE           ;POINT TO NEXT ENTRY
0373 10DE     11400            DJNZ    SEAR10          ;GO IF NOT 18TH
0375 C9       11410            RET                     ;18TH-RETURN
              11420 ;
              11430 ;DATA
              11440 ;
0376          11450 PDATA      EQU     $               ;START OF PROGRAM RAM
0376 FFFF     11460            DEFW    -1              ;(TTABLE)
0378 FFFF     11470            DEFW    -1
037A FFFF     11480            DEFW    -1
037C FFFF     11490            DEFW    -1
037E FFFF     11500            DEFW    -1
0380 FFFF     11510            DEFW    -1
0382 FFFF     11520            DEFW    -1
0384 FFFF     11530            DEFW    -1
0386 FFFF     11540            DEFW    -1
0388 FFFF     11550            DEFW    -1
038A FFFF     11560            DEFW    -1
038C FFFF     11570            DEFW    -1
038E FFFF     11580            DEFW    -1
0390 FFFF     11590            DEFW    -1
0392 FFFF     11600            DEFW    -1
0394 FFFF     11610            DEFW    -1
```

program listing.

```
0396 FFFF                 DEFW     -1
0398 FFFF                 DEFW     -1
039A FFFF                 DEFW     -1
039C FFFF                 DEFW     -1
039E FFFF                 DEFW     -1
03A0 FFFF                 DEFW     -1
03A2 FFFF                 DEFW     -1
03A4 FFFF                 DEFW     -1
03A6 FFFF                 DEFW     -1
03A8 FFFF                 DEFW     -1
03AA FFFF                 DEFW     -1
03AC FFFF                 DEFW     -1
03AE FFFF                 DEFW     -1
03B0 FFFF                 DEFW     -1
03B2 FFFF                 DEFW     -1
03B4 FFFF                 DEFW     -1
03B6 FFFF                 DEFW     -1
03B8 FFFF                 DEFW     -1
03BA FFFF                 DEFW     -1
03BC FFFF                 DEFW     -1
          ;*********END OF LOCATIONS TO BE PROGRAMMED******
0048      PDATAS   EQU    $-PDATA              ;SIZE
0824      TTABLE   EQU    PROGR                ;LOCATION OF (TTABLE)
0000               END
00000 TOTAL ERRORS
```

Fig. 18-4 cont'd. Timer program listing.

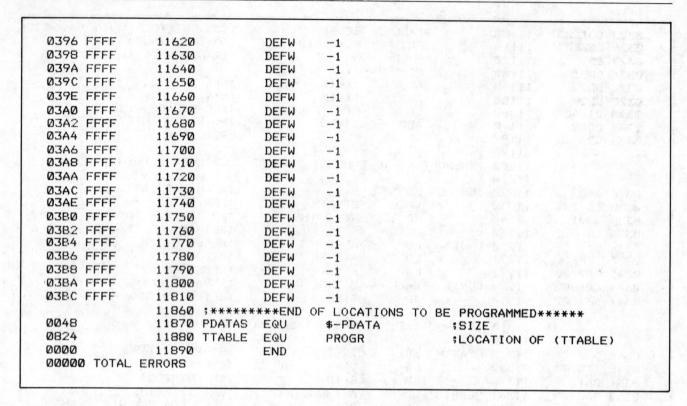

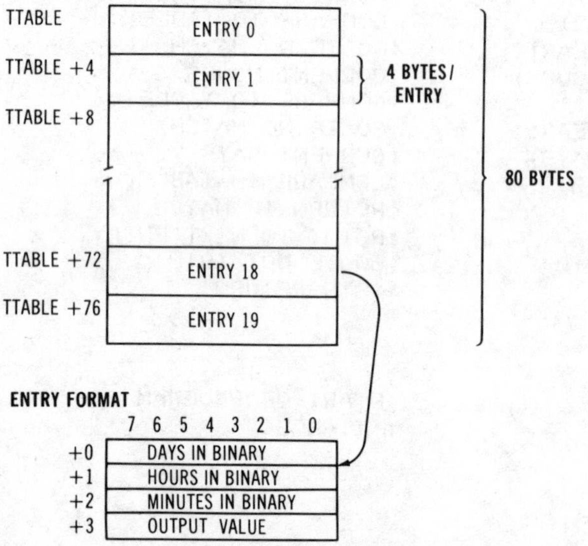

Fig. 18-5. Timer TTABLE.

The accuracy of the Timer is dependent on the adjustment of the $\overline{NMI}$ signal. By using the technique described in Chapter 9 it is possible to "fine tune" the real-time clock to excellent accuracy for timing applications.

TIME10 reverses the process by finding the location of a specified entry number (FINDN) and displaying the DD, HH, MM, and mm of the entry.

TIME20 finds the location of a specified entry number and "kills" it by filling the entry with all ones.

TIME30 starts the Timer by zeroing the real-time-clock values. It then loops continuously and scans the Time table entries (TTABLE), comparing them with the real-time-clock DDHHMM values. If a match is found, the mm value for the entry is output to OUT1–OUT6, and the program delays 1 second before reentering the scanning loop.

The only variable in TIME is the time table TTABLE. It is made up of 18 entries as shown in Fig. 18-5.

CHAPTER 19

Music Synthesizer

This chapter describes a Music Synthesizer application of the EZ-80. We have seen in previous chapters how audio could be generated by toggling one output line between 1 and 0 at a constant rate. Such an implementation, however, produces only a constant tone at constant volume. The Music Synthesizer described here has the capability of producing four octaves of frequencies from high C down to lowest C or approximately 65 to 956 hertz in 12 steps per octave (C, C♯, D, D♯, E, F, F♯, G, G♯, A, A♯, and B). Notes may be 1/16, 1/8, 1/4,, 1/2, or whole notes, or even dotted values (half again as long). Quarter and half rests are also implemented.

Other parameters that may be varied are tempo, loudness, and envelope. Tempo, of course, is the speed of the music, and may be set at 80, 110, or 130 beats per minute. Loudness may be set to soft, medium, or loud at any time. The envelope of the note may also be varied according to four patterns, as shown in Fig. 19-1. The "Normal" envelope is a note of constant volume as determined by the current "loudness" setting. The "Stacatto" envelope is a note of short duration. The "Triangle Down" envelope produces a "pinging" or harpsichordlike sound. The "Triangle Up" envelope produces the reverse type of sound. The ability to vary the loudness and envelope is the thing that sets the Music Synthesizer application apart from simple tone generators.

Another feature of the Synthesizer is the ability to repeat any section of the song as many times as required. The "song" is made up of four bits, or nibbles (nibls). An example of a typical song is the sequence 13, 2, 12, 12, 0, 0, 2, 4, 0, 4, 2, 13, 1, 7, 13, 2, 0, 0, 2, 4, 12, 8, 0, 12, 10, 13, 1, 11, 15, which plays part of Yankee Doodle. By introducing "repeat" codes, the song may be repeated five times 14, 5 (sequence) 14, 0. The repeats may be put anywhere within the song.

An "editor" allows songs to be entered into RAM or to be displayed one nibl at a time. Songs may be entered into RAM, but may also be burned into EPROM if the user desires. This application is somewhat longer than the typical EZ-80 application and requires a 2716 EPROM. The area available for user songs in EPROM is about 750 bytes. Each byte holds about 1½ notes, permitting about 1100 notes in EPROM or 100 notes in RAM, not counting repeats. Songs may be "debugged" in RAM and then coded into EPROM if the user desires.

OPERATING INSTRUCTIONS

The codes for the Music Synthesizer are shown in Chart 19-1. Each code consists of one or two 4-bit nibls. A note is defined by one nibl, but the duration of a note is defined by two nibls, a "12" plus a code for the duration (whole, ½, etc.). Once the duration has been defined, every note will be of that duration until the duration is redefined. For example, 12, 12, 0, 2, 12, 14, 0, 2 represents ¼ duration (12, 12), a ¼C, a ¼D, ⅛ duration (12, 14), a ⅛C, and ⅛D.

The octave is set by a "13" code. (13,0) sets the lowest octave, (13,1) the next highest, (13,2) the middle C octave, and (13,3) the high C octave. As

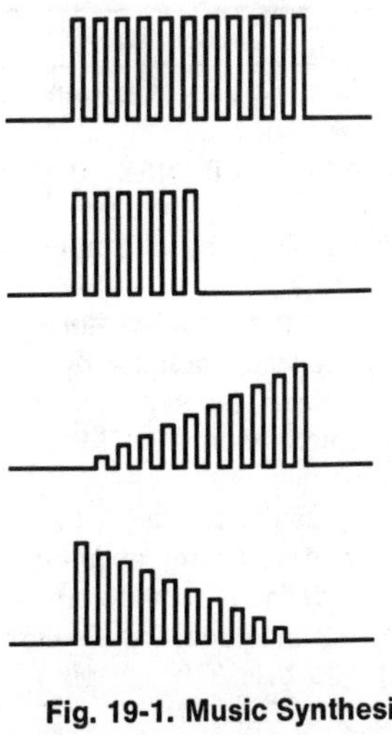

Fig. 19-1. Music Synthesizer envelopes.

Chart 19-1. Music Synthesizer Codes

Notes		**Envelope**	
C	0	Normal	13,4
C#	1	Staccatto	13,5
D	2	Triangle Up	13,6
D#	3	Triangle Down	13,7
E	4	**Tempo**	
F	5	80 beats/minute	13,8
F#	6	110 beats/minute	13,8
G	7	130 beats/minute	13,10
G#	8	**Loudness**	
A	9	Soft	13,11
A#	10	Medium	13,12
B	11	Loud	13,13
Note Duration		**Rests**	
Whole	12,0	1/4	13,14
1/2•	12,4	1/2	13,15
1/2	12,8	**Repeat**	
1/4•	12,10	Repeat n times	14,n
1/4	12,12	End repeat	14,0
1/8•	12,13	**End Song**	15
1/8	12,14		
1/16	12,15		
Octaves			
0 (low)	13,0		
1	13,1		
2	13,2		
3 (high)	13,3		

in the case of duration, the octave is in force until redefined.

The envelope is set by a "13" code with a 4-7 argument. (13,4), (13,5), (13,6), and (13,7) set "Normal," "Staccatto," "Triangle Up," and "Triangle Down" envelopes. The envelope is modified by the current "loudness" setting to generate one of 12 envelopes.

Tempo is set by a "13" code with an 8–10 argument that sets 80, 110, or 130 beats per minute, respectively.

Table 19-1. Music Synthesizer Commands

Command	Description
0E	Play music starting at current location defined.
1nnE	Set data nn (0–15) into current nibl defined by location counter. Increment location counter by one after store of data.
2E	Display nibl at current location. Increment location counter by one after access. Keep display until next key push. Entering an "ENTER" will display next nibl.
3nnnnE	Set nibl location counter to the byte defined by the quotient of (nnnn/2) and the nibl defined by the remainder of (nnnn/2). nnnn may be 0–4351 (byte 0 nibl 0 to byte 87F nibl 1). E = "ENTER"

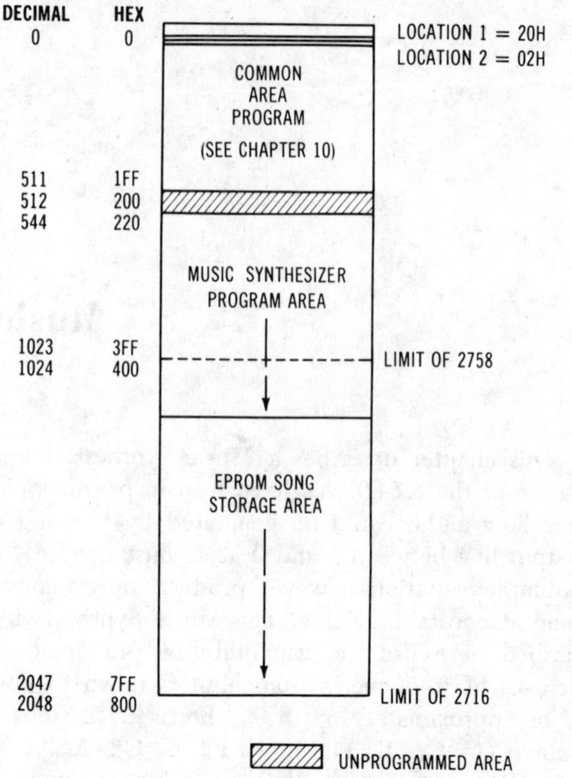

Fig. 19-2. Music Synthesizer memory mapping.

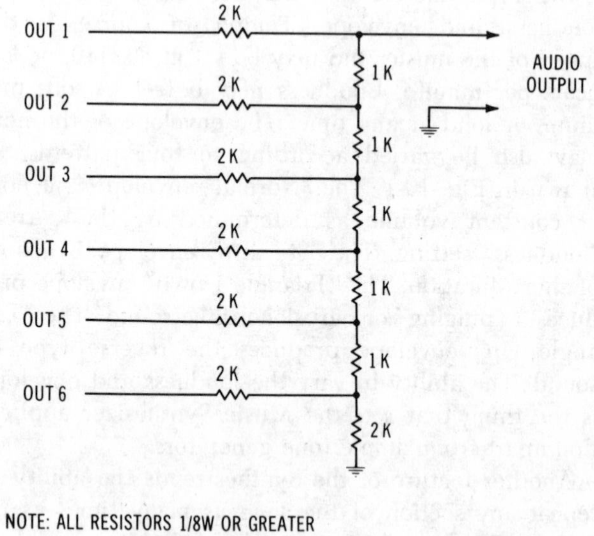

Fig. 19-3. Music Synthesizer output.

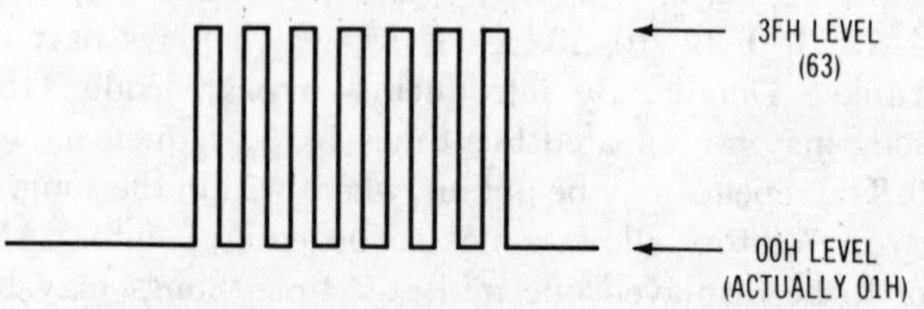

Fig. 19-4. Music Synthesizer loudness control.

```
                00099 *LIST OFF
                09999 *LIST ON
                10000 ;*************************************************
                10010 ;                 MUSIC SYNTHESIZOR              *
                10020 ;                      00-04                     *
                10030 ;*************************************************
                10040 ;
0220            10050          ORG     220H           ;NEXT EPROM AREA
0220            10060 MUSC     EQU     $              ;START OF MUSIC SYNTH
0220 318008     10070          LD      SP,880H        ;INITIALIZE STACK
0223 212605     10080          LD      HL,PDATA       ;START OF RAM DATA
0226 011100     10090          LD      BC,PDATAS      ;SIZE OF DATA
0229 CD0300     10100          CALL    INIT           ;INITIALIZE
022C 210000     10110 MUSC90   LD      HL,0           ;ZERO HL
022F 220808     10120          LD      (LEDBUF),HL    ;ZERO LEFT DIGITS
0232 220A08     10130          LD      (LEDBUF+2),HL  ;ZERO RIGHT DIGITS
0235 213E02     10140          LD      HL,MUSCT       ;FUNCTION TABLE ADDR
0238 110300     10150          LD      DE,0003H       ;0=MINIMUM,0-3 VALID
023B C31E00     10160          JP      BRANCH         ;BRANCH OUT
023E 180D       10170 MUSCT    JR      MUSC00         ;0=PLAY MUSIC
0240 1805       10180          JR      MUSCB1         ;1=SET DATA
0242 1806       10190          JR      MUSCB2         ;2=DISPLAY DATA
0244 C3E003     10200          JP      MUSC30         ;3=SET LOCN COUNTER
0247 C36703     10210 MUSCB1   JP      MUSC10
024A C3B003     10220 MUSCB2   JP      MUSC20
                10230 ;
                10240 ;MUSC00.PLAY MUSIC
                10250 ;
024D            10260 MUSC00   EQU     $
024D CD0904     10270 MUSC02   CALL    HALF           ;GET 4 BITS
0250 F2A902     10280          JP      P,MUSC06       ;GO IF NOT NOTE
0253 F5         10290          PUSH    AF             ;SAVE NOTE
0254 DD217E04   10300          LD      IX,FREQT       ;FREQ TABLE ADDRESS
0258 CD2A04     10310          CALL    GETDSP         ;GET FREQUENCY
025B 3A2E08     10320          LD      A,(OCT)        ;GET OCTAVE #
025E 47         10330          LD      B,A            ;TRANSFER TO B
025F CD3804     10340          CALL    SHIFT          ;SHIFT RIGHT
0262 223208     10350          LD      (FREQ),HL      ;SAVE FREQ FOR PLAY
0265 F1         10360          POP     AF             ;RESTORE NOTE
0266 DD219604   10370          LD      IX,DURT        ;DURATION TAB ADDR
026A CD2A04     10380          CALL    GETDSP         ;GET DURATION
026D E5         10420          PUSH    HL             ;SAVE RESULT
026E 0604       10430          LD      B,4            ;FOR 1/16TH
0270 CD3804     10440          CALL    SHIFT          ;GET 1/16TH
0273 D1         10450          POP     DE             ;GET 16/16THS
0274 EB         10460          EX      DE,HL          ;DE=1/16TH,HL=16/16THS
0275 3A2F08     10470          LD      A,(NDUR)       ;GET NOTE DURATION
0278 47         10480          LD      B,A            ;TRANSFER TO B
0279 CD4204     10490          CALL    SUBT           ;SUBT DE FROM HL B TIMES
027C E5         10500          PUSH    HL             ;SAVE RESULT
027D 0603       10510          LD      B,3            ;FOR 1/8
027F CD3804     10520          CALL    SHIFT          ;GET 1/8
0282 D1         10530          POP     DE             ;GET 8/8
0283 EB         10540          EX      DE,HL          ;DE=1/8,HL=8/8
0284 3A2808     10550          LD      A,(TEMP)       ;GET TEMPO
0287 47         10570          LD      B,A            ;TRANSFER TO B
0288 04         10571          INC     B              ;BUMP CODE
```

Fig. 19-5. Music Synthesizer program listing.

```
0289 B7       10572          OR     A              ;TEST  FOR 80 CPM
028A 2002     10573          JR     NZ,MUSC03      ;GO IF MORE
028C 0600     10574          LD     B,0            ;FOR 80 CPM
028E CD4204   10580 MUSC03   CALL   SUBT           ;SUBT DE FROM HL 0,2,0R 3 T.
0291 0603     10590          LD     B,3            ;FOR 1/8
0293 CD3804   10600          CALL   SHIFT          ;GET 1/8
0296 3A2E08   10602          LD     A,(OCT)        ;GET OCTAVE #
0299 47       10604          LD     B,A            ;TRANSFER TO B
029A 3E03     10606          LD     A,3            ;FOR SUBT
029C 90       10607          SUB    B              ;3-OCT#
029D 47       10608          LD     B,A            ;SETUP FOR SHIFT
029E CD3804   10609          CALL   SHIFT          ;SHIFT RIGHT
02A1 223008   10610          LD     (DURA),HL      ;SAVE FOR PLAY
02A4 CD4B04   10620          CALL   NOTE           ;PLAY NOTE
02A7 18A4     10625          JR     MUSC00         ;CONTINUE
              10630 ;
              10640 ;NOT NOTE HERE
              10650 ;
02A9 FE0C     10660 MUSC06   CP     12             ;TEST FOR NOTE DURATION
02AB 2009     10670          JR     NZ,MUSC07      ;GO IF NOT DURATION
02AD CD0904   10680          CALL   HALF           ;GET ARGUMENT
02B0 322F08   10690          LD     (NDUR),A       ;STORE
02B3 C34D02   10700          JP     MUSC00         ;GO FOR NEXT NOTE
02B6 FE0D     10710 MUSC07   CP     13             ;TEST FOR OCT,ENV,TEMP,LOUD
02B8 206C     10720          JR     NZ,MUSCA4      ;GO IF 14 OR 15
02BA CD0904   10730          CALL   HALF           ;GET ARGUMENT
02BD FE04     10740          CP     4              ;TEST FOR OCTAVE
02BF F2C802   10750          JP     P,MUSC09       ;GO IF NOT OCTAVE
02C2 322E08   10760          LD     (OCT),A        ;STORE OCTAVE #
02C5 C34D02   10770          JP     MUSC00         ;GO FOR NEXT NOTE
02C8 FE08     10780 MUSC09   CP     8              ;TEST FOR ENVELOPE
02CA F2EB02   10790          JP     P,MUSCA1       ;GO IF NOT ENVELOPE
02CD D604     10800          SUB    4              ;ENVELOPE NOW 0-3
02CF 323408   10801          LD     (ENVT),A       ;SAVE ENVELOPE TYPE
02D2 47       10810 MUSCA0   LD     B,A            ;SAVE
02D3 3A2708   10820          LD     A,(LOUD)       ;LOUDNESS 0-2
02D6 07       10830          RLCA                  ;LOUD*2
02D7 07       10840          RLCA                  ;LOUD*4
02D8 B0       10850          OR     B              ;NOW LL,EE 0 TO 11
02D9 47       10855          LD     B,A            ;HASH*1
02DA 07       10860          RLCA                  ;HASH*2
02DB 07       10870          RLCA                  ;HASH*4
02DC 07       10880          RLCA                  ;HASH*8
02DD 80       10885          ADD    A,B            ;HASH*9
02DE 4F       10890          LD     C,A            ;NOW IN C
02DF 0600     10900          LD     B,0            ;NOW IN BC
02E1 21BA04   10910          LD     HL,ETAB        ;START OF ENVELOPE TAB
02E4 09       10920          ADD    HL,BC          ;POINT TO ENVELOPE
02E5 222908   10930          LD     (ENVP),HL      ;SAVE FOR OUTPUT
02E8 C34D02   10940          JP     MUSC00         ;GO FOR NEXT NOTE
02EB FE0B     10950 MUSCA1   CP     11             ;TEST FOR TEMPO
02ED F2F802   10960          JP     P,MUSCA2       ;GO IF NOT TEMPO
02F0 D608     10965          SUB    8              ;ADJUST
02F2 322808   10970          LD     (TEMP),A       ;STORE TEMPO
02F5 C34D02   10980          JP     MUSC00         ;GO FOR NEXT NOTE
02F8 FE0E     10990 MUSCA2   CP     14             ;TEST FOR LOUDNESS
02FA F20803   11000          JP     P,MUSCA3       ;GO IF NOT LOUDNESS
```

Fig. 19-5 cont'd. Music

```
02FD D60B     11010         SUB   11            ;NOW 0-2
02FF 322708   11020         LD    (LOUD),A      ;STORE LOUDNESS
0302 3A3408   11025         LD    A,(ENVT)      ;GET ENVELOPE TYPE
0305 C3D202   11026         JP    MUSCA0        ;GO FOR NEW ENVELOPE
0308 D60E     11040 MUSCA3  SUB   14            ;REST ARG NOW 0 OR 1
030A 47       11050         LD    B,A           ;SAVE ARG
030B 3A2808   11060         LD    A,(TEMP)      ;GET TEMP
030E 07       11070         RLCA                ;SHIFT LEFT ONE
030F 80       11080         ADD   A,B           ;MERGE REST
0310 07       11085         RLCA
0311 4F       11090         LD    C,A           ;HASH IN C
0312 0600     11100         LD    B,0           ;HASH IN BC
0314 DD21AE04 11110         LD    IX,RTABLE     ;REST TABLE
0318 DD09     11120         ADD   IX,BC         ;POINT TO REST ENTRY
031A DD6E00   11130         LD    L,(IX)        ;GET LS BYTE
031D DD6601   11140         LD    H,(IX+1)      ;GET MS BYTE
0320 CD1800   11150         CALL  DELAY         ;DELAY FOR REST
0323 C34D02   11160         JP    MUSC00        ;GO FOR NEXT NOTE
0326 FE0F     11170 MUSCA4  CP    15            ;TEST FOR END
0328 CA2C02   11180         JP    Z,MUSC90      ;GO IF END
032B CD0904   11190         CALL  HALF          ;GET ARGUMENT
032E B7       11200         OR    A             ;TEST FOR ZERO
032F 201F     11210         JR    NZ,MUSCA5     ;GO IF NOT ZERO
0331 3A2D08   11220         LD    A,(RPTC)      ;GET REPEAT COUNT
0334 3D       11230         DEC   A             ;DECREMENT BY 1
0335 322D08   11240         LD    (RPTC),A      ;STORE FOR NEXT
0338 CA4D02   11250         JP    Z,MUSC00      ;GO IF DONE
033B 2A2B08   11260         LD    HL,(RADD)     ;REPEAT ADDRESS
033E CB3C     11270         SRL   H             ;SHIFT RIGHT 1
0340 CB1D     11280         RR    L
0342 222408   11290         LD    (PNTR),HL     ;RESET POINTER
0345 3E00     11300         LD    A,0           ;0 TO A
0347 3001     11310         JR    NC,MUSCA6     ;GO IF ZERO CARRY
0349 3C       11320         INC   A             ;1 TO A
034A 322608   11330 MUSCA6  LD    (NIBL),A      ;STORE NIBL CODE
034D C34D02   11340         JP    MUSC00        ;GO FOR NEXT NOTE
0350 322D08   11350 MUSCA5  LD    (RPTC),A      ;STORE REPEAT COUNT
0353 2A2408   11360         LD    HL,(PNTR)     ;GET CURRENT PNTR
0356 3A2608   11370         LD    A,(NIBL)      ;GET NIBL POINTER
0359 B7       11380         OR    A             ;TEST FOR 0
035A 2007     11390         JR    NZ,MUSCA8     ;GO IF 1
035C 29       11400         ADD   HL,HL         ;ADDR*2
035D 222B08   11420 MUSCA7  LD    (RADD),HL     ;SAVE FOR REPEAT
0360 C34D02   11430         JP    MUSC00        ;GO FOR NEXT NOTE
0363 29       11450 MUSCA8  ADD   HL,HL         ;ADDR*2
0364 23       11455         INC   HL            ;NIBL
0365 18F6     11460         JR    MUSCA7        ;GO TO STORE
              11470 ;MUSC10.SET LOCATION TO SPECIFIED DATA
              11480 ;
0367 111000   11490 MUSC10  LD    DE,16         ;MAXIMUM
036A DD211408 11500 MUSC11  LD    IX,INBUF+1    ;START OF DATA
036E 3A2308   11510         LD    A,(NOCHR)     ;GET # OF CHARS INPUT
0371 47       11520         LD    B,A           ;MOVE TO B
0372 05       11530         DEC   B             ;ADJUST FOR FUNCTION CODE
0373 CD1200   11540         CALL  BCDBIN        ;CONVERT
0376 3806     11550         JR    C,MUSC12      ;GO IF OK
0378 CD1B00   11560         CALL  BLINK         ;OVER LIMIT-BLINK
037B C32C02   11570         JP    MUSC90        ;GO FOR NEXT FUNCTION
```

Synthesizer program listing.

```
037E DD2A2408 11580 MUSC12  LD    IX,(PNTR)      ;GET CURRENT LOCATION
0382 3A2608   11590         LD    A,(NIBL)       ;GET NIBL POINTER
0385 EE01     11600         XOR   1              ;FLIP
0387 322608   11610         LD    (NIBL),A       ;STORE FOR NEXT
038A DD7E00   11620         LD    A,(IX)         ;GET VALUE
038D 2811     11630         JR    Z,MUSC13       ;GO IF SECOND
038F E60F     11640         AND   0FH            ;MASK OUT LS NIBL
0391 CB25     11650         SLA   L              ;LEFT JUSTIFY NIBL
0393 CB25     11660         SLA   L
0395 CB25     11670         SLA   L
0397 CB25     11680         SLA   L
0399 B5       11690         OR    L              ;MERGE NEW DATA
039A DD7700   11700         LD    (IX),A         ;STORE MERGED RESULT
039D C32C02   11710         JP    MUSC90         ;GET NEXT COMMAND
03A0 E6F0     11720 MUSC13  AND   0F0H           ;MASK OUT MS NIBL
03A2 B5       11730         OR    L              ;MERGE NEW DATA
03A3 DD7700   11740         LD    (IX),A         ;STORE MERGED RESULT
03A6 2A2408   11750         LD    HL,(PNTR)      ;GET CURRENT LOCATION
03A9 23       11760         INC   HL             ;BUMP BY 1
03AA 222408   11770         LD    (PNTR),HL      ;STORE
03AD C32C02   11780         JP    MUSC90         ;GET NEXT COMMAND
              11790 ;
              11800 ;MUSC20.DISPLAY CURRENT LOCATION.
              11810 ;
03B0 2A2408   11820 MUSC20  LD    HL,(PNTR)      ;GET CURRENT LOCATION
03B3 3A2608   11830         LD    A,(NIBL)       ;GET NIBL POINTER
03B6 EE01     11840         XOR   1              ;FLIP
03B8 322608   11850         LD    (NIBL),A       ;STORE FOR NEXT
03BB 7E       11860         LD    A,(HL)         ;GET BYTE
03BC 280A     11870         JR    Z,MUSC21       ;GO IF SECOND
03BE CB3F     11880         SRL   A              ;RIGHT JUSTIFY VALUE
03C0 CB3F     11890         SRL   A
03C2 CB3F     11900         SRL   A
03C4 CB3F     11910         SRL   A
03C6 1806     11920         JR    MUSC22         ;GO FOR STORE
03C8 E60F     11930 MUSC21  AND   0FH            ;GET NIBL
03CA 23       11940         INC   HL             ;BUMP POINTER
03CB 222408   11950         LD    (PNTR),HL      ;STORE
03CE 6F       11960 MUSC22  LD    L,A            ;NOW IN L
03CF 2600     11970         LD    H,0            ;NOW IN HL
03D1 DD210708 11980         LD    IX,LEDBUF-1    ;LED BUFFER
03D5 CD1500   11990         CALL  BINBCD         ;CONVERT AND DISPLAY
03D8 CD0C00   12000 MUSC25  CALL  KEYSCN          ;TEST KEY PUSH
03DB 28FB     12010         JR    Z,MUSC25        ;GO IF NONE
03DD C32C02   12020         JP    MUSC90         ;GET NEXT COMMAND
              12030 ;
              12040 ;MUSC30. SET LOCATION COUNTER.
              12050 ;
03E0 110011   12060 MUSC30  LD    DE,4352        ;(RAM+1)*2
03E3 DD211408 12070         LD    IX,INBUF+1     ;START OF DATA
03E7 3A2308   12080         LD    A,(NOCHR)      ;GET # OF CHARS INPUT
03EA 47       12090         LD    B,A            ;MOVE TO B
03EB 05       12100         DEC   B              ;ADJUST FOR FUNCTION CODE
03EC CD1200   12110         CALL  BCDBIN         ;CONVERT
03EF 3806     12120         JR    C,MUSC31       ;GO IF OK
03F1 CD1B00   12130         CALL  BLINK          ;OVER LIMIT-BLINK
03F4 C32C02   12140         JP    MUSC90         ;GO FOR NEXT FUNCTION
03F7 CB3C     12150 MUSC31  SRL   H              ;FIND BYTE LOCATION
```

Fig. 19-5 cont'd. Music

```
04EA 00        13870          DEFB    0
04EB 00        13880          DEFB    0
04EC 00        13890          DEFB    0
04ED 00        13900          DEFB    0
04EE 00        13910          DEFB    0
04EF FF        13920          DEFB    0FFH
04F0 00        13930          DEFB    0                 ;MEDIUM,TRIANGLE UP
04F1 02        13940          DEFB    2
04F2 04        13950          DEFB    4
04F3 05        13960          DEFB    5
04F4 07        13970          DEFB    7
04F5 09        13980          DEFB    9
04F6 00        13990          DEFB    0
04F7 00        14000          DEFB    0
04F8 FF        14010          DEFB    0FFH
04F9 09        14020          DEFB    9                 ;MEDIUM,TRIANGLE DOWN
04FA 07        14030          DEFB    7
04FB 05        14040          DEFB    5
04FC 04        14050          DEFB    4
04FD 02        14060          DEFB    2
04FE 00        14070          DEFB    0
04FF 00        14080          DEFB    0
0500 00        14090          DEFB    0
0501 FF        14100          DEFB    0FFH
0502 3F        14110          DEFB    3FH               ;LOUD, NORMAL
0503 3F        14120          DEFB    3FH
0504 3F        14130          DEFB    3FH
0505 3F        14140          DEFB    3FH
0506 3F        14150          DEFB    3FH
0507 00        14160          DEFB    0
0508 00        14170          DEFB    0
0509 00        14180          DEFB    0
050A FF        14190          DEFB    0FFH
050B 3F        14200          DEFB    3FH               ;LOUD,STACCATO
050C 3F        14210          DEFB    3FH
050D 3F        14220          DEFB    3FH
050E 00        14230          DEFB    0
050F 00        14240          DEFB    0
0510 00        14250          DEFB    0
0511 00        14260          DEFB    0
0512 00        14270          DEFB    0
0513 FF        14280          DEFB    0FFH
0514 00        14290          DEFB    0                 ;LOUD,TRIANGLE UP
0515 0D        14300          DEFB    13
0516 1A        14310          DEFB    26
0517 26        14320          DEFB    38
0518 33        14330          DEFB    51
0519 3F        14340          DEFB    63
051A 01        14350          DEFB    1
051B 01        14360          DEFB    1
051C FF        14370          DEFB    0FFH
051D 3F        14380          DEFB    63                ;LOUD,TRIANGLE DOWN
051E 33        14390          DEFB    51
051F 26        14400          DEFB    38
0520 1A        14410          DEFB    26
0521 0D        14420          DEFB    13
0522 00        14430          DEFB    0
0523 00        14440          DEFB    0
```

Synthesizer program listing.

```
                12740 ;
044B DD2A2908  12750 NOTE    LD     IX,(ENVP)      ;GET PNTR TO ENVELOPE
044F 11FFFF    12765         LD     DE,-1          ;FOR DECREMENT
0452 FD2A3008  12767 LOOPB   LD     IY,(DURA)      ;DURATION OF ONE SEGMENT
0456 DD7E00    12770         LD     A,(IX)         ;GET ENVELOPE VALUE
0459 BA        12780         CP     D              ;TEST FOR -1
045A C8        12790         RET    Z              ;GO IF 8TH
045B 2A3208    12800 LOOPA   LD     HL,(FREQ)      ;FREQ COUNT
045E 2B        12810         DEC    HL             ;ADJUST FOR JP C
045F DD7E00    12820         LD     A,(IX)         ;VALUE
0462 2F        12825         CPL                   ;INVERT FOR OUTPUT
0463 D301      12830         OUT    (1),A          ;OUTPUT
0465 19        12840 LOOP1   ADD    HL,DE          ;-1 TO COUNT
0466 DA6504    12850         JP     C,LOOP1        ;LOOP HERE
0469 2A3208    12860         LD     HL,(FREQ)      ;FREQ COUNT
046C 2B        12870         DEC    HL             ;ADJUST FOR JP C
046D 3EFF      12880         LD     A,0FFH         ;0
046F D301      12890         OUT    (1),A          ;OUTPUT
0471 19        12900 LOOP2   ADD    HL,DE          ;-1 TO COUNT
0472 DA7104    12910         JP     C,LOOP2        ;LOOP HERE
0475 FD19      12920         ADD    IY,DE          ;DECREMENT DURATION
0477 DA5B04    12930         JP     C,LOOPA        ;GO FOR DURATION
047A DD23      12940         INC    IX             ;BUMP ENVELOPE PNTR
047C 18D4      12950         JR     LOOPB          ;GO FOR NEXT SEGMENT
                12960 ;
                12970 ;FREQUENCY TABLE.OPTIMIZED FOR MIDDLE C.
                12980 ;
047E 6701      12990 FREQT   DEFW   359            ;C
0480 5301      13000         DEFW   339            ;C SH
0482 3F01      13010         DEFW   319            ;D
0484 2F01      13020         DEFW   303            ;D SH
0486 1B01      13030         DEFW   283            ;E
0488 0B01      13040         DEFW   267            ;F
048A FB00      13050         DEFW   251            ;F SH
048C EF00      13060         DEFW   239            ;G
048E E300      13070         DEFW   227            ;G SH
0490 D300      13080         DEFW   211            ;A
0492 C700      13090         DEFW   199            ;A SH
0494 BB00      13100         DEFW   187            ;B
                13110 ;
                13120 ;DURATION TABLE. DURATION OF WHOLE NOTES
                13130 ;IN COUNTS.
                13140 ;
0496 C705      13150 DURT    DEFW   1479           ;C
0498 1806      13160         DEFW   1560           ;C SH
049A 6F06      13170         DEFW   1647           ;D
049C CB06      13180         DEFW   1739           ;D SH
049E 2B07      13190         DEFW   1835           ;E
04A0 9007      13200         DEFW   1936           ;F
04A2 FB07      13210         DEFW   2043           ;F SH
04A4 6A08      13220         DEFW   2154           ;G
04A6 E008      13230         DEFW   2272           ;G SH
04A8 5A09      13240         DEFW   2394           ;A
04AA D909      13250         DEFW   2521           ;A SH
04AC 610A      13260         DEFW   2657           ;B
                13270 ;
                13280 ;REST TABLE.
                13290 ;
```

Fig. 19-5 cont'd. Music

```
04AE  EE02    13300  RTABLE  DEFW    750      ;80 CPM,1/4
04B0  DC05    13310          DEFW    1500     ;80 CPM,1/2
04B2  5802    13320          DEFW    600      ;100 CPM,1/4
04B4  B004    13330          DEFW    1200     ;100 CPM,1/2
04B6  F401    13340          DEFW    500      ;120 CPM,1/4
04B8  E803    13350          DEFW    1000     ;120 CPM,1/2
              13360  ;
              13370  ;ENVELOPE TABLE.4 AT SOFT,4 AT MED,4 AT LOUD.
              13380  ;
04BA  03      13390  ETAB    DEFB    03H      ;SOFT,NORMAL
04BB  03      13400          DEFB    03H
04BC  03      13410          DEFB    03H
04BD  03      13420          DEFB    03H
04BE  03      13430          DEFB    03H
04BF  00      13440          DEFB    0
04C0  00      13450          DEFB    0
04C1  00      13460          DEFB    0
04C2  FF      13470          DEFB    0FFH
04C3  03      13480          DEFB    03H      ;SOFT,STACCATO
04C4  03      13490          DEFB    03H
04C5  03      13500          DEFB    03H
04C6  00      13510          DEFB    0
04C7  00      13520          DEFB    0
04C8  00      13530          DEFB    0
04C9  00      13540          DEFB    0
04CA  00      13550          DEFB    0
04CB  FF      13560          DEFB    0FFH
04CC  00      13570          DEFB    0        ;SOFT, TRIANGLE UP
04CD  01      13580          DEFB    1
04CE  02      13590          DEFB    2
04CF  04      13600          DEFB    4
04D0  05      13610          DEFB    5
04D1  06      13620          DEFB    6
04D2  00      13630          DEFB    0
04D3  00      13640          DEFB    0
04D4  FF      13650          DEFB    0FFH
04D5  06      13660          DEFB    6        ;SOFT,TRIANGLE DOWN
04D6  05      13670          DEFB    5
04D7  04      13680          DEFB    4
04D8  02      13690          DEFB    2
04D9  01      13700          DEFB    1
04DA  00      13710          DEFB    0
04DB  00      13720          DEFB    0
04DC  00      13730          DEFB    0
04DD  FF      13740          DEFB    0FFH
04DE  09      13750          DEFB    9H       ;MEDIUM,NORMAL
04DF  09      13760          DEFB    9H
04E0  09      13770          DEFB    9H
04E1  09      13780          DEFB    9H
04E2  09      13790          DEFB    9H
04E3  00      13800          DEFB    0
04E4  00      13810          DEFB    0
04E5  00      13820          DEFB    0
04E6  FF      13830          DEFB    0FFH
04E7  09      13840          DEFB    9H       ;MEDIUM.STACCATO
04E8  09      13850          DEFB    9H
04E9  09      13860          DEFB    9H
```

Synthesizer program listing.

```
03F9 CB1D      12160          RR    L            ;BY SHIFT OF HL
03FB 222408    12165          LD    (PNTR),HL    ;SET PNTR
03FE 3E00      12170          LD    A,0          ;0 TO A
0400 3001      12180          JR    NC,MUSC32    ;GO IF C=0
0402 3C        12190          INC   A            ;1 TO A
0403 322608    12200 MUSC32   LD    (NIBL),A     ;0 OR 1 TO NIBL
0406 C32C02    12210          JP    MUSC90       ;GET NEXT COMMAND
               12220 ;
               12230 ;HALF.SUBROUTINE TO GET 4 BIT NIBL.
               12240 ;
0409 2A2408    12250 HALF     LD    HL,(PNTR)    ;GET CURRENT LOC
040C 3A2608    12260          LD    A,(NIBL)     ;GET NIBL POINTER
040F EE01      12270          XOR   1
0411 322608    12280          LD    (NIBL),A     ;FLIP
0414 7E        12290          LD    A,(HL)       ;GET BYTE
0415 280A      12300          JR    Z,HALF10     ;GO IF 2ND HALF
0417 CB3F      12310          SRL   A
0419 CB3F      12320          SRL   A
041B CB3F      12330          SRL   A
041D CB3F      12340          SRL   A
041F 1806      12350          JR    HALF20       ;CONTINUE
0421 E60F      12360 HALF10   AND   0FH          ;GET 4 BITS
0423 23        12370          INC   HL           ;BUMP PNTR
0424 222408    12380          LD    (PNTR),HL    ;RESTORE
0427 FE0C      12390 HALF20   CP    12           ;TEST FOR NOTE
0429 C9        12400          RET                ;RETURN
               12410 ;
               12420 ;GETDSP.SUBROUTINE TO GET ENTRY FOR 2 BYTE ENTRY TABLE.
               12430 ;
042A CB27      12440 GETDSP   SLA   A            ;N*2
042C 4F        12450          LD    C,A          ;NOW IN C
042D 0600      12460          LD    B,0          ;NOW IN BC
042F DD09      12470          ADD   IX,BC        ;POINT TO ENTRY
0431 DD6E00    12480          LD    L,(IX)       ;GET LS VALUE
0434 DD6601    12490          LD    H,(IX+1)     ;GET MS VALUE
0437 C9        12500          RET                ;RETURN
               12510 ;
               12520 ;SHIFT.SUBROUTINE TO SHIFT HL RIGHT B TIMES.
               12530 ;
0438 78        12540 SHIFT    LD    A,B          ;COUNT TO A
0439 B7        12550          OR    A            ;TEST FOR ZERO
043A C8        12560          RET   Z            ;RETURN IF ZERO
043B CB3C      12570 SHIF1    SRL   H            ;SET C
043D CB1D      12580          RR    L            ;SHIFT IN C
043F 10FA      12590          DJNZ  SHIF1        ;CONTINUE N TIMES
0441 C9        12600          RET                ;RETURN
               12610 ;
               12620 ;SUBT.SUBROUTINE TO SUBTRACT DE FROM HL B TIMES.
               12630 ;
0442 78        12640 SUBT     LD    A,B          ;TRANSFER CNT TO A
0443 B7        12650          OR    A            ;TEST FOR ZERO
0444 C8        12660          RET   Z            ;RETURN IF ZERO
0445 B7        12662 SUB20    OR    A            ;0 TO C
0446 ED52      12664          SBC   HL,DE        ;HL-DE TO HL
0448 10FB      12670          DJNZ  SUB20        ;GO IF MORE
044A C9        12680          RET                ;RETURN
               12720 ;
               12730 ;NOTE.SUBROUTINE TO PLAY ONE NOTE.
```

Fig. 19-5 cont'd. Music Synthesizer program listing.

```
0524 00          14450          DEFB     0
0525 FF          14460          DEFB     0FFH
                 14470 ;DATA AREA
                 14480 ;
0526             14490 PDATA    EQU      $          ;START OF PROGRAM RAM
0526 0000        14500          DEFW     0          ;(PNTR)
0528 00          14510          DEFB     0          ;(NIBL)
0529 00          14520          DEFB     0          ;(LOUD)
052A 00          14530          DEFB     0          ;(TEMP)
052B BA04        14540          DEFW     ETAB       ;(ENVP)
052D 0000        14550          DEFW     0          ;(RADD)
052F 00          14560          DEFB     0          ;(RPTC)
0530 00          14570          DEFB     0          ;(OCT)
0531 00          14580          DEFB     0          ;(NDUR)
0532 0000        14590          DEFW     0          ;(DURA)
0534 0000        14600          DEFW     0          ;(FREQ)
0536 00          14605          DEFB     0          ;(ENVT)
                 14610 ;*******END OF LOCATIONS TO BE PROGRAMMED*******
0011             14620 PDATAS   EQU      $-PDATA    ;SIZE
                 14630 ;
                 14640 ;EPROM MUSIC CAN START HERE
                 14650 ;
0824             14660 PNTR     EQU      PROGR      ;LOCATION OF (PNTR)
0826             14670 NIBL     EQU      PNTR+2     ;LOCATION OF (NIBL)
0827             14680 LOUD     EQU      NIBL+1     ;LOCATION OF (LOUD)
0828             14690 TEMP     EQU      LOUD+1     ;LOCATION OF (TEMP)
0829             14700 ENVP     EQU      TEMP+1     ;LOCATION OF (ENVP)
082B             14710 RADD     EQU      ENVP+2     ;LOCATION OF (RADD)
082D             14720 RPTC     EQU      RADD+2     ;LOCATION OF (RPTC)
082E             14730 OCT      EQU      RPTC+1     ;LOCATION OF (OCT)
082F             14740 NDUR     EQU      OCT+1      ;LOCATION OF (NDUR)
0830             14750 DURA     EQU      NDUR+1     ;LOCATION OF (DURA)
0832             14760 FREQ     EQU      DURA+2     ;LOCATION OF (FREQ)
0834             14765 ENVT     EQU      FREQ+2     ;LOCATION OF (ENVT)
0000             14770          END
00000 TOTAL ERRORS
```

Fig. 19-5 cont'd. Music Synthesizer program listing.

Loudness is set by a "13" code with an 11–13 argument that sets soft, medium, or loud.

Rests are set by a "13" code with an argument of 14 (¼ rest) or 15 (½ rest).

All "12" and "13" type codes define conditions that remain in force until redefined, and do not have to be (and should not be) redefined for each note.

Repeats are defined by "14" type codes. The repeat is set by a "14" code with an argument of 1 to 15. The next location after the repeat codes is saved as the starting location to be repeated. A "14" code with a zero argument marks the end of the repeat sequence. The repeat sequence will be repeated for the number of times defined in the first argument.

The last code is a "15," marking the end of the song and returning control to the command input routine.

When the Music Synthesizer is first powered up or reset, there are four commands that may be entered as shown in Table 19-1. The "3nnn" command sets a location counter for entering, displaying, or playing song data. The location counter is set to "nnn," which is a decimal number representing the EPROM or RAM address of the data. This address, however, is the address of the nibl and is therefore twice the size of the normal RAM/EPROM address, as each

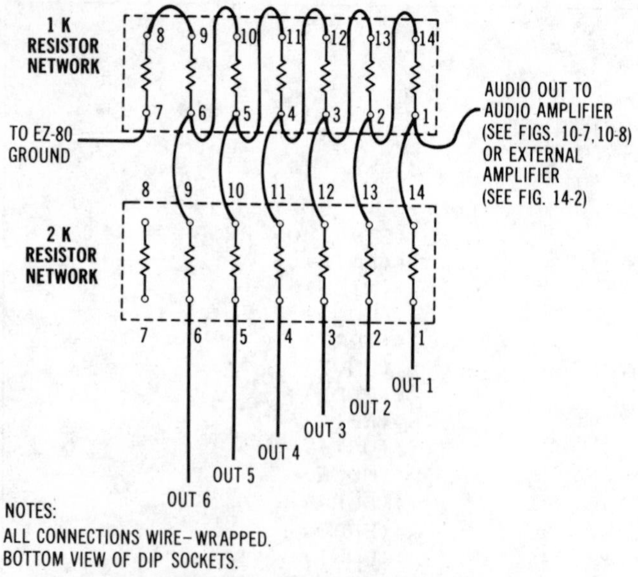

Fig. 19-6. Music Synthesizer construction.

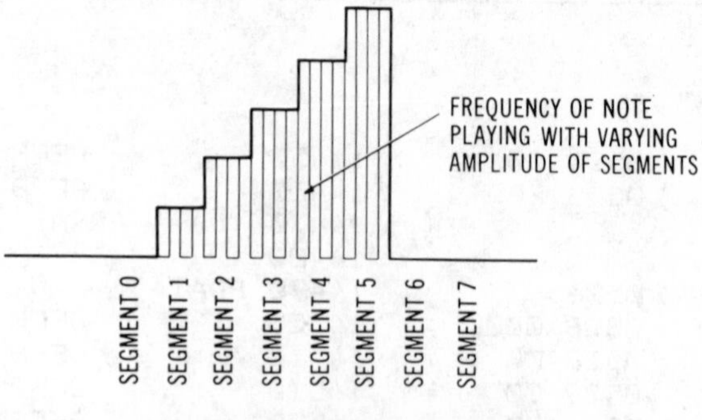

Fig. 19-8. Envelope generation.

byte contains two 4-bit nibls. The left-hand nibl is designed "0" and the right-hand nibl is designated "1." Location 4225 specifies byte 4225/2 = 2112 (840H in RAM) and the remainder of 1 indicates nibl 1 at location 2112.

Command "1nn" sets data defining the song into RAM. The location counter must have previously been set to a valid RAM/nibl location. The value nn may be 0–15 and defines a code shown in Chart 19-1. The location counter will automatically be incremented to the next nibl after the entry is made.

Command "2" displays data in the current RAM or EPROM location. The current location counter must have previously been set to the desired memory/nibl location. Pressing any key ends the display and allows input of the next command. Pressing

Subroutine SHIFT shifts the HL register right the number of times specified by the count in the B register. Subroutine SUBT subtracts the contents of DE from HL the number of times specified by the count in the B register.

Many of the variables have already been mentioned. The rest table RTABLE specifies a delay count based

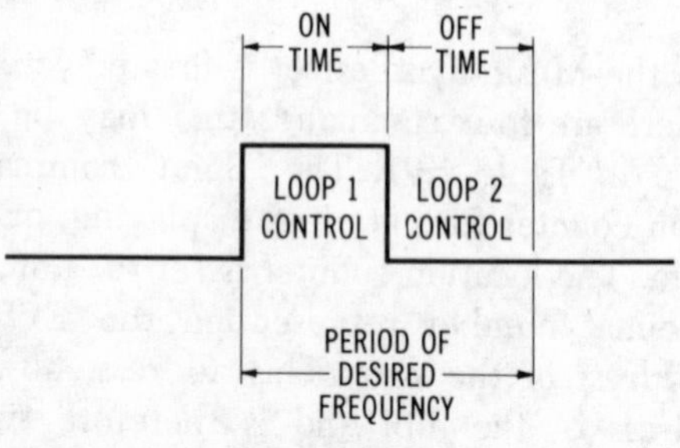

Fig. 19-7. Frequency generation.

upon the current tempo (TEMP) and rest value (¼ or ½). The Envelope Table (ETAB) contains eight values for the eight segments of the envelope plus a terminating value of 0.

"ENTER" displays sequential locations, automatically incrementing to the next for each display. This mode allows the user to examine music codes for validity.

Command "0" starts execution of the song specified by the current location counter. The song may be in RAM or in EPROM at the user's choice. Multiple songs may be stored in RAM or EPROM and specified by the proper location counter address. Return is made to command input when the Synthesizer encounters a "15" or end code.

The Music Synthesizer is programmed into 2716 EPROM as shown in Fig. 19-2 and starts at location 220H. Set EPROM locations 1 and 2 to 20H and 2 respectively.

APPLICATIONS HARDWARE

The Music Synthesizer uses OUT1–OUT6 as outputs to a resistor ladder network as shown in Fig. 19-3. This ladder network is a digital-to-analog converter that converts a 6-bit digital value to an analog signal level. The maximum signal level is about 3.5 volts for an output of 111111. Half of that level is 011111. Each bit represents about 3.5 volts/64, or 0.055 volt, and the output is approximately linear over the range of voltages.

Loudness (or envelope) is controlled by varying the digital output values to OUT1–OUT6. The greater the digital value output, the louder the signal will be. For a "normal" note with a "loud" output, the level will be either 0 or maximum, as shown in Fig. 19-4. Medium and soft result in lowered value outputs. Using different envelope patterns results in varying levels, and therefore varying waveshapes. The user is urged to modify the envelope tables in the program to create his or her own patterns.

The output of the ladder network can be fed into the audio amplifier described in Chapter 10 or into an external amplifier. The suggested physical layout for this application is shown in Fig. 19-5.

THEORY OF OPERATION

The heart of the Music Synthesizer (Fig. 19-6) is a subroutine called "NOTE." NOTE consists of four loops. The innermost two loops (LOOP1 and LOOP2) turn on the output lines and then turn off the output lines for a precise period. The time that the lines are on and off correspond to the frequency of the note desired. Variable FREQ contains a count that is decremented by 1 each time through LOOP1 (on loop) or LOOP2 (off loop) to create a (relatively) precise on/off time that matches the period of the frequency desired (see Fig. 19-7).

One cycle of a note would not be audible, so there is an outer loop (LOOPA) that counts how many cycles should be output. As the period of each note varies with the frequency of the note, this count is different for every frequency. It is put into variable DURA before the NOTE subroutine is called. LOOPA outputs approximately the correct number of cycles for the frequency of the note (which depends upon the note value and the octave) and the duration of the note (which depends upon the note duration and tempo).

To produce varying envelopes, the values defining different points on the envelope must be accessed and output. LOOPB performs this function. Every envelope is defined by eight segments on the envelope, as shown in Fig. 19-8. LOOPA outputs exactly one-eighth the duration of the note and then LOOPB gets the next envelope value to be used during the "ON" portion of output. A −1 value defines the end of the envelope. The proper envelope has been previously defined before NOTE is called and variable ENVP points to its location.

When a song is to be played, routine MUSC00 is entered. MUSC00 gets a nibl from the song data area. Much of the processing in MUSC0 (from MUSC06 on) is to process "non-note" nibls. This involves getting the next argument and storing it in variables such as LOUD (loudness), NDUR (note duration), OCT (octave), ENVP (envelope pointer), TEMP (tempo), RPTC (repeat count), and RADD (repeat address). During this code some processing is done to store the variables in convenient form for the NOTE subroutine to minimize the "overhead" for playing a note.

When a note is to be played in MUSC00, the proper frequency count is obtained from the frequency table (FREQT) and modified by the octave number. The frequency table holds the proper count for all notes of the lowest octave. This count is halved for each octave above the lowest. The result is stored in FREQ for the NOTE subroutine.

The second portion of playing a note in MUSC00 involves figuring out the duration count to be stored in DURA. A value from the duration table (DURT) is obtained based upon the note to be played. This is halved for every octave below the highest. This result is then adjusted for the number of 16ths in the note (NDUR), and then adjusted further for the tempo (TEMP). The result is divided by eight (for the eight segments) and stored in DURA.

Whew! Subroutine NOTE is then called to play the note.

The remainder of the Music Synthesizer is made up of the editor portion to access or change data to be played and subroutines. MUSC10, MUSC20, and MUSC30 operate similarly to the Microcomputer Educator in setting a location counter, displaying data based upon the location counter, or storing data to the current location. Location (NIBL), however, contains the current nibl position (0 or 1) and these routines operate in nibl addressing, display, and entry rather than in byte fashion.

Subroutine HALF obtains the current nibl based upon the byte pointer (PNTR) and nibl pointer (NIBL). The 4 bits are right justified to produce a value of 0–15 for ease in handling.

Subroutine SHIFT shifts the HL register right the number of times specified by the count in the B register. Subroutine SUBT subtracts the contents of DE from HL the number of times specified by the count in the B register.

Many of the variables have already been mentioned. The Rest Table RTABLE specifies a delay count based on the current tempo (TEMP) and rest value (¼ or ½). The Envelope Table (ETAB) contains eight values for the eight segments of the envelope plus a terminating value of 0.

CHAPTER 20

Blue Sky Projects

The preceding chapters have presented some interesting applications for a dedicated inexpensive microcomputer such as the EZ-80. In this chapter we'll discuss some other possible applications—ones which we will not implement here, but that are certainly well within the realm of possibility. These fall roughly into three areas: other EZ-80 control applications, distributed processing, and intelligent controller applications.

OTHER EZ-80 CONTROL APPLICATIONS

The EZ-80 can be used to control a variety of outputs, as we have seen in previous chapters. The relay described in the applications will handle up to 125 watts, or may be used to drive still other relays or solid-state electronics to control virtually any slow-speed control application such as lights, motors, solenoids, and appliances. All of these applications are "discrete" outputs—the output is either off or on.

The outputs of the EZ-80 may be converted to an analog signal by a digital to analog (dac) converter. The simplest form of this is described in Chapter 19 for the Music Synthesizer, where a ladder network is used to implement a dac whose output varies from 0 to 3.5 volts. The same scheme may be used to control external devices that require analog voltages, such as small dc motors. An analog amplifier will have to be used between the output of the dac and the control application to provide more drive capability and a voltage level conversion.

Inputs for control applications are a major problem because of the noise present on input lines for even short runs of several feet. In the Burglar Alarm application we bypassed the problem by using relay inputs where the relay contacts were physically close to the EZ-80. There are many approaches to solving the noise problem for inputs. The one we'll discuss here is differential line drivers/receivers.

Differential line drivers and receivers are devices for generating and detecting digital signals over lines that run up to hundreds of feet. They are highly immune to line noise, can operate at high frequencies, and provide a high current drive capability. A communication system using twisted pair is shown in Fig. 20-1. The 8820 device is a dual differential *receiver* and the 8830 device is a dual differential *driver*. They are interconnected by a *twisted pair* line. The twisted pair line is simply that—two pieces of wire twisted around each other to give approximately known impedance and noise cancellation effects. The 8820 and 8830 devices can be used on the EZ-80 by the setup shown in Fig. 20-2. One set of twisted pair must be run for each input or output to the EZ-80.

What about analog inputs to a computer such as the EZ-80? It is very convenient to have a microcomputer measure *analog inputs* that represent external conditions such as temperature, humidity, speed, and others. Commerical analog-to-digital converters (adc's) are available for this function, but they are generally somewhat expensive. Simple schemes for implementing an adc usually incorporate a programmable dac and a comparator, as shown in Fig. 20-3. The dac is programmed a step at a time (or in binary fashion, halving the remaining range each time) until the corresponding input analog voltage is matched. The scheme we'll consider here, though, relies on *pulse generation.*

The pulse generator adc is shown in Fig. 20-4. It uses an external resistance or voltage as an analog of a real world signal, such as temperature or humidity. There are many available *transducers* that convert external parameters into resistance or voltage; the converted resistance or voltage is then supplied to the MC4024 device as a voltage. The MC4024 outputs a square wave whose frequency is (approximately) linearly dependent upon the input control voltage. The square wave output is fed into one of the input lines IN1–IN5 of the EZ-80. By measuring the time interval between pulses, the frequency of the MC4042 can be determined, the control voltage value can be derived, and the analog value, such as tem-

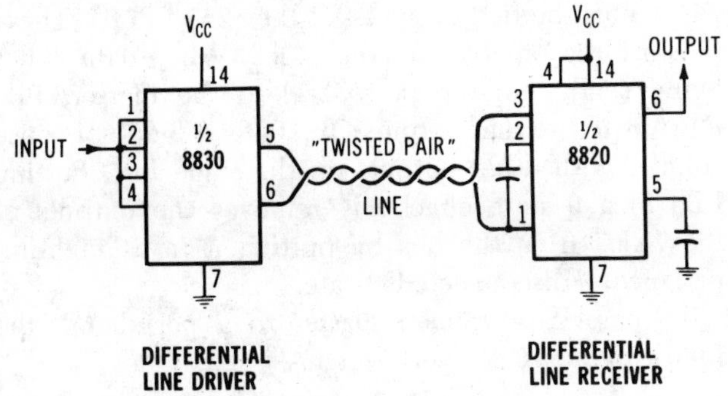

Fig. 20-1. Differential line drivers/receivers.

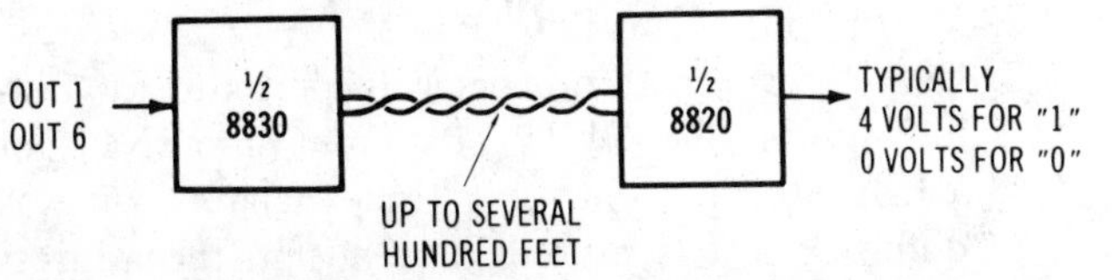

(A) Output from EZ-80 to remote receiver.

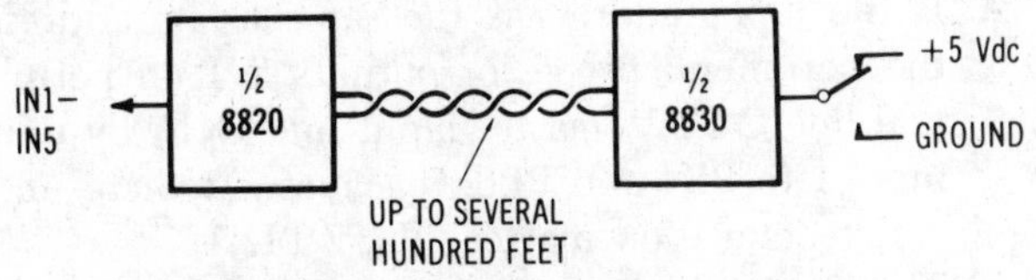

(B) Input to EZ-80 from remote receiver.

Fig. 20-2. EZ-80 differential system.

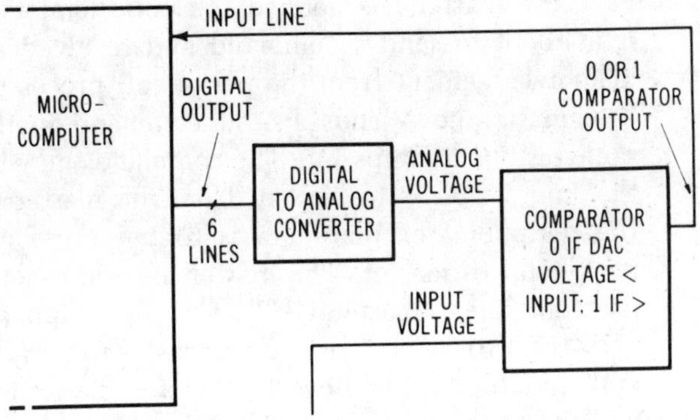

TRY	DIGITAL OUTPUT	COMPARATOR OUTPUT	DESCRIPTION
1	100000	0	INPUT VOLTAGE NOT 32-63 HALVE 0-31 RANGE
2	010000	0	INPUT NOT 16-31 HALVE 0-15 RANGE
3	001000	1	INPUT 8-15 HALVE 8-15
4	001100	0	INPUT NOT 12-15 HALVE 8-11 RANGE
5	001001	0	INPUT NOT 9-10 INPUT MUST BE 8

Fig. 20-3. Analog to digital conversion.

perature, may be found. In general, the conversion from time interval and analog value is a simple divide of the form:

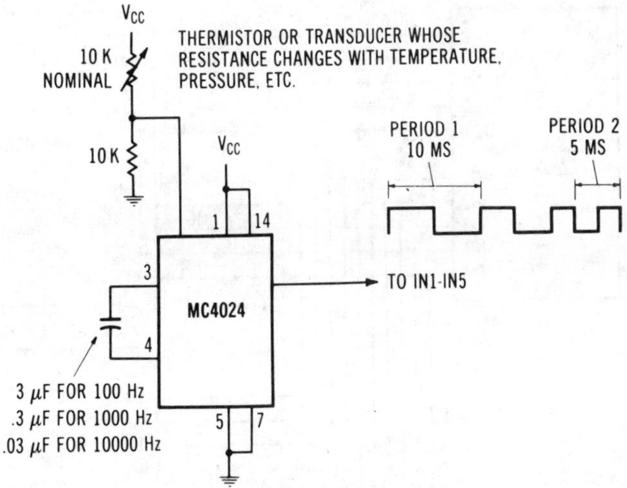

Fig. 20-4. Pulse generator adc.

$$\text{analog value} = \frac{k}{\text{time interval}}$$

where k is a constant value.

The circuitry shown in Fig. 20-4 can be used to monitor analog inputs such as room temperature, wind speed, light intensity, humidity, and others if the suitable transducer is used and a *linear* portion of the frequency curve is chosen.

DISTRIBUTED PROCESSING

The EZ-80 was designed to be inexpensive and to use readily available parts. It therefore lends itself to parallel processing of the form shown in Fig. 20-5. In this case each EZ-80 can perform its own dedicated function and a master EZ-80 can communicate

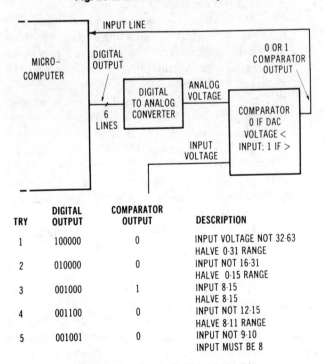

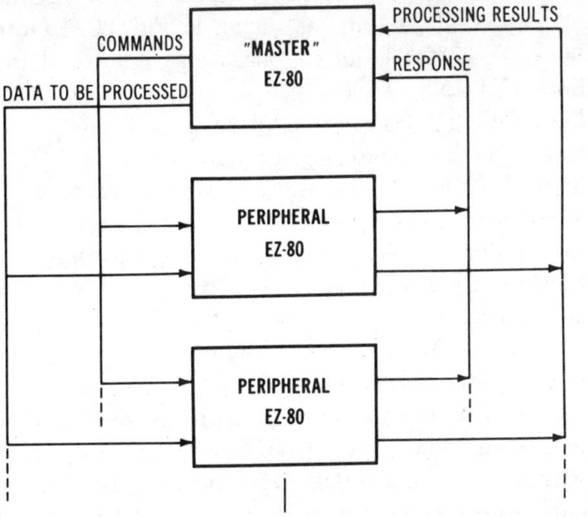

Fig. 20-5. Distributed processing using EZ-80s.

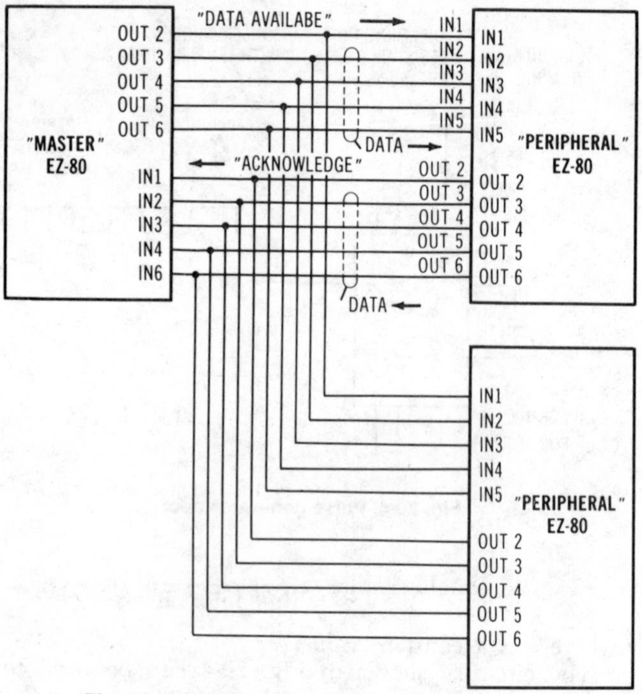

Fig. 20-6. EZ-80 bus for distributed processing.

with the others to monitor the system in general. The network of microcomputers can be physically close and working in parallel to process parts of the same problem, or they can be physically far apart in a control system. The peripheral processors may require no keyboard or LED displays and this will reduce their cost significantly.

How do the cpu's communicate in such a system? Two approaches are presented here, one in which the processors are physically close, and a second in which they are a relatively long distance apart.

In the case of processors that are close together, we can create a "bus" as shown in Fig. 20-6. Output lines OUT2–OUT6 of the master go out to all input lines IN1–IN5 of each peripheral processor. Output lines OUT3–OUT6 are used to pass 4 bits of data from the master to a peripheral processor. Output line OUT2 from the master is a "data available" line to indicate there is data on lines OUT3-OUT6 from the master which is to be read in by the peripheral. Master output lines OUT3–OUT6 are read in by each peripheral processor on input lines IN2–IN5. Master output line OUT2 is read in by each peripheral processor on line IN1.

Data sent from a peripheral processor is sent over peripheral lines OUT3–OUT6. These lines go to master input lines IN2–IN5. An "acknowledge signal" from a microprocessor is sent out from peripheral line OUT2 and is read in from master line IN1. A slight modification must be performed for each peripheral processor. Pins 15 and 8 of each peripheral 74368 must be tied to pin 24 of the 8255 (PB6). These pins are the "enable" for the 74368. When data is not being sent from the peripheral to the master, PB6 *must be a 0* so that outputs OUT2–OUT6 do not cause conflict with other outputs on the same bus. Putting PB6 in a 0 state effectively removes the outputs of the 74367 from the bus by putting it in a "high-impedance" (disconnected) state.

To pass data from a master to a peripheral, the following steps are performed:

1. Master puts address of peripheral on lines OUT3–OUT6 (0–15).
2. Master puts 1 on line OUT2.
3. Every peripheral processor is periodically testing master line OUT2 (its input line IN1) for a 1. If a 0 is present, it continues whatever it was doing. If a 1 is present, it reads in the address on lines master OUT3–OUT6 (its input lines IN2–IN5).
4. If the input address is the same as its address, the peripheral processor outputs a 1 on peripheral line OUT2 (master input line IN1) by writing a 1 to PB4 and PB6. It leaves a 1 there until it detects a 0 on master OUT2 (IN1).
5. The master looks for a 1 on its IN1 (peripheral OUT2). As soon as it receives the "acknowledge," it puts a 0 on master OUT2.
6. Now the master has notified the peripheral that it is about to send a command and received an acknowledgement from the peripheral processor. The master now sends a 4-bit command in the same fashion as Steps 1–5. The commands may be that more data is to be sent from the master to the peripheral or that data is to be sent from peripheral to master. The master and peripheral use four lines (master OUT3-OUT6, peripheral IN2–IN5) to transfer data from master to peripheral and four other lines to transfer data from peripheral to master (master IN2–IN5 and peripheral OUT3–OUT6). Master lines OUT2 is used as a "data available" line and peripheral line OUT2 is used as an "acknowledge" line in the transfers.

Data can be sent in 4-bit segments fairly rapidly using this protocol, on the order of 25,000 bytes per second. All communication is initiated by the master with the addressed peripheral responding. Interperipheral communication may be done through the master. Such distributed processing could provide a means to "number-crunch" data on one processor, while another performed control functions. It is a way to parallel a number of tasks on different processors.

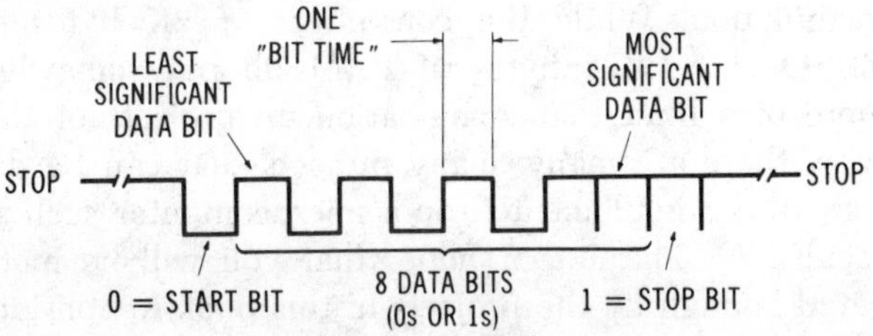

Fig. 20-7. Serial data format.

In the case of distributed processors that are separated by some distance, a similar scheme could be used if twisted-pair differential drivers/receivers were employed (with some modification to the circuitry previously shown). However, a more feasible approach is to use a double-twisted pair, one pair for sending data and one pair for receiving data. Data would be sent in *serial* fashion as a bit stream rather than as 4 bits at a time. In this case each master output line of OUT2–OUT6 would be dedicated as a differential driver and each master input line IN1–IN5 as a differential receiver. The possible five peripheral processors would be addressed by outputting on the appropriate line and receiving data on the appropriate input line.

Data sent in serial fashion can follow the somewhat standard conventions used in data communications, a *start bit, 8 data bits,* and a *stop bit,* as shown in Fig. 20-7. Each output is on or off for one bit time. Standard bit times range from 10 milliseconds to 100 microseconds. A good value to use would be on the order of 200 microseconds. Each 8-bit value sent out would take 2 milliseconds to send in this case. A 0 (start) would be output, followed by 8 data bits (least significant bit first), followed by a 1 (stop) bit. Each peripheral processor would be monitoring the input line from the master looking for a 0 bit, and then reading in the following bit stream by delaying one bit time and reading in at 200-microsecond intervals. Commands sent by the master would be similar to the commands described above.

Table 20-1. 8255 Configuration Codes

	Control Word							
Lines	**80H**	**82H**	**81H**	**83H**	**88H**	**8AH**	**89H**	**8BH**
PA7–PA0	out	out	out	out	out	out	out	out
PC7–PC4	out	out	out	out	in	in	in	in
PC3–PC0	out	out	in	in	out	out	in	in
PB7–PB0	out	in	out	in	out	in	out	in
Lines	**90H**	**92H**	**91H**	**93H**	**98H**	**9AH**	**99H**	**9BH**
PA7–PA0	in	in	in	in	in	in	in	in
PC7–PC4	out	out	out	out	in	in	in	in
PC3–PC0	out	out	in	in	out	out	in	in
PB7–PB0	out	in	out	in	out	in	out	in

INTELLIGENT CONTROLLER APPLICATIONS

Stripped of keyboard and display, the EZ-80 makes a good intelligent controller for a computer system, with 1K or 2K of EPROM and 128 bytes of RAM. The 24 lines from the 8255 may be used to receive data from an S-100 or other computer system, as shown in Fig. 20-8 and Table 20-1, to process the data, and to transmit it to a printer or other peripheral. Conversely, the EZ-80 may receive data from a peripheral, buffer it, process it, and then send it on to the controlling computer system. Data may be transferred at rates of up to 50,000 bytes per second when the EZ-80 is used in this type of application.

As a typical example of such a use, Fig. 20-9 shows an EZ-80 used as a Morse Code Translator/Sender in a ham radio application. The EZ-80 receives the audio and translates from code to ASCII characters. The main computer periodically requests new characters from the EZ-80 and handles logging the message on

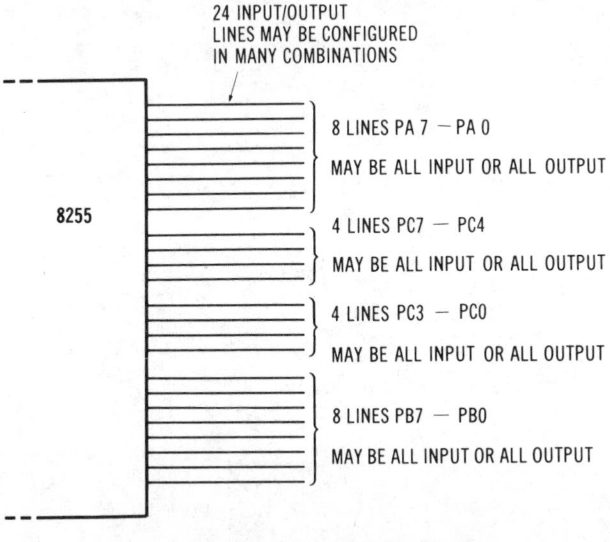

Fig. 20-8. Reconfiguring the 8255 i/o lines.

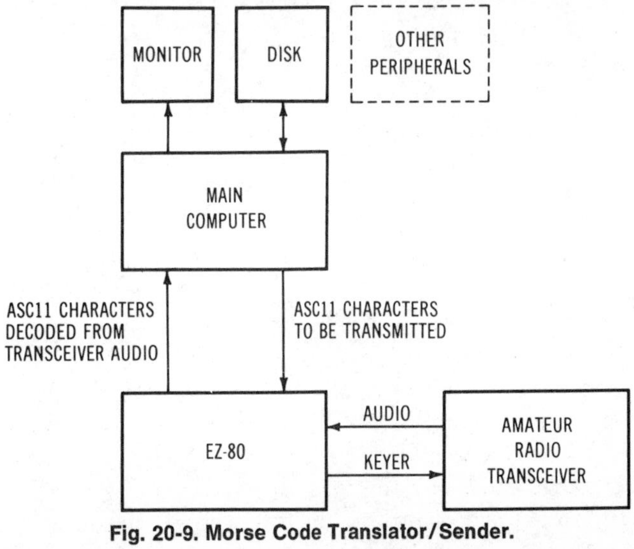

Fig. 20-9. Morse Code Translator/Sender.

disk, looking for previous contacts with the station, printing the received message, and so forth. When messages are to be sent, the main computer passes a message in ASCII, which is then translated by the EZ-80 into code.

The preceding applications are perfectly feasible. To use a hackneyed phrase, the applications for such a microcomputer are limited only by the reader's imagination. While the constraints of 2K bytes of EPROM and 128 bytes of RAM do put somewhat more of a limit than imagination on projects of this type, there are many, many projects that can be designed and implemented on a microcomputer such as the EZ-80. The author hopes that you will be motivated enough by the projects in this book to consider trying some of your own.

Appendices

APPENDIX A

Binary Operations

TO CONVERT FROM DECIMAL TO BINARY

1. Divide decimal by 2. Save remainder:

$$2\overline{)50} = 25 \text{ R}0$$

2. Repeat until zero remains:

$$2\overline{)25} = 12 \text{ R}1 \quad 2\overline{)12} = 6 \text{ R}0 \quad 2\overline{)6} = 3 \text{ R}0 \quad 2\overline{)3} = 1 \text{ R}1 \quad 2\overline{)1} = 0 \text{ R}1$$

3. Arrange remainders in reverse order (last to first):

110010

4. This is equivalent binary number:

$$110010_2 = 50_{10}$$

TO CONVERT FROM BINARY TO DECIMAL

1. Take first binary digit and multiply by 2:

110010
$1 \times 2 = 2$

2. Add to next binary digit:

110010
$1 \times 2 = 2 + 1 = 3$

3. Repeat for remainder of binary digits:

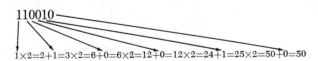

110010
$1{\times}2{=}2{+}1{=}3{\times}2{=}6{+}0{=}6{\times}2{=}12{+}0{=}12{\times}2{=}24{+}1{=}25{\times}2{=}50{+}0{=}50$

4. The result is the equivalent binary number.

TO ADD TWO BINARY NUMBERS

1. Adding $0 + 0 = 0$, adding $0 + 1 = 1$, adding $1 + 1 = 0$ with a carry, adding $1 + 1 + \text{carry} = 1$ with a carry.
2. Start from right as in decimal addition and add with carries.

$$\begin{array}{r} 10010 = 18 \\ +11110 = 30 \\ \hline 110000 = 48 \end{array}$$

TO SUBTRACT TWO BINARY NUMBERS

1. Subtracting $0 - 0 = 0$, subtracting $1 - 0 = 1$, subtracting $0 - 1 = 1$ with a borrow, subtracting $1 - 1 = 0$.
2. Start from right as in decimal subtraction and subtract with borrows:

$$\begin{array}{r} 11010 = 26 \\ -01111 = 15 \\ \hline 1011 = 11 \end{array}$$

SIGNED BINARY NUMBERS (TWOS COMPLEMENT)

1. Most significant bit is sign. If msb = 0, number is +, if msb = 1, number is negative.

01111111 is positive, 10101010 is negative

2. If positive number, convert remainder to decimal:

01111111
↓
+ 127

3. If negative number, change all ones to zeros and all zeros to one:

10101010
↓
01010101

Add one:

10101010
↓

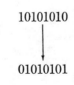

```
01010101
      +1
--------
01010110
```

Now convert all but sign bit to decimal and add minus sign:

```
10101010
    |
    v
01010101
      +1
--------
01010110
    \
    -86
```

TO ADD SIGNED BINARY NUMBERS

1. Add as in simple addition:

```
 01010100 = +84
+10101010 = -86
---------
 11111110 = - 2
```

2. Convert result:

```
11111110
    |
    v
00000001
      +1
--------
00000010
    |
   -2
```

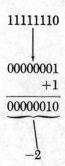

APPENDIX B

Hexadecimal Operations

TO CONVERT FROM BINARY TO HEX

1. Group binary number into groups of four digits:

   1010▵1010▵1111▵1011

2. Convert each 4-digit group as follows:

Binary	*Hexadecimal*
0000	0
0001	1
0010	2
0011	3
0100	4
0101	5
0110	6
0111	7
1000	8
1001	9
1010	A
1011	B
1100	C
1101	D
1110	E
1111	F

1010▵1010▵1111▵1011

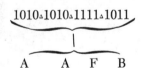

A A F B

TO CONVERT FROM HEX TO BINARY

1. Convert each hex digit to a binary four-bit group as above:

   A32F

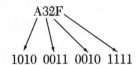

   1010 0011 0010 1111

TO CONVERT FROM DECIMAL TO HEX

1. Divide hex by 16. Save remainder:

   $16\overline{)1234}$ = 77 R2

2. Repeat until 0 remains:

   $16\overline{)77}$ = 4 R13 $16\overline{)4}$ = 0 R4

3. Arrange remainders in reverse order (last to first):

   4 13 2

4. Convert to hex digits:

   4 13 2

   ↓

   4 D 2

5. This is equivalent hexadecimal number:

   4D2H = 1234

TO CONVERT FROM HEX TO DECIMAL

1. Take first hex digit and multiply by 16:

   4D2H

   $4 \times 16 = 64$

2. Add to next hex digit:

   4D2H

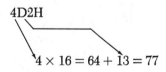

   $4 \times 16 = 64 + 13 = 77$

3. Repeat for remainder of hexadecimal digits:

   4D2H

   $4 \times 16 = 64 + 13 = 77 \times 16 = 1232 + 2 = 1234$

4. The result is the equivalent binary number.

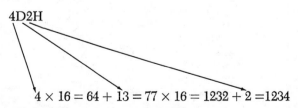

APPENDIX C

Conversion Tables for Decimal 0-255

BINARY	DEC	HEX
00000000	000	00
00000001	001	01
00000010	002	02
00000011	003	03
00000100	004	04
00000101	005	05
00000110	006	06
00000111	007	07
00001000	008	08
00001001	009	09
00001010	010	0A
00001011	011	0B
00001100	012	0C
00001101	013	0D
00001110	014	0E
00001111	015	0F
00010000	016	10
00010001	017	11
00010010	018	12
00010011	019	13
00010100	020	14
00010101	021	15
00010110	022	16
00010111	023	17
00011000	024	18
00011001	025	19
00011010	026	1A
00011011	027	1B
00011100	028	1C
00011101	029	1D
00011110	030	1E
00011111	031	1F
00100000	032	20
00100001	033	21
00100010	034	22
00100011	035	23
00100100	036	24
00100101	037	25
00100110	038	26
00100111	039	27
00101000	040	28
00101001	041	29
00101010	042	2A
00101011	043	2B
00101100	044	2C
00101101	045	2D
00101110	046	2E
00101111	047	2F
00110000	048	30
00110001	049	31
00110010	050	32

BINARY	DEC	HEX
00110011	051	33
00110100	052	34
00110101	053	35
00110110	054	36
00110111	055	37
00111000	056	38
00111001	057	39
00111010	058	3A
00111011	059	3B
00111100	060	3C
00111101	061	3D
00111110	062	3E
00111111	063	3F
01000000	064	40
01000001	065	41
01000010	066	42
01000011	067	43
01000100	068	44
01000101	069	45
01000110	070	46
01000111	071	47
01001000	072	48
01001001	073	49
01001010	074	4A
01001011	075	4B
01001100	076	4C
01001101	077	4D
01001110	078	4E
01001111	079	4F
01010000	080	50
01010001	081	51
01010010	082	52
01010011	083	53
01010100	084	54
01010101	085	55
01010110	086	56
01010111	087	57
01011000	088	58
01011001	089	59
01011010	090	5A
01011011	091	5B
01011100	092	5C
01011101	093	5D
01011110	094	5E
01011111	095	5F
01100000	096	60
01100001	097	61
01100010	098	62
01100011	099	63
01100100	100	64
01100101	101	65

BINARY	DEC	HEX
01100110	102	66
01100111	103	67
01101000	104	68
01101001	105	69
01101010	106	6A
01101011	107	6B
01101100	108	6C
01101101	109	6D
01101110	110	6E
01101111	111	6F
01110000	112	70
01110001	113	71
01110010	114	72
01110011	115	73
01110100	116	74
01110101	117	75
01110110	118	76
01110111	119	77
01111000	120	78
01111001	121	79
01111010	122	7A
01111011	123	7B
01111100	124	7C
01111101	125	7D
01111110	126	7E
01111111	127	7F
10000000	128	80
10000001	129	81
10000010	130	82
10000011	131	83
10000100	132	84
10000101	133	85
10000110	134	86
10000111	135	87
10001000	136	88
10001001	137	89
10001010	138	8A
10001011	139	8B
10001100	140	8C
10001101	141	8D
10001110	142	8E
10001111	143	8F
10010000	144	90
10010001	145	91
10010010	146	92
10010011	147	93
10010100	148	94
10010101	149	95
10010110	150	96
10010111	151	97

BINARY	DEC	HEX
10011000	152	98
10011001	153	99
10011010	154	9A
10011011	155	9B
10011100	156	9C
10011101	157	9D
10011110	158	9E
10011111	159	9F
10100000	160	A0
10100001	161	A1
10100010	162	A2
10100011	163	A3
10100100	164	A4
10100101	165	A5
10100110	166	A6
10100111	167	A7
10101000	168	A8
10101001	169	A9
10101010	170	AA
10101011	171	AB
10101100	172	AC
10101101	173	AD
10101110	174	AE
10101111	175	AF
10110000	176	B0
10110001	177	B1
10110010	178	B2
10110011	179	B3
10110100	180	B4
10110101	181	B5
10110110	182	B6
10110111	183	B7
10111000	184	B8
10111001	185	B9

BINARY	DEC	HEX
10111010	186	BA
10111011	187	BB
10111100	188	BC
10111101	189	BD
10111110	190	BE
10111111	191	BF
11000000	192	C0
11000001	193	C1
11000010	194	C2
11000011	195	C3
11000100	196	C4
11000101	197	C5
11000110	198	C6
11000111	199	C7
11001000	200	C8
11001001	201	C9
11001010	202	CA
11001011	203	CB
11001100	204	CC
11001101	205	CD
11001110	206	CE
11001111	207	CF
11010000	208	D0
11010001	209	D1
11010010	210	D2
11010011	211	D3
11010100	212	D4
11010101	213	D5
11010110	214	D6
11010111	215	D7
11011000	216	D8
11011001	217	D9
11011010	218	DA
11011011	219	DB
11011100	220	DC

BINARY	DEC	HEX
11011101	221	DD
11011110	222	DE
11011111	223	DF
11100000	224	E0
11100001	225	E1
11100010	226	E2
11100011	227	E3
11100100	228	E4
11100101	229	E5
11100110	230	E6
11100111	231	E7
11101000	232	E8
11101001	233	E9
11101010	234	EA
11101011	235	EB
11101100	236	EC
11101101	237	ED
11101110	238	EE
11101111	239	EF
11110000	240	F0
11110001	241	F1
11110010	242	F2
11110011	243	F3
11110100	244	F4
11110101	245	F5
11110110	246	F6
11110111	247	F7
11111000	248	F8
11111001	249	F9
11111010	250	FA
11111011	251	FB
11111100	252	FC
11111101	253	FD
11111110	254	FE
11111111	255	FF

APPENDIX D

Z-80 Instruction Set

A Register Operations

Complement CPL
Decimal DAA
Negate NEG

Adding/Subtracting Two 8-Bit Numbers

A and Another Register
ADC A,r SBC A,r
ADD A,r SUB A,r
A and Immediate Operand
ADC A,n SBC A,n
ADD A,n SUB A,n
A and Memory Operand
ADC A,(HL) ADD A,(HL) SBC (HL) SUB (HL)
ADC A,(IX+d) ADD A,(IX+d) SBC (IX+d) SUB (IX+d)
ADC A,(IY+d) ADD A,(IY+d) SBC (IY+d) SUB (IY+d)

Adding/Subtracting Two 16-Bit Numbers

HL and Another Register Pair
ADC HL,ss ADD HL,ss SBC HL,ss
IX and Another Register Pair
ADD IX,pp ADD IY,rr

Bit Instructions

Test Bit
Register BIT b,r
Memory BIT b,(HL) BIT b,(IX+d) BIT b,(IY+)
Reset Bit
Register RES b,r
Memory RES b,(HL) RES b,(IX+d) RES b,(IY+d)
Set Bit
Register SET b,r
Memory SET b,(HL) SET b,(IX+d) SET b,(IY+d)

Carry Flag

Complement CCF
Set SCF

Compare Two 8-Bit Operands

A and Another Register CP r
A and Immediate Operand CP n
A and Memory Operand
CP (HL) CP (IX+d) CP (IY+d)
Block Compare
CPD,CPDR,CPI,CPIR

Decrements and Increments

Single Register
DEC r INC r DEC IX DEC IY INC
Register Pair
DEC ss INC ss DEC IX DEC IY INC IX DEC IY
Memory
DEC HL DEC (IX+d) DEC (IY+d)

Exchanges

DE and HL EX DE,HL
Top of Stack
EX (SP),HL EX (SP),IX EX (SP),IY

Input/Output

I/O To/From A and Port
IN A,(n) OUT (n),A
I/O To/From Register and Port
IN r,(C) OUT (C),r
Block
IND,INDR,INR,INIR,OTDR,OTIR,OUTD,OUTI

Interrupts

Disable DI
Enable EI
Interrupt Mode
IM 0 IM 1 IM 2
Return From Interrupt
RETI RETN

Jumps

Unconditional
JP (HL) JP (IX) JP (IY) JP (nn) JR e
Conditional
JP cc,nn JR C,e JR NZ,e JR Z,e
Special Conditional
DJNZ e

Loads

A Load Memory Operand
LD A,(BC) LD A,(DE) LD A,(nn)

A and Other Registers
LD A,I LD A,R LD I,A LD R,A
Between Registers, 8-Bit
LD r,r'
Immediate 8-Bit
LD r,n
Immediate 16-Bit
LD dd,nn LD IX,nn LD IY,nn
Register Pairs From Other Register Pairs
LD SP,HL LD SP,IX LD SP,IY
From Memory, 8-Bits
LD r,(HL) LD r,(IX+d) LD r,(IY+d)
From Memory, 16-Bits
LD HL,(nn) LD IX,(nn) LD IY,(nn) LD dd,(nn)
Block
LDD,LDDR,LDI,LDIR

Logical Operations 8 Bits With A

A and Another Register
AND r OR r XOR r
A and Immediate Operand
AND n OR n XOR n
A and Memory Operand
AND (HL) OR (HL) XOR (HL)
AND (IX+d) OR (IX+d) XOR (IX+d)
AND (IY+d) OR (IY+d) XOR (IY+d)

Miscellaneous

Halt HALT
No Operation NOP

Prime/Non-Prime

Switch AF
EX AF,AF'
Switch Others
EXX

Shifts

Circular (Rotate)
A Only RLA, RLCA, RRA, RRCA
All Registers RL r RLC r RR r RRC r
Memory
RL (HL) RLC (HL) RR (HL) RRC (HL)
RL (IX+d) RLC (IX+d) RR (IX+d) RRC (IX+d)
RL (IY+d) RLC (IY+d) RR (IY+d) RRC (IY+d)
Logical
Registers SRL r
Memory SRL (HL) SRL (IX+d) SRL (IY+d)
Arithmetic
Registers SLA r SRA r
Memory
SLA (HL) SRA (HL)
SLA (IX+d) SRA (IX+d)
SLA (IY+d) SRA (IY+d)

Stack Operations

PUSH IX PUSH IY PUSH qq POP IX POP IY POP qq

Stores

Of A Only
LD (BC),A LD (DE),A LD (HL),A LD (nn),A
All Registers
LD (HL),r LD (IX+d),r LD (IY+d),r
Immediate Data
LD (HL),n LD (IX+d),n LD (IY+d),n
16-Bit Registers
LD ((nn),dd LD (nn),IX LD (nn),IY

Subroutine Action

Conditional CALLs CALL cc,nn
Unconditional CALLs CALL nn
Conditional Return RET cc
Unconditional Return RET cc
Special CALL RST p

APPENDIX E

Z-80 Operation Code Listings

Mnemonic	Format	Description	S	Z	P/V	C
ADC HL,ss	11101101 01ss1010	HL+ss+CY to HL	●	●	●	●
ADC A,r	10001 r	A+r+CY to A	●	●	●	●
ADC A,n	11001110 n	A+n+CY to A	●	●	●	●
ADC A,(HL)	10001110	A+(HL)+CY to A	●	●	●	●
ADC A,(IX+d)	11011101 10001110 d	A+(IX+d)+CY to A	●	●	●	●
ADC A,(IY+d)	11111101 10001110 d	A+(IY+d)+CY to A	●	●	●	●
ADD A,n	11000110 n	A+n to A	●	●	●	●
ADD A,r	10000 r	A+r to A	●	●	●	●
ADD A,(HL)	10000110	A+(HL) to A	●	●	●	●
ADD A,(IX+d)	11011101 10000110 d	A+(IX+d) to A	●	●	●	●
ADD A,(IY+d)	11111101 10000110 d	A+(IY+d) to A	●	●	●	●
ADD HL,ss	00ss1001	HL+ss to HL				●
ADD IX,pp	11011101 00pp1001	IX+pp to IX				●
ADD IY,rr	11111101 00rr1001	IY+rr to IY				●
AND r	10100 r	A AND r to A	●	●	●	0
AND n	11100110 n	A AND n to A	●	●	●	0
AND (HL)	10100110	A AND (HL) to A	●	●	●	0
AND (IX+d)	11011101 10100110 d	A AND (IX+d) to A	●	●	●	0
AND (IY+d)	11111101 10100110 d	A AND (IY+d) to A	●	●	●	0
BIT b,r	11001011 01 b r	Test bit b of r	●	●	●	
BIT b,(HL)	11001011 01 b 110	Test bit b of (HL)	●	●	●	
BIT b,(IX+d)	11011101 11001011 d 01 b 110	Test bit b of (IX+d)	●	●	●	
BIT b,(IY+d)	11111101 11001011 d 01 b 110	Test bit b of (IY+d)	●	●	●	
CALL cc,nn	11 c 100 n n	CALL subroutine at nn if cc				
CALL nn	11001101 n n	Unconditionally CALL nn				
CCF	00111111	Complement carry flag				●
CP r	10111 r	Compare A:r	●	●	●	●
CP n	11111110 n	Compare A:n	●	●	●	●
CP (HL)	10111110	Compare A:(HL)	●	●	●	●
CP (IX+d)	11011101 10111110 d	Compare A:(IX+d)	●	●	●	●

Mnemonic	Format			Description	S	Z	P/V	C
CP (IY+d)	11111101	10111110	d	Compare A:(IY+d)	●	●	●	●
CPD	11101101	10101001		Block Compare, no repeat	●	●	●	
CPDR	11101101	10111001		Block Compare, repeat	●	●	●	
CPI	11101101	10100001		Block Compare, no repeat	●	●	●	
CPIR	11101101	10110001		Block Compare, repeat	●	●	●	
CPL	00101111			Complement A (1's comple)				
DAA	00100111			Decimal Adjust A	●	●	●	
DEC r	00 r 101			Decrement r by one	●	●	●	
DEC (HL)	00110101			Decrement (HL) by one	●	●	●	
DEC (IX+d)	11011101	00110101	d	Decrement (IX+d) by one	●	●	●	
DEC (IY+d)	11111101	00110101	d	Decrement (IY+d) by one	●	●	●	
DEC IX	11011101	00101011		Decrement IX by one				
DEC IY	11111101	00101011		Decrement IY by one				
DEC ss	00ss1011			Decrement register pair				
DI	11110011			Disable interrupts				
DJNZ e	00010000	e-2		Decrement B and JR if B≠0				
EI	11111011			Enable interrupts				
EX (SP),HL	11100011			Exchange (SP) and HL				
EX (SP),IX	11011101	11100011		Exchange (SP) and IX				
EX (SP),IY	11111101	11100011		Exchange (SP) and IY				
EX AF,AF'	00001000			Set prime AF active				
EX DE,HL	11101011			Exchange DE and HL				
EXX	11011001			Set prime B-L active				
HALT	01110110			Halt				
IM 0	11101101	01000110		Set interrupt mode 0				
IM 1	11101101	01010110		Set interrupt mode 1				
IM 2	11101101	01011110		Set interrupt mode 2				
IN A,(n)	11011011	n		Load A with input from n				
IN r,(C)	11101101	01 r 000		Load r with input from (C)	●	●	●	
INC r	00 r 100			Increment r by one	●	●	●	
INC (HL)	00110100			Increment (HL) by one	●	●	●	
INC (IX+d)	11011101	00110100	d	Increment (IX+d) by one	●	●	●	
INC (IY+d)	11111101	00110100	d	Increment (IY+d) by one	●	●	●	
INC IX	11011101	00100011		Increment IX by one				
INC IY	11111101	00100011		Increment IY by one				
INC ss	00ss0011			Increment register pair				
IND	11101101	10101010		Block I/O input from (C)	●	●	●	
INDR	11101101	10111010		Block I/0 input, repeat	●	●	●	
INI	11101101	10100010		Block I/O input from (C)	●	●	●	
INIR	11101101	10110010		Block I/0 input, repeat	●	●	●	
JP (HL)	11101001			Unconditional jump to (HL)				
JP (IX)	11011101	11101001		Unconditional jump to (IX)				
JP (IY)	11111101	11101001		Unconditional jump to (IY)				
JP cc,nn	11 c 010	n	n	Jump to nn if cc				
JP nn	11000011	n	n	Unconditional jump to nn				

Mnemonic	Format				Description	S	Z	P/V	C
JR C,e	00111000	e-2			Jump relative if carry				
JR e	00011000	e-2			Unconditional jump relative				
JR NC,e	00110000	e-2			Jump relative if no carry				
JR NZ,e	00100000	e-2			Jump relative if non-zero				
JR Z,e	00101000	e-2			Jump relative if zero				
LD A,(BC)	00001010				Load A with (BC)				
LD A,(DE)	00011010				Load A with (DE)				
LD A,I	11101101	01010111			Load A with I	●	●	●	
LD A,(nn)	00111010	n	n		Load A with location nn				
LD A,R	11101101	01011111			Load A with R	●	●	●	
LD (BC),A	00000010				Store A to (BC)				
LD (DE),A	00010010				Store A to (DE)				
LD (HL),n	00110110	n			Store n to (HL)				
LD dd,nn	00dd0001	n	n		Load register pair with nn				
LD dd,(nn)	11101101	01dd1011	n	n	Load register pair with location nn				
LD HL,(nn)	00101010	n	n		Load HL with location nn				
LD (HL),r	01110 r				Store r to (HL)				
LD I,A	11101011	01000111			Load I with A				
LD IX,(nn)	11011101	00101010	n	n	Load IX with nn				
LD IX,nn	11011101	00100001	n	n	Load IX with location nn				
LD (IX+d),n	11011101	00110110	d	n	Store n to (IX+d)				
LD (IX+d),r	11011101	01110 r	d		Store r to (IX+d)				
LD IY,nn	11111101	00100001	n	n	Load IY with nn				
LD IY,(nn)	11111101	00101010	n	n	Load IY with location nn				
LD (IY+d),n	11111101	00110110	d	n	Store n to (IY+d)				
LD (IY+d),r	11111101	01110 r	d		Store r to (IY+d)				
LD (nn),A	00110010	n	n		Store A to location nn				
LD (nn),dd	11101101	01dd0011	n	n	Store register pair to loc'n nn				
LD (nn),HL	00100010	n	n		Store HL to location nn				
LD (nn),IX	11011101	00100010	n	n	Store IX to location nn				
LD (nn),IY	11111101	00100010	n	n	Store IY to location nn				
LD R,A	11101101	01001111			Load R with A				
LD r,r'	01 r r'				Load r with r'				
LD r,n	00 r 110	n			Load r with n				
LD r,(HL)	01 r 110				Load r with (HL)				
LD r,(IX+d)	11011101	01 r 110	d		Load r with (IX+d)				
LD r,(IY+d)	11111101	01 r 110	d		Load rf with (IY+d)				
LD SP,HL	11111001				Load SP with HL				
LD SP,IX	11011101	11111001			Load SP with IX				
LD SP,IY	11111101	11111001			Load SP with IY				
LDD	11101101	10101000			Block load, f'ward, no repeat			●	
LDDR	11101101	10111000			Block load, f'ward, repeat			0	
LDI	11101101	1010000			Block load, b'ward, no repeat			●	
LDIR	11101101	10110000			Block load b'ward, repeat			0	
NEG	11101101	01000100			Negate A (two's complement)	●	●	●	●

Mnemonic	Format				Description	S	Z	P/V	C
NOP	00000000				No operation				
OR r	10110 r				A OR r to A	●	●	●	0
OR n	11110110	n			A OR n to A	●	●	●	0
OR (HL)	10110110				A OR (HL) to A	●	●	●	0
OR (IX+d)	11011101	10110110	d		A OR (IX+d) to A	●	●	●	0
OR (IY+d)	11111101	10110110	d		A OR (IY+d) to A	●	●	●	0
OTDR	11101101	10111011			Block output, b'ward, repeat	●	●	●	
OTIR	11101101	10110011			Block output, f'ward, repeat	●	●	●	
OUT (C),r	11101101	01 r 001			Output r to (C)				
OUT (n),A	11010011	n			Output A to port n				
OUTD	11101101	10101011			Block output, b'ward, no rpt	●	●	●	
OUTI	11101101	10100011			Block output, f'ward, no rpt	●	●	●	
POP IX	11011101	11100001			Pop IX from stack				
POP IY	11111101	11100001			Pop IY from stack				
POP qq	11qq0001				Pop qq from stack				
PUSH IX	11011101	11100101			Push IX onto stack				
PUSH IY	11111101	11100101			Push IY onto stack				
PUSH qq	11qq0101				Push qq onto stack				
RES b,r	11001011	10 b r			Reset bit b of r				
RES b,(HL)	11001011	10 b 110			Reset bit b of (HL)				
RES b,(IX+d)	11011101	11001011	d	10 b 110	Reset bit b of (IX+d)				
RES b,(IY+d)	11111101	11001011	d	10 b 110	Reset bit b of (IY+d)				
RET	11001001				Return from subroutine				
RET cc	11 c 000				Return from subroutine if cc				
RETI	11101101	01001101			Return from interrupt				
RETN	11101101	01000101			Return from non-maskable int				
RL r	11001011	00010 r			Rotate left thru carry r	●	●	●	●
RL (HL)	11001011	00010110			Rotate left thru carry (HL)	●	●	●	●
RL (IX+d)	11011101	11001011	d	00010110	Rotate left thru carry (IY+d)	●	●	●	●
RL (IY+d)	11010101	11001011	d	00000110	Rotate left thru carry (IY+d)	●	●	●	●
RLA	00010111				Rotate A left thru carry				●
RLC r	11001011	00000 r			Rotate left circular r	●	●	●	●
RLC (HL)	11001011	00000110			Rotate left circular (HL)	●	●	●	●
RLC (IX+d)	11011101	11001011	d	00000110	Rotate left circular (IX+d)	●	●	●	●
RLC (IY+d)	11111101	11001011	d	00000110	Rotate left circular (IY+d)	●	●	●	●
RLCA	00000111				Rotate left circular A				●
RLD	11101101	01101111			Rotate bcd digit left (HL)	●	●	●	
RR r	11001011	00011 r			Rotate right thru carry r	●	●	●	●
RR (HL)	11001011	00011110			Rotate right thru carry (HL)	●	●	●	●
RR (IX+d)	11011101	11001011	d	00011110	Rotate right thru cy (IX+d)	●	●	●	●
RR (IY+d)	00011110	11001011	d	00011110	Rotate left thru cy (IY+d)	●	●	●	●
RRA	00011111				Rotate A right thru carry				●
RRC r	11001011	00001 r			Rotate r right circular	●	●	●	●
RRC (HL)	11001011	00001110			Rotate (HL) right circular	●	●	●	●
RRC (IX+d)	11011101	11001011	d	00001110	Rotate (IX+d) right circular	●	●	●	●

Mnemonic	Format	Description	S	Z	P/V	C
RRC (IY+d)	11111101 | 11001011 | d | 00001110	Rotate (IY+d) right circular	●	●	●	●
RRCA	00001111	Rotate A right circular				●
RRD	11101101 | 01100111	Rotate bcd digit right (HL)	●	●	●	
RST p	11 t 110	Restart to location p				
SBC A,r	10011 r	A-r-CY to A	●	●	●	●
SBC A,n	11011110 | n	A-n-CY to A	●	●	●	●
SBC A,(HL)	10011110	A-(HL)-CY to A	●	●	●	●
SBC A,(IX+d)	11011101 | 10011110 | d	A-(IX+d)-CY to A	●	●	●	●
SBC A,(IY+d)	11111101 | 10011110 | d	A-(IY+d)-CY to A	●	●	●	●
SBC HL,ss	11101101 | 01ss0010	HL-ss-CY to HL	●	●	●	●
SCF	00110111	Set carry flag				1
SET b,(HL)	11001011 | 11 b 110	Set bit b of (HL)				
SET b,(IX+d)	11011101 | 11001011 | d | 11 b 110	Set bit b of (IX+d)				
SET b,(IY+d)	11111101 | 11001011 | d | 11 b 110	Set bit b of (IY+d)				
SET b,r	11001011 | 11 b r	Set bit b of r				
SLA r	11001011 | 00100 r	Shift r left arithmetic	●	●	●	●
SLA (HL)	11001011 | 00100110	Shift (HL) left arithmetic	●	●	●	●
SLA (IX+d)	11011101 | 11001011 | d | 00100110	Shift (IX+d) left arithmetic	●	●	●	●
SLA (IY+d)	11111101 | 11001011 | d | 00100110	Shift (IY+d) left arithmetic	●	●	●	●
SRA r	11001011 | 00101 r	Shift r right arithmetic	●	●	●	●
SRA (HL)	11001011 | 00101110	Shift (HL) right arithmetic	●	●	●	●
SRA IX+d)	11011101 | 11001011 | d | 00101110	Shift (IX+d) right arithmetic	●	●	●	●
SRA (IY+d)	11111101 | 11001011 | d | 00101110	Shift (IY+d) right arithmetic	●	●	●	●
SRL r	11001011 | 00111 r	Shift r right logical	●	●	●	●
SRL (HL)	11001011 | 00111110	Shift (HL) right arithmetic	●	●	●	●
SRL (IX+d)	11011101 | 11001011 | d | 00111110	Shift (IX+d) right arithmetic	●	●	●	●
SRL (IY+d)	11111101 | 11001011 | d | 00111110	Shift (IY+d) right arithmetic	●	●	●	●
SUB r	10010 r	A-r to A	●	●	●	●
SUB n	11010110 | n	A-n to A	●	●	●	●
SUB (HL)	10010110	A-(HL) to A	●	●	●	●
SUB (IX+d)	11011101 | 10010110 | d	A-(IX+d) to A	●	●	●	●
SUB (IY+d)	11111101 | 10010110 | d	A-(IY+d) to A	●	●	●	●
XOR r	10101 r	A EXCLUSIVE OR r to A	●	●	●	0
XOR n	11101110 | n	A EXCLUSIVE OR n to A	●	●	●	0
XOR (HL)	10101110	A EXCLUSIVE OR (HL) to A	●	●	●	0
XOR (IX+d)	11011101 | 10101110 | d	A EXCLUSIVE OR (IX+d) to A	●	●	●	0
XOR (IY+d)	11111101 | 10101110 | d	A EXCLUSIVE OR (IY+d) to A	●	●	●	0

Key:

Instruction Fields:

- b bit field 0-7
- c condition field 0=NZ, 1=Z, 2=NC, 3=C, 4=PO, 5=PE, 6=P, 7=M
- d indexing displacement +127 to −128
- dd register pair: 0=BC, 1=DE, 2=HL, 3=SP
- e relative jump displacement +127 to −128
- n immediate or address value
- pp register pair: 0=BC, 1=DE, 2=IX, 3=SP
- qq register pair: 0=BC, 1=DE, 2=IY, 3=SP
- r register: 0=B, 1=C, 2=D, 3=E, 4=H, 5=L, 7=A
- r′ register: same as r
- ss register pair: 0=BC, 1=DE, 2=HL, 3=SP
- t RST field: Location=t*8

Condition Codes:

- ● = affected
- 0 = reset
- 1 = set
- = unaffected

APPENDIX F

EZ-80 PC Board Layout

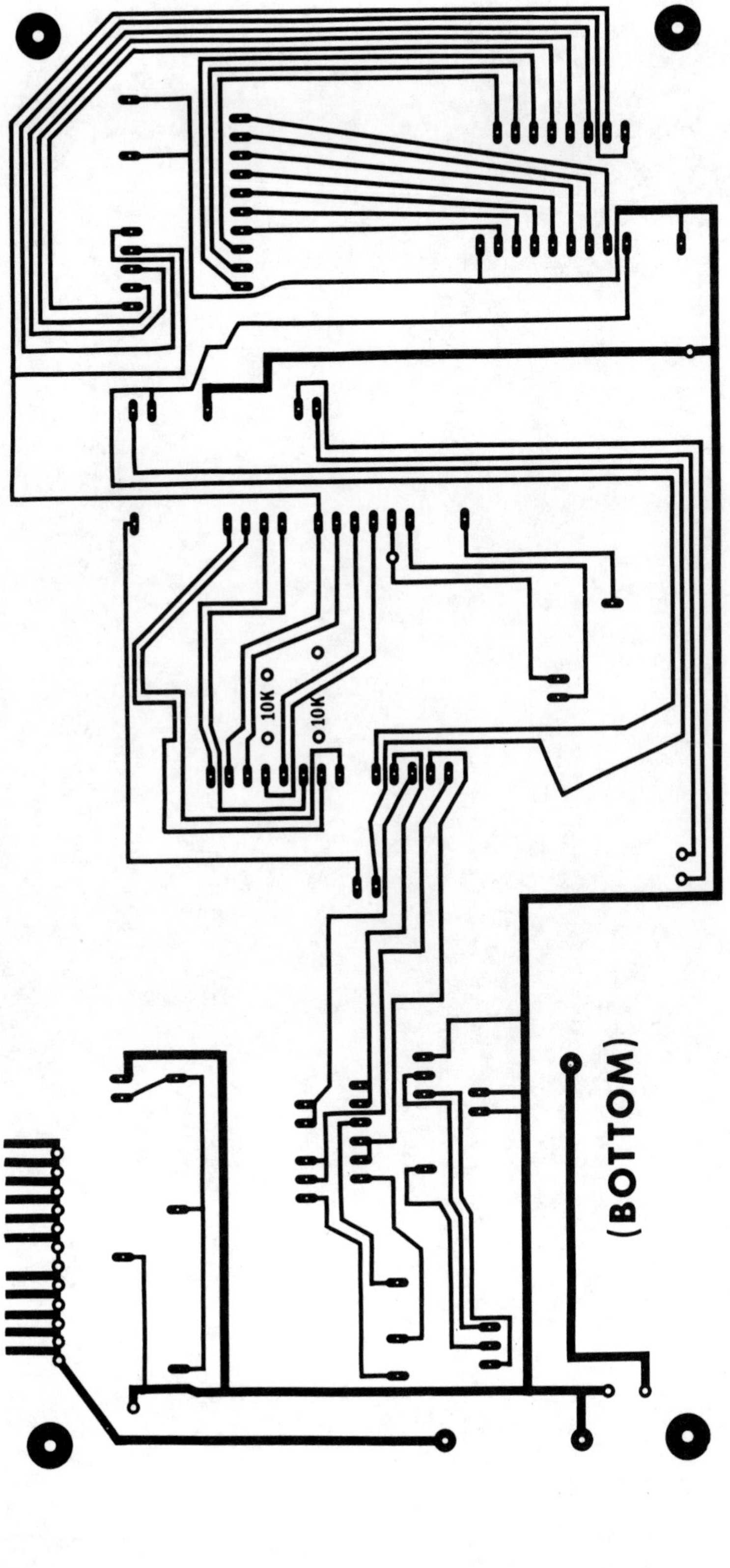

Notes:

1. Pin numbers may differ slightly with schematics shown in this book, especially in output and input line logic.
2. PC board artwork designed for double-sided board without plated through holes. Solder all pads on component side and all pads on reverse side to complete connections between traces on both sides of board.

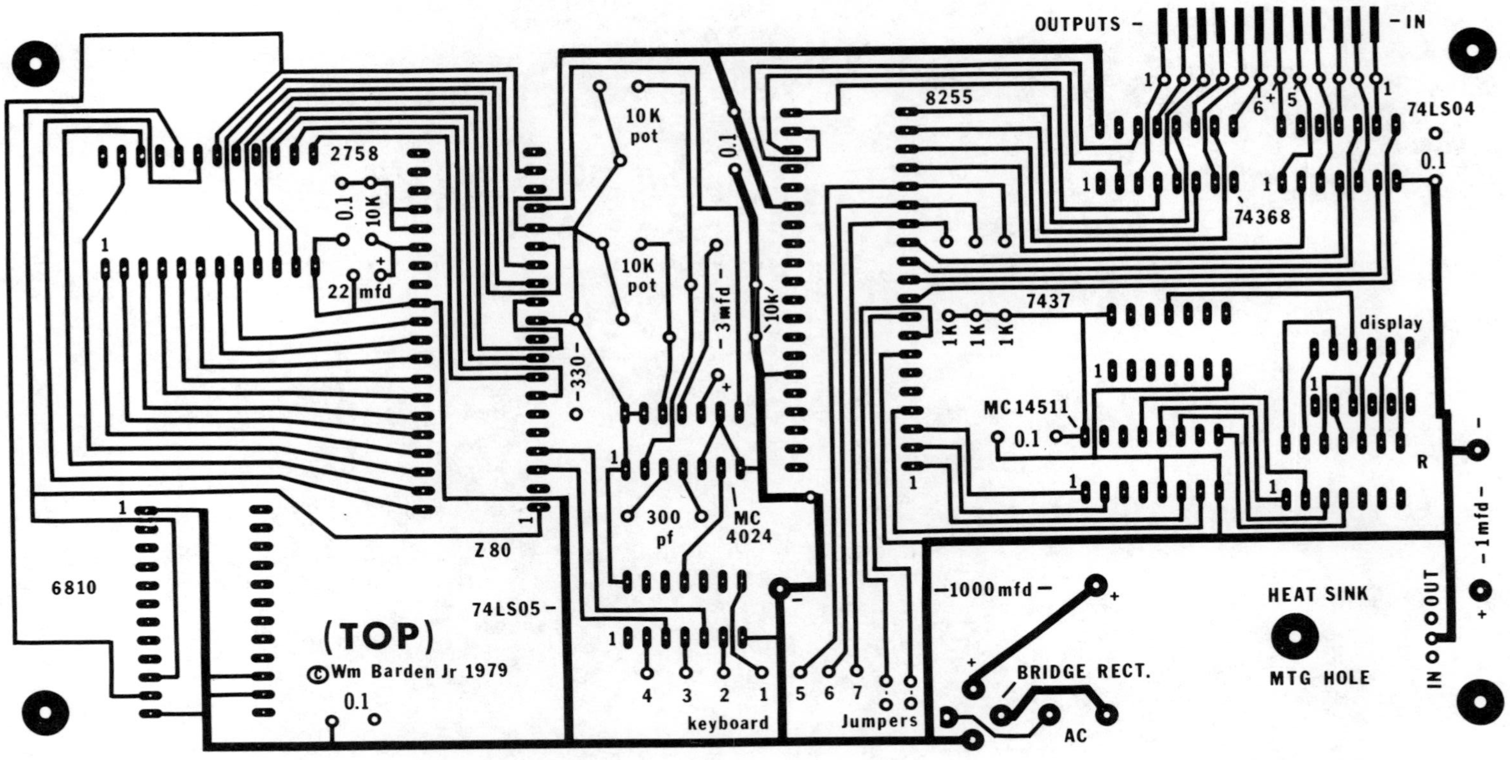

Notes:

1. Pin numbers may differ slightly with schematics shown in this book, especially in output and input line logic.

2. PC board artwork designed for double-sided board without plated through holes. Solder all pads on component side and all pads on reverse side to complete connections between traces on both sides of board.

Index